Maritime Engineering
& Ports III

THIRD INTERNATIONAL CONFERENCE ON
THE MANAGEMENT, OPERATION, DESIGN AND BUILDING OF PORTS,
MARINAS AND OTHER MARITIME WORKS

MARITIME ENGINEERING & PORTS III

CONFERENCE DIRECTORS

C.A. Brebbia
Wessex Institute of Technology, UK

W.R. Blain
Wessex Institute of Technology, UK

G. Sciutto
SCIRO S.r.l., Italy

INTERNATIONAL SCIENTIFIC ADVISORY COMMITTEE

M Cullen
J J F Elwin
V Esteban
R A Falconer
W Galor
N Guler
P Holmes
J Olivella
N Panagopoulos
A J Rogan
F Sakellariadou
A Stateczny
J C Van Ham
D Young

Organised by:
Wessex Institute of Technology, UK

Maritime Engineering & Ports III

Editors:

C.A. Brebbia
Wessex Institute of Technology

G Sciutto
SCIRO S.r.l., Italy

WITPRESS Southampton, Boston

C.A. Brebbia
Wessex Institute of Technology

G Sciutto
SCIRO S.r.l., Italy

Published by

WIT Press
Ashurst Lodge, Ashurst, Southampton, SO40 7AA, UK
Tel: 44 (0) 238 029 3223; Fax: 44 (0) 238 029 2853
E-Mail: witpress@witpress.com
http://www.witpress.com

For USA, Canada and Mexico

Computational Mechanics Inc
25 Bridge Street, Billerica, MA 01821, USA
Tel: 978 667 5841; Fax: 978 667 7582
E-Mail: info@compmech.com
US site: http://www.compmech.com

British Library Cataloguing-in-Publication Data

A Catalogue record for this book is available
from the British Library

ISBN: 1-85312-923-2
ISSN: 1462-6071

*The texts of the papers in this volume were set
individually by the authors or under their supervision.
Only minor corrections to the text may have been carried
out by the publisher.*

Printed in Great Britain by IBT Global, London

PREFACE

Nowadays a port is no longer a simple interchange point where goods are stored and prepared to continue their journey by sea. The globalisation process led to different logistic constraints which changed the port concept: now transport operators consider the quays as gates where goods must pass through in the safest and quickest way. To achieve this result, operators have to implement novel information and communication technologies onto the port areas.

Moreover, the importance of the port economy is now extended to a much more wider area than before. The performance of a single port can affect the economy of an entire region. Therefore, it is very important to understand and manage the complex changes that are currently taking place in the port industry and in its operation management sectors.

The "Ports and Marinas 2002" conference offers a unique forum where institutions and private and public enterprises present the research and industrial activities recently developed. This book which contains the proceedings of the meeting examines thoroughly the latest changes in the field of design and building of ports, taking into account the new technologies affecting these sectors. The problems related to the port operations are also highlighted in this book.

Technology in the port sector has also been analysed in order to boost both the use of the information systems and the man-machine interfaces; besides that, the technological aspects related to new systems of loading and unloading goods and to marine engineering works have been underlined in order to link maintenance with the design, including that of marinas. Engineers are also faced with environmental aspects affecting ports and marinas.

The Editors would like to thank the International Scientific Advisory Commitee members, who have reviewed abstracts and papers; their generous work was essential to the success of this conference. They extend their thanks to the authors too, who appreciated both the scientific contents of this event and the magic atmosphere of the location when walking along the ancient stone paved lanes of Rhodes.

The Editors
Rhodes 2002

Contents

Section 2: Environmental aspects

Section 3: Hydrodynamic aspects

Section 4: Construction and design of ports

Section 5: Marine engineering works

Section 6: Container systems

Section 1
Port management

Port development vs. technological development: the challenge of keeping the pace

G. Sciutto[1], A. Derito[1], A. Traverso[2], G. Dellepiane[2], G. Pietronave[2]
[1]Sciro S.r.l., Genoa, Italy.
[2]CIRT (Centro Interuniversitario di Ricerche Transporti), University of Genoa, Italy.

Abstract

This paper presents an overview of the main features regarding both the port planning procedures and the information and communication technology development. All the projects regarding port infrastructures have to get through several steps before they pass to the operative phase. Firstly, an analysis of the current situation is necessary, underlining the results to be achieved based on a predictable future situation. However, there is a long period of time between this analysis and the moment in which the project may actually get started. This long period prevents analysts from making precise predictions about what the situation will be by the time the infrastructures will be built and the information systems will be implemented. All the civil projects are defined for a 20-30 years future horizon, while the information systems and the technological features foresee a sensibly shorter life period, usually 5-7 years.

Planning a new port, or the enhancement of an already existent one, that time span difference leads to a situation where new infrastructures are run with a technology level generally corresponding to a former period. As a consequence, the whole effort afforded to build a modern port system is weakened by the fact that the brand-new port is matching the future challenges using the "day-before" technology.

1 Port development

The construction of a new port, as well as the enhancement of an already existing one, involves a high number of planning procedures and many economic factors to be kept into account. Furthermore, since the 70's the environmental issues have become more and more important, turning into fundamental aspects with the introduction of the EIE (Environmental Impact Evaluation).

In general, any intervention aiming to boost the performances of a port area requires several procedures which may be divided in three big steps to be passed through:

1. analysis and work projects
2. project conforming to the Master Plan
3. getting the projects under way

Hereafter each of these groups will be analysed in order to provide an idea of the time required to overcome all the necessary steps.

1.1 Analysis and work projects

The philosophy that lies behind any intervention on a port, either to build a new one or to improve the performances of an already existing terminal, is to rise competitiveness to goods to be moved by sea. This meets two different type of needs, depending on the goods already have a land connection between the point of origin and destination, or they have not. In other words, setting up more port facilities can be analysed in case the sea transport is just an option or in case it is the only solution.

As for the first case, promoting the port as a fundamental junction for the intermodal transport means that a share of goods transported by road is moved to the sea, in order to shift the balance between modes of transport. For instance, this is just the aim of the European transport policy, underlined in the last "White Paper". Road's share of goods market in Europe has been growing constantly, from 41% in '90 to 44% in '98; if no action is taken, this share is expected to reach 47% by 2010, according to experts evaluations.

When the sea transport is not an option, we have the case where two distinct world areas improve their commercial connections with an increase of goods transported from one to another. This is the case of the big traffic volumes already existing between America, Far East and Europe; in this scenario, the location and the facilities of the main European ports have risen in importance for the "Pendulum routes". There is also the case where the port facilities led the decision of sea routes where the ports are simply chosen for their ability in quickly and safely transferring a big amount of goods from one ship to another. This is the typical case of the hub-spoke sea transport organisation, where the transhipment ports play a key role.

To have proper infrastructures linking the port with its hinterland is a necessity, because a port with bad connections with the main inland transport network may result in a bottleneck, when it is not a harmful thing for the area where it is located. It is worthless indeed to concentrate all the financial efforts to increase depths of harbour waters if a quick connection with the inland is not provided. In this way, the increase of traffic volumes moved by the best handling system will surely turn in a "logistic nightmare" for the multimodal terminal operator once the goods have to be moved out of the port area.

In general, all the works involved in a port development project can be divided in three big groups:

a.   civil engineering
b.   mechanical engineering
c.   information technology

All the projects regarding quays and wharves, as well as offices, warehouses and other goods facilities belong to the first group. Moreover, in this group there are also the dredging works in order to reach the necessary depth of harbour waters and all the infrastructures needed to link the port area with the main transport inland networks.

The handling devices, like cranes and other handling and storage facilities belong to the second group. At this point of the planning it is necessary to define the number and the dimensions of this kind of devices. Any type of handling machines operating in a terminal (Ship to Shore Cranes, Rubber Tired Gantry Cranes, Rail Mounted Gantry Cranes, reach stackers, front loaders, trailers, tractors, etc.), as well as their features, have to be defined in order to match up to expectations in terms of handling capacity.

Regarding the third group, the contribution of Information Technology has become very important in order to get the best results with the minimum effort.

The latest features of Information Technology systems cover a wide range of applications: from security devices for the crane spread system to the location of containers in the yard, such technology may help the port system to work more efficiently. In spite of that, it is pointed out that automation tends to be avoided by the big terminal operators worldwide. Of course, initial capital costs of automation will be greater than conventional equipment, and probably only partly balanced by reduced civil installation costs. But now many suppliers are providing reduced maintenance and life-cycle costs for automated equipment; once these aspects have been entered into the equation, it will be quite clear that the overall cost will be lowered (thanks to the manpower savings too). As the container revolution changed the rules 40 years ago, it seems that terminal operators will agree on recognising the advantages of the automation options.

To sum up, the first phase of planning procedure consists in collecting all the required data to analyse the situation related to the port and its area, focusing on the needs of having an improvement of the port facilities. This data will have to take into account both the connections with the main inland transportation networks and the expected traffic volumes that the new terminal will have to deal with. All the elements required to draw the new features of the port are expected to allow designers to define the equipment main characteristics, although they are defined in a preliminary way. Technically, it is estimated that this first phase lasts about one year.

But to draw the main characteristics of the new port (or new terminal) could last more if we thoroughly consider the three phases mentioned above. On one hand, the civil projects have already a sort of codification in order to define the way they have to be carried out. But on the other, the information technology aspects of the projects (and all the mechanical issues directly correlated) are surely more undetermined. Due to that, the automation in port handling system tends to be underestimated. Another reason may well be the varying division of responsibility that is set in different ports and countries. In fact, the terminal operator often represent only a short-term franchise holder in the port system, and the equipment is the responsibility of a different party. Experts claim that, if unconventional development is to occur, full responsibility for the terminal equipment and security of tenure are highly desirable features.

For these reasons, normally the phase of collecting data and preparing the preliminary projects (civil, mechanical and technological) may well last a couple of years.

1.2 Project conforming to the Master Plan

Any intervention on a port area has to comply with the specifications and the rules the institutions have given to manage that area. The legal instrument to define those rules and limitations is the Master Plan.

In general, the Master Plan is to consider the expectations, plans and programs of local jurisdictions, state agencies, business and residential communities. Beside that, it must keep into account environmental issues related to the sustainable development of the whole area. In pursuing those results, it is no coincidence that the planning procedure involves many players: port authority, ministries, regional and local subjects are all involved in the Master Plan decision process. The delicate nature of its role makes it represent the synthesis of collective utility. Beside that, the globalisation process, changing the rules of the world commerce, brings with it certain risks for the whole port region economic system. Up to just a few years ago, the presence of the port was always an advantage for the city and the country that hosted it, but today it seems that those times have come to an end. On one hand, ports are even more essential compared to the respective hinterland, as a basic node in logistic networks. On the other hand, it is pointed out that the higher external costs (in terms of exploitation of coastal and retro-coastal areas, air pollution, land networks congestion), do not lead to a guaranteed positive cost-benefit ratio any longer. Due to that, the port Master Plan becomes much more important than in the past, not only for the single port but also for the reference economic system.

Although it is extremely difficult to exactly outline which specifications have to be considered in a Master Plan, due to the peculiarities of different states and ports, it is possible to highlight the main procedures to be carried out. It is possible to define six big steps:

1) identify the planning process and the community outreach process and reviewing available planning background material;
2) delineation of the study zone. A market analysis will provide documentation on the local commercial and industrial needs.
3) preparation of an Economic Development Action Plan. This action incorporates an analysis pertaining to the property's development;
4) develop the Implementation Strategies and Policies

5) Draft Master Plan and refined Zone database. An Economic Development Action Plan will be prepared;
6) preparation of the Final Master Plan.

As for the community involvement, the first public engagement will occur in stage 2 with a preliminary "listening forum". Then, after having prepared the Draft Master Plan, a series of public meetings will be held. At the conclusion of these community outreach sessions, feedback summaries will be prepared and the draft plan will be refined.

The indications stressed into the Master Plan have to comply with limitations for a sustainable development. For this purpose the EIA (Environmental Impact Assessment) Directive was introduced by the European Community in 1985 and was amended in 1997. This procedure ensures that environmental consequences of projects are identified and assessed before authorisation is given. The public may give its opinion and all results are taken into account in the project authorisation procedure. The involvement of the public is limited, however, by the fact that the public is often informed on the decision only afterwards.

Environmental impacts are classified into different ways according to the focus of the study; therefore, they can be local, regional or global as well as temporary or permanent, reversible or not reversible, etc. An environmental impact can affect or modify ground, atmosphere, superficial and underground water, inhabitants life quality. An impact can be positive or negative, depending on it improves or deteriorates the existing conditions, or neutral, if it does not alter those conditions. Negative impacts, particularly, must be neutralised, mitigating them by putting into practice the actions suggested in the project authorisation procedure.

As for the time required for the entire Master Plan decision process, it is obvious that it depends on the importance and the gravity of the expected impacts. In general, however, we can say that the process takes 2 years to be accomplished. But there is also the case where the local community, with its ever-increasing intolerance toward any additional port expansion, makes the whole process last longer than expected. In this case, we can even reach a period time of 3 years.

1.3 Getting the projects under way

Once the positive EIA is obtained, the projects can get started, the civil works firstly. Obviously, at this time the detailed projects will be already prepared, a favourable decision by the institutions about the EIA being expected. Feedback coming from the project evaluation describing the actions to be taken to mitigate the negative impacts may postpone the start of the works. However, once the preliminary project have been presented to the institutions for their approval, the designers start with the detailed plans, waiting for the definitive start of the work. If the corrections to be made are not so important, the works can start immediately, provided that the corrections indicated will be implemented as soon as possible.

Due to the enormous variety of type of works, it is quite impossible to explain thoroughly this phase of the port development process. However, it is said that, in general, the whole quays and building construction phase takes about four years. This is the phase that lasts more: the last leg (to implement the mechanical handling facilities, lay down the technological devices and test them) keeps an additional year.

To sum up, it is believed that the entire port development process lasts 8-12 years, depending on the works gravity and global interest, the risk of environmental damages it may cause, and the community agreement degree.

2 Information Technology development

The introduction of technology in the manifold human activities in the last years has obtained a considerable acceleration thanks to the multiple occasions in which the coupling between technology and traditional *modus operandi* have proved to be competitive and convenient.

One of the fields in which the introduction of technology, and in particular of Information Technology, has moved its first steps in the last two decades is the ports environment. Computer-aided design systems, satellite-based navigation systems, automatic vehicle driving and similar applications have entered the world of ports and the overall water transportation chain in a considerable number of actual realities. The Port of Rotterdam seems to be one of the most interesting realities since a dozen of years ago, and it represents the first example of massive Information Technology deployment, at least in Europe.

These considerations introduce the following argument, that consists in the importance related to a good choice of the most appropriate technology to be used in port activities.

With reference to Chapter 1.1, regarding the three groups in which a port development project is realised (civil engineering, mechanical engineering, and information technology), it is easy to realise that the last group has an average development rate higher than the remaining groups. Technology is a highly dynamic element, and the magnitude order of its development rate may be 5 to 10 times huger than the one of other engineering fields like the civil and mechanical ones. Nevertheless, it is possible to state that the risk is that the scenario which has to be built up at the moment when the project is planned, is relatively easier (so, more reliable) to be drawn about the civil and mechanical parts rather than for the Information Technology part.

As for the Information Technology development, we can say that to build up a reliable scenario, in which designers may foresee the suitable system working, typically covers a period no longer than 4 years.

An apparent solution would seem to be the post-position of the planning of Information Technology utilisation after the completion of the civil and mechanical designs; but this solution is not easily viable because civil and mechanical designs should not be implemented disregarding the information technology tools.

3 Modularity

One of the important issues of the design of Information Technology application to port environment is the modularity of the systems. This is an important feature especially when it is kept into account what stated in the previous Chapter, that is the high rate of development that characterises Information Technology. The high speed which features the field of Information Technology forces the civil and mechanical engineers to build up a scenario of technological tools. That scenario is usually full of uncertainties and randomness that are definitely hard to overcome, especially considering the long period of time that separates the start up of civil and mechanical design and the completion of the designed port infrastructure. Within this framework, modularity provides engineers with a flexible and adaptable solution, which may grant them the possibility to update their civil and mechanical designs according to the ongoing development of Information Technology.

The concept presented above may seem the solution to overcome the difference in evolution times of infrastructure technology and information technology; indeed this is the most frequently used approach to the problem. But the intention of this paper is to present a new approach which seems to lead to the presence of innovative technology in the port infrastructure at the time of completion of the project, and not at the time of design as it is nowadays.

4 A new skill: the technology advisor

As mentioned above, there is a great difference between the horizon-times of the civil plans and of the information technology systems. In general, we can divide the whole process in six big legs:

1. analysis and collect data
2. preliminary plans
3. EIA procedure
4. detail plans
5. civil works
6. mechanical handling system and information technology devices implementation

We can take a simplified overview of the entire process in Figure 1. It is clear that the time schedule shown can suffer some modifications, depending on the cases. For example, the EIA procedure (leg 3) may take only 2 years, so the civil works can get started just after the detail plans preparation, in order to avoid any waste of time.

The focus of this paper is to point out that the detail plans, with the civil and mechanical designs, cannot disregard the information technology tools that they will have to deal with. But the detail plans leg starts far before the terminal could be run. As shown in Figure 1, the gap between these phases could be long enough to nullify the previsions about the technology systems, or rather, to make the systems run with a 3-4 years old technology level.

Legs	Years									
	1	*2*	*3*	*4*	*5*	*6*	*7*	*8*	*9*	*10*
1										
2										
3										
4										
5										
6										

Figure 1: Port development time schedule

Due to that, a new skill is to play a basic role: the Technology Advisor. His duty is to make reliable previsions about how the Information Technology market will have changed within a time horizon far longer than the usual. This new actor has to manage thoroughly the IT world, to understand all the changes this market sector presents in order to foresee a reliable long-term scenario. His decisions will have to be kept into account during the leg 3 (plan details), in order to make the terminal operators, in the final phase, able to set running systems with a technological level as much up-do-date as possible. The Technology Advisor role is highlighted in Figure 2, where the port development time schedule presented in Figure 1 is enriched with the presence of this innovative subject.

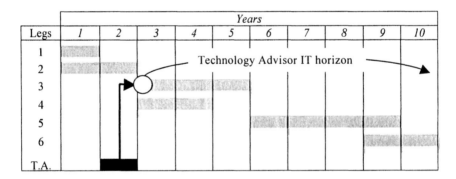

Figure 2: the role of the Technology Advisor (T.A.)

The basic role of the Technology Advisor is indeed to indicate what affordable results the IT will have reached by the time the handling system will have been implemented. The strategic task of the Technological Advisor is to be abreast of technical progress in the IT field, providing useful indications which will support the civil and mechanical engineers. In fact, civil works will have to permit the implementation of such a *soft* technology that, nowadays, costs too much, but, within a eight years period, it could be of common use.

A clear proof of what mentioned above is provided by the wiring works in process right now in some port terminals; all of us know the discomforts deriving from the operations interruption and the physical demolition of part of the infrastructures. This fact underlines that, if somebody had had the duty of forecasting a possible future situation, now many operators would not have to put up with this kind of problems.

The time schedule shown in Figure 2 seems to be exaggerated, but it becomes realistic when considering the time needed to achieve some big port development project worldwide. For example, Le Havre "Port 2000" project started in 1994, suffered a heavy stop in 1998 and now, after the required institutions agreements, is expected to be put in by 2003, waiting for the definitive environmental works that will have been over by the end of 2004.

5 New opportunities

By adopting the Technology Advisor suggestions, it is expected that terminal operators will be in a privileged market position once the port handling systems will have been implemented. It is expected indeed that designers would plan with a wider IT previsional market scenario, which will let them to run a system with a more up-to-date technology level.

The work done by the Technology Advisor will be useful even if the IT foreseen level will exist both before or after the prevision given. In case the IT market development presents a time lag compared with the Technology Advisor predictions, then operators will still have to use a conventional technology, but with all the infrastructures already prepared to hold new systems. So that, the upgrade process will be relatively easy. The wireworks is a suitable example: at the detail plans phase, it is expected to foresee a "multiservice tube" just under the quays, or even inside the lampposts. Even if it stays idle for a period of time, it is likely to be utilised as soon as necessary. On the contrary, if the IT market will develop in a faster way than the Technology Advisor suggested, operators will work systems with a smaller technology delay with respect to their competitors. Therefore, in both cases operators will work closer to the real technology level.

To make the Technology Advisor role definitively strategic, however, a deep revision of the planning and decision procedures is strongly recommended. If it is quite impossible to reduce the time required to set up the civil works, at least it is possible to reduce the idle times existing in the whole port development process. In Figure 2 the gaps existing between leg 3 and leg 4 (detail plans preparation and EIA procedure) and between leg 5 and leg 6 (civil works, mechanical handling system and information technology devices implementation) have to be shortened if more efficient port development is to occur.

A prime reason for reluctance on the part of some terminal operators to consider automation may well derive from a sort of "vicious circle": the slower the procedures, the harder the traffic volumes estimations, the less reliable the prevision (done either by the designer or by the Technology Advisor), the less the investors are attracted, the lower probability that massive automation is implemented. Only by reducing the idle times in the port development process it is possible to balance the unavoidable risks deriving from such wide-ranging predictions; this is the only way to make the Technology Advisor's work more important and easier at the same time, in order to make planning with a wider technology range more profitable.

6 Conclusions

It is to be noticed that the Technology Advisor skills play a basic role in the new port planning only when there is a growth in the Gross Domestic Product (GDP). This is the main point, indeed, which is impossible to create the necessary conditions to promote port automation without. Indeed, it is said that any IT improvement to be implemented in order to cut down logistical costs and to mitigate environmental impacts requires a tangible GDP growth.

The IT implementation could turn onto a rise of external economies, according to expert. The catalysing action of logistic services with high added value, the establishment of large international players in transports and logistics, the induced demand in term of goods and services for goods and persons represent the major benefits of IT exploitation. Moreover, it would be totally useless to improve the port IT systems paying no attention to an efficient use of space and to the allocation of extensive areas where logistic services with high added value may be located.

Another point that could play against the port automation process is that, at first sight, the direct occupation seems to drop. Only a wide range analysis of the effects brought by an unconventional development on the entire social and economic structure of the territory will be able to determine whether or not the social cost- benefit ratio will be positive.

Finally, an appropriate LCC (Life Cycle Cost) analysis of the systems implemented in the new port can be helpful to this purpose. In fact, it is possible to determine the replacement of part of the system on a pre-fixed basis, creating so direct occupation especially with regard to the mechanical handling machines.

References

[1]   Commission of the European Communities, *White Paper – European transport policy for 2010: time to decide*, Brussels, 2001
[2]   Musso, E., Costi e benefici ma anche rischi di autogol. *Sailing list*, June 2001, pp.7-8
[3]   Macleod, R., So, what's the excuse this time?. *Cargo System*, August 2001, pp. 62-63
[4]   Goasguen, R., Port 2000: "On est entré dans le vif du sujet". *Le Marin*, October 2001 – special issue, p. 12
[5]   Woodbridge, C., Access all areas. *Containerisation Internaional*, January 2002, pp.69-71

Port expansion and public-private partnership: the case of Rotterdam

J.C. van Ham and J.F.M. Koppenjan
Faculty of Technology, Policy and Management,
Delft University of Technology, The Netherlands

Abstract

The role of public authorities in the development of infrastructure is evident. Increasingly, private parties show interest in infrastructure projects. The relationship between public and private parties can take various shapes. From a theoretical point of view, four models of co-operation between public and private parties are discussed. The realisation of the second Maasvlakte, a large scale port expansion in Rotterdam, will serve as an example. The project started in the early 1990s as a traditional (unilateral) port planning procedure. Private involvement enters the picture for the first time in 1998. A constructing firm, container handling company and financial institution launched the Binnenmeerplan. This innovative private initiative introduced the concept of a phased construction of the second Maasvlakte. Simultaneously, the Dutch government carried out a study project and the Combination model, which incorporates both the objectives of public parties and of the business community was developed. The Combination model can be perceived as a breakthrough because it demonstrates that solutions for problems such as existing planning procedures and EU directives can be found. Albeit the enthusiasm from both parties was overwhelming, the government exchanged the Combination model for the Parallel model. In this model, the role of central government is restricted to spatial planning and land use, regional and local government will act as project developer. At the moment two arguments in the discussion prevail: innovation and risk sharing. Therefore, parts of the project will be put on tender: Design Build Finance and Maintain (DBFM)-arrangements for the dikes and Build Operate and Transfer (BOT)-contracts for the terminals. However, it is at least doubtful whether BOT-contracts will work in the Hamburg - Le Havre range.

1 Introduction

In the second half of the 20th century, public-private partnerships have gained in importance, first in the USA and later in Europe (Teisman [1]). These partnerships took various shapes, due to the different settings and institutional contexts in which they were developed. In the USA private companies, citizens and local governments co-operated in order to revitalise inner cities, whereas in Canada decentralisation and empowerment were important issues, which were central to partnerships. In Britain as well as in the Netherlands partnerships were put forward as a solution to budget deficits in a period of economic decline. But at the same time it is uncertain whether parties are able to successfully give shape to a public-private co-operation. Cultural and institutional differences between public and private parties and the risks attached to bringing the two together constitute a serious threat to successful public-private partnership (Jacobs [2]).

The development of successful public-private partnerships will form one of the most important challenges facing organisations in the public and private domain in the years to come. This paper deals with the need and options for creating public-private partnerships but also with the difficulties and risks involved. This problem will be illustrated by examining the public-private partnership relating to the expansion of the port of Rotterdam.

2 Public-private co-operation in infrastructure projects

The process of project development comprises various phases. In order to position the stage of a project a general scheme that contains all phases from early identification to realisation and exploitation of the project, will be employed (Twijnstra Gudde [3]):

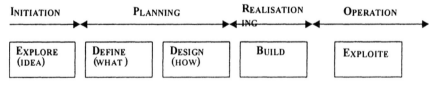

Figure 1. Project Phases

During the initiation phase the problem and potential solutions are the centre of attention; activities include (extensive) exploration of the problem and mapping the parties involved. Public-private partnership in this stage usually is without obligations. When the problem and its solution gradually become clear the project enters into the planning phase. Now the 'what' and 'how'-questions needs to be answered. In the part of definition phase the aims, scope and constraints must be defined whereas in the latter part a detailed technical design as well as financial arrangements are needed. When an agreement has been reached the building phase can commence. In a life cycle approach construction and maintenance are combined in the design. Ultimately, the project is ready for use. Public as well as private parties are qualified to operate infrastructure projects.

With regard to the process of project development of infrastructures, relations between public and private parties can take various shapes. In this paper four types of co-operation are distinguished: public projects being contracted out, private initiatives, public project with innovative tendering and public-private partnership.

2.1 Contracting out

Contracting out is the traditional way of developing and realising public infrastructure. The phase of conceptual development and planning is done by government and results in a public program of detailed specifications. On the basis of this program the project is put to tender. The selected private constructing company builds the project and delivers it to the public authority. Exploitation is mostly in the hands of government or tendered separately to a private party. Putting exploitation to contract is a relatively new practice (Kessides [4]).

Although governments have developed engineering departments with a lot of technical know how, they often lack knowledge of the market and their orientation on societal developments is limited. In the course of years, private constructors have become dependent on governments. They also lack a market orientation and a drive to develop and apply technological innovations. Within the specification formulated by the government, there is little room for innovation and experiments. Typical for these of projects is the separation in various phases of project development (conceiving the concept, planning, design, construction and exploitation). This restricts the quality of (the exploitation of) the infrastructure system, efficiency, and the opportunities for commercial exploitation.

2.2 Public involvement in private initiatives

During the last years a number of private initiatives were launched concerning the realisation of what traditionally is considered to be public infrastructure. In the field of building roads that were postponed due to a lack of public budget, private initiatives were presented. But also with respect to major, highly innovative projects such as the construction of a magnetic elevated train between Amsterdam and the North of the Netherlands, private plans are proposed. These private initiatives are to a certain extent the other side of the picture of the above mentioned public projects. Especially the first phases of the project are developed by private parties (Van Mill [5]). Often, commercial exploitation of the project is part of the concept. For instance, the magnetic high-speed railway proposals include a plan for commercial exploitation of the locations in the surrounding of the railway stations. Public parties are asked to adopt these private plans and to give formal approval for their construction. Often they are asked to provide a substantial financial contribution to the projects to cover the unprofitable (public) parts of the project. In this case, contrary to public projects where the government ex ante defines the project unilaterally, the government is asked to legitimise and subsidise private projects ex post. It is unlikely that the government will approve of such a role. However, it is difficult for private parties to accept that the government is using their proposals for their own projects. In this case, enthusiasm will evaporate quickly. So, it remains to be seen whether the recent upsurge in private initiatives is the starting point of a new practice that will result in privately developed projects and/or public-private partnerships.

2.3 Innovative tendering

Innovative tendering encompass contracts such as Design and Build (DB), Design, Build and Operate (DBO), Design, Build and Maintain (DBM) and, if financial risks are included, Design, Build, Finance and Maintain (DBFM) and Build, Operate and Transfer (BOT) (Walker and Smith [6]). Usually, public programs are not as detailed as in case of contracting out. They are formulated at the level of output specifications and functional requirements. This offers private companies the opportunity to optimise their activities within the prescribed requirements. If public authorities try to direct developments by using output criteria and contractors are allowed to keep (part of) their gained savings, this is a strong incentive for innovative behaviour at the operational level. If the exploitation phase is part of the contract, the public aim is often to generate private funds in excess of the traditional contribution.

Because the project and the functional requirements are unilaterally determined by government, it remains to be seen whether the project is suited for commercial exploitation. This may be the reason why private parties were not inclined to invest in recent public infrastructure projects

2.4 Public-private partnership

Public-private partnership occurs when public and private parties co-operate during several phases of project development, including the phases of concept development and planning. As a result the quality of the integrated design is higher than if parties had operated on their own. In the earlier discussed types of relationships public and private gains, risks, tasks and responsibilities were, more or less, kept apart. Thus a financial trade off between design, construction and exploitation becomes apparent. Partnership presupposes that they are shared (Teisman [1], Graeber [7]). Partnerships do not start out with a clear public program of functional requirements or specifications, or with a well-conceived private plan. It starts with a general idea that is interesting enough for public as well as private parties to enter into a joint process in which this idea is elaborated. During this process parties do not commit themselves to a detailed contract which is meant to rule out all uncertainties and risks. What they do in participating in the partnership is consciously accepting risks. The fact that parties have committed themselves to the project despite these risks is a guarantee for further investments in order to make the project successful and generates mutual trust (Hindmoor [8]).

The partnership is aimed at realising joint products: innovative projects which are characterised by synergy. In order to satisfy the societal demands innovations in the field of technology, processes, procedures and institutions must be used. Especially public parties will be concerned about the impacts of infrastructure on the environment. However, impacts of the project only become known during actual project development. Public parties should safeguard conditions for the articulation of public interest during the process of project development and make couplings between public and private parties engaged in this process. Synergy means that the unique combination of private and public efforts results in a commercial exploitation of a project that also contributes to the realisation of public interests.

3 Port Development in Rotterdam

3.1 Introduction

When the stock of port-related sites in Rotterdam started to run low in the late 1980s, the Municipal Port Management issued a warning statement. The Port Plan 2010, a future vision from 1991, anticipated that (until 2010) 1250 hectares of port acreage would be needed. This space could be found through more efficient and intensive use of existing sites, by filling in harbour basins and the construction of new port areas. In this respect, the expansion of the Maasvlakte and/or construction of a second Maasvlakte was introduced (GHR [9]). Initially, the municipal port management thought of developing this port project in the traditional unilateral way with a financial contribution of the central government. The policy objectives for the Greater Rotterdam (Rijnmond) area are:

- strengthen the position of Mainport Rotterdam by finding a solution to the shortage of space for port and industrial activities that exists in the Rotterdam docks, in Rijnmond and/or in the south-western part of the Netherlands;
- improve the quality of the living environment in Rijnmond by utilising the options which solutions to the shortage of space offer.

On the basis of the national scope of the project, a Key Planning Decision Plus procedure (KPD+) was eligible.

3.2 The Combination model

In the summer of 1999 the progress report 'PMR on course' was published. At that moment, private involvement entered the picture for the first time (PMR [10]). A working group, consisting of 7 private and 12 public parties, studied the possibilities of public-private partnership (SPB [11]). The Private Involvement Study Project looked at which forms of co-operation are possible, which game rules apply and what contribution private parties could make. The process was described as a voyage of discovery. The PMR-director stated later: "At the first meeting everyone was watching each other closely but during the second meeting prejudices were put aside. After the third time we had come to terms. It was a nice process to experience. I remember it with pleasure." (Fukke et al. [12]).

It was recognised that private parties would not be able to realise the port expansion on their own. Preliminary calculations showed that the investment costs for the second Maasvlakte without and with its own maritime access amount to 2 and 3 million Euro respectively. The sharing of the (financial) risks in the construction and exploitation phase is the basis for public-private partnership. Three types of risks were identified: political, construction and exploitation risks.

Various models of public-private partnership were designed. Based on their intention to co-operate, private parties wanted to be involved in the plan formation phase. Several options, ranging from zero commitment to equal partnership, have been discussed. Because private parties want to influence the construction and exploitation risks, zero commitment is left out. The option of co-makership focuses on designing, constructing and exploiting the new Maasvlakte together and according to the wishes of the government. More partnership is apparent in the option partnering where parties also look for solutions together. Finally, the Combination Model was drawn up to interweave the public-private partnership in the existing planning procedure.

The Combination Model incorporates both the objectives of the government and the business community and comprises a number of phases. Initially a public programme of project specifications will be drawn up. This programme is discussed with social organisations, private parties and then with the Dutch Lower House. After the first political decision-making step, laying down the specifications for design, the status changes into a sort of pre-KPD+ part 1. On the basis of this document, the European tender takes place in two stages. First the consortium profile is examined and then the submitted plan. In this way, both content and credibility are scrutinised. Once the consortium and proposal have been selected, the public authorities will establish a public-private partnership with the consortium that then draws up KPD+ part 1.

Given the involvement of many parties in the preparation it was anticipated that it would be possible to run more quickly through the next steps of KPD+ procedure. Due to the possibility of modifications to the plans occurring during these phases, modification and exit rules must be laid down in order to prevent any claims being made against central government.

3.3 The Binnenmeer plan

In November 1998, a consortium comprising a constructing firm (Ballast Nedam), a container handling company (ECT) and a financial institution (ING Bank) launched the Binnenmeer concept. This plan is based on the phased construction of the second Maasvlakte. Such an approach had never been presented before and offers evident advantages. However, it remains to be seen whether the content side of the plan will altogether meet the specifications for design which has yet to be drawn up.

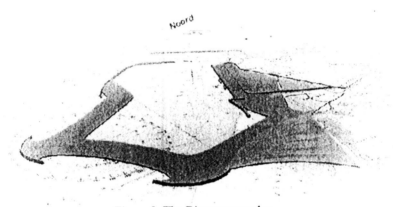

Figure 2. The Binnenmeer plan

Moreover, the plans' financial format displays a very traditional notion of the role of public and private parties; the government is held responsible for the construction of the sea walls while the construction of quays and port sites can be largely financed by private funds. As a consequence of this role division, the government must bear the greater part of the project costs and private parties enjoy the economic benefits of the project.

In the report 'PMR on course', the project organisation PMR chooses a different distribution of public and private investments than has been suggested. The government contribution requested by the consortium will be based on, among other things, of a social cost-benefit analysis. Notwithstanding its innovative concept that was copied in other plans, the Binnenmeer plan played no role in policy discussions.

3.4 The Parallel model

Much to the disappointment of private parties, the Cabinet exchanged the Combination model for the so called Parallel model. In this model, the role of central government is restricted to spatial planning and land use, regional and local government will act as project developer. These arrangements were laid down in an official agreement that describes each party's responsibilities. For the time being, the city of Rotterdam is responsible for the development of a second Maasvlakte.

In a business case, carried out by the municipal port management, the (un)profitable parts of the project were identified. From a purely financial point of view, it seems that the construction and exploitation of a new Maasvlakte is not profitable. However, the government insists on substantial private involvement. Rough calculations suggest that, given a rate on investment of 8% for private parties, the contribution of public parties varies between 48% and 65% (CPB/NEI [13]). Meanwhile, the feasibility of an independent land and property company has been studied. Obviously, public parties will take part in this company. Future users of the new port area are precluded because of a possible conflict of interest.

Since public authorities are responsible for decisions concerning planning, grant and use of land, construction and maintenance, the question remains what the contribution of private parties might be. At the moment two arguments prevail: innovation and risk sharing. Therefore, parts of the project will be tendered. For example: the design and construction of the dikes can be combined with maintenance. This lifecycle approach may offer new concepts. If a DBFM-contract is in place, risk sharing is also included. In relation to new terminals BOT-contracts can be considered. In this way, stevedores will design, build and operate terminals on their own account. After a certain time they hand the terminal over to the land owner or exploitation company. This model resembles common practice in the port of Hong Kong.

3.5 Epilogue

In relation to the port extension of Rotterdam 4 different approaches have been suggested that come close to the archetypal forms of public-private relationship described in chapter 2. In the beginning the traditional way of project development that comes close to contracting out, was considered. The Combination model shows how public-private partnership could have played a role in the development of the port of Rotterdam. In the proposed approach, public and private parties managed to find an arrangement that gives shape to the involvement of private parties within the existing national procedures and meets the EU directives for private tenders. Thus, two important barriers to public-private partnership were removed.

The importance of the Combination model was not so much that it provided a standard type of arrangement for port projects. It is unlikely that this model is the only feasible arrangement and that it will solve every problem involved in partnerships. Its importance lies rather in the fact that it has produced a breakthrough in thinking about public-private partnerships.

However, public-private partnership lost momentum. Parties didn't co-operate closely enough to succeed in jointly developing a second Maasvlakte. Public as well as private parties resumed old roles (Fukke [12]). Since the Combination model was abandoned and the Parallel model is put in place, the principal-agent relationship has returned. However, innovative tendering instead of contracting out will be applied.

Between times, a private initiative (the Binnenmeer-plan) was launched too. Although the innovative design was appealing, the proposed division of tasks and risks was very traditional and the plan never played an essential role in policy discussions about public-private co-operation.

4. Conclusions

In the decision making on the involvement of private parties in the expansion of the Rotterdam port different models have been discussed. The process can be seen as a 'voyage of discovery' in which public and private parties jointly explore the possibilities for co-operation. In this interaction process both public as private parties were able to get acquainted with each other potential role in the project. Also, innovative, substantive ideas were exchanged, such as the implementation of the land reclamation in phases, which was suggested in the Binnenmeer concept and later made part of the Parallel model.

Despite these initial explorations, public parties hesitated to organise the project as a public-private partnership. This was partly due to the relatively modest financial contribution of private parties to the project. Also there was the risk of creating conflicts of interests, especially by involving future operators in the partnership. The Parallel model does not exclude the possibility of private parties joining the independent development company. But it is not at all sure that they will have an interest in doing so. The involvement of private parties in the rest of the project is organised according to the model of innovative tendering. So, the port expansion of Rotterdam ends up as a predominant public project. After an initial involvement of private parties in the conceptualisation and planning of the project, which has resulted in some innovative ideas, their further contribution to the project as a whole will be limited. Perhaps this is a typical reaction when institutional innovations are introduced. After an enthusiastic start, parties become aware of costs and risks (Kingdon [14]). Instead of finding ways to jointly accept and manage risks, they chose for risk avoidance. Risks are divided up and settled in contractual arrangements. These contracts regulate relations in such a way that interactions are discouraged in stead of furthered (Van Ham en Koppenjan [15]).

Advantages are there without doubt: reductions of risks for both public as private parties, clear demarcations of the public and private domain and so on (compare Jacobs [2]). But it also means that chances for further innovative project development are missed. What is more, one may wonder whether the choice for a Hong Kong like model matches with the institutional context and market position of the Rotterdam Port. After all, Hong Kong is the only major port in the region, while Rotterdam is confronted with major competitors. This gives future users a strong negotiation position. It remains to be seen whether working with Built, Operate and Transfer contracts will be as favourable for public parties as one might theoretically expect.

References

[1] Teisman G R, *New arrangements and management principles for public-private partnership*, paper presented at the Third International research Symposium on Public Management, Birmingham, 25-26 March 1999.

[2] Jacobs J, *Systems of survival; a dialogue on moral foundations of commerce and politics*, Random House, London 1992.

[3] Twijnstra Gudde, *Op de goede weg*, Amersfoort, 2000.

[4] Kessides, C, *Institutional options for the provision of infrastructure*, World Bank, Washington, 1993.

[5] Mill, B. van, *Dilemma-management bij de vorming van private consortia*, MSc-thesis, Delft University of Technology, Delft, 2000.

[6] Walker, C and Smith A J, *Privatized infrastructure: the Built Operate Transfer approach*, Thomas Telford Publications, London, 1995/6.

[7] Graeber, G, *The embedded firm: understanding networks: actors, resources and processes in interfirm co-operation*, Routledge, London, 1993.

[8] Hindmoor, A, *The importance of being trusted: transaction costs and policy network theory*, in: Public Administration, vol. 76 Spring, pp. 25-43, 1998.

[9] GHR (Municipal Port Management Rotterdam), *Havenplan 2010*, Rotterdam, 1991.

[10] PMR (Project Mainport Development Rotterdam), *PMR op koers*, The Hague, 1999.

[11] SPB (Studyproject Private Involvement), *Samen aan boord*, The Hague, 1999.

[12] Fukke, J et al., *Op de goede weg*, Twijnstra Gudde, Amersfoort, 2000.

[13] CPB/NEI (Central Planbureau / Nederlands Economisch Instituut*)*, *Bedrijfseconomische aspecten van landaanwinning bij PMR* (notitie 00/21), The Hague, 2000.

[14] Kingdon, J W, *Agendas, policy and alternatives*, Little, Brown and Company, Boston / Longman, New York, 1984/1995.

[15] Ham J C van en Koppenjan J F M, *Building Public Private Partnerships*, In: Public Management Review, vol.3 no. 4, Routledge, London, 2001.

Enemy at the gates: introduction of Multi-Agents in a terminal information community

L. Henesey & J Törnquist
Department of Software Engineering and Computer Science
Blekinge Institute of Technology, Sweden

Abstract

Container terminals in Europe play a significant role as nodes within logistics chains. The management of container transportation system is a decentralized, often poorly structured, complex, and changeable problem domain. Therefore we propose that a Multi-Agent System (MAS) approach would offer port and terminal actors (e.g. rail operators), a suitable means of control, coordination, and management in the container terminal domain. Ports, as nodes, accept and deliver freight from various modes of transport and offer services that add value to the freight. In order to plan the activities in the terminals, continuous and reliable information on the cargos' physical status (e.g. position, condition) is paramount to other activities. Integrating the information flows from the various transport providers and actors would improve the planning for the terminals and benefit planning and scheduling for the others in the chain. Through the introduction of "information society" to a logistics chain, transport providers and actors can improve individual performance and service by sharing information with each other. In the suggested MAS approach, the actors involved in the physical and information flows will be mapped with agents that will have the abilities to search, coordinate, communicate, and negotiate with other agents in order to complete their specified goal(s). Information society members could benefit from information sharing with the use of Multi-Agents, especially in cases of deviations or other kinds of problems. Knowing problems at an early stage can increase the ability to limit negative impacts. Thus, this approach may serve as the basis for a decision support system (DSS).

1 Introduction

There exist many bottlenecks in terms of information and flow of cargo in container terminals. Information refers to the content of, and means and procedures for communication, inside the port and information possessed by external actors [13]. Congestion and increasing cargo dwell times is a common scene in many of the world's ports as well as in the road and railway networks and at airports in Europe[5]. In order to avoid further bottlenecks, especially due to increasing road transports, the European Union has stated their aim of "turning intermodality into reality" [5]. This will be achieved by technical harmonization and interoperability between systems [5]. Intermodal transportation can be defined as "movement of goods in one and the same loading unit or vehicle that uses successively several modes of transport without handling of the goods themselves in changing modes" according to the definition of The European Conference of Ministers of Transport provided in [15]. In the White Paper [5], the EU policy of delimiting the predicted increase in road transport by increasing use of intermodal transportation, is intended to be achieved by shifting the balance between transport modes, i. e. substituting road transports with transports by short sea shipping, rail and inland waterway when possible [22]. An intermodal transports chain can be characterized by using railway and/or shipping for long distance transfer of goods between two points and road transport for collection and distribution of goods. In some relations this has been achieved by devoted intermodal corridors, but not to the same extent as expected. Not only transportation itself is important, but also the activities occurring in the transport chain, such as cross-docking. Intermodal transports are often joined with high costs in comparison with unimodal transports due to the need of terminal operations in the process of changing transport mode, and terminal operations constitute a large part of the total intermodal cost [3]. Another obstacle is the dependency on a large number of actors in the chain and the critical integration between them [11]. Integration can be, and is in this context, the need of sharing important information that may have an influence on the daily planning. This paper will focus on the importance of collaboration between different parties improving intermodal transportation, and in particular the rail-port interface since it affects the overall performance of the total transport chain. The paper will first briefly discuss the measurements and driving forces in transportation, then present a MAS approach for rail traffic, a container terminal and their interface. The MAS approach will be presented as an alternative method for improving the container terminal interface system.

2 Performance measures

The measurements of performance used in transport chains vary greatly as well as the definitions of performance [6]. However, one performance indicator often used is accuracy in time of delivery (ToD). Through measuring the accuracy in ToD for different transport modes, the degree of reliability of the transport mode can be viewed. In this context reliability refers to trustworthiness, i. e. if the requirements of a transport are fulfilled to a certain established level. Reliability is one of the key factors when choosing transport mode as well as lead-time and price [17]. In the final report of the project *Intermodal Quality* (IQ) [3] the decisive factors in the modal choice between intermodal and road transports are addressed. The project has identified that first price is determinant and second the match to the individual logistics requirements, closely followed by degree of flexibility. However, as stated in the same report, there are relations between quality and price, which together determine the attractiveness of a specific transport mode or combination of transport modes.

3 Intermodal transport

There are socio-environmental impacts that affect transportation to a varying extent such as the surrounding traffic flow. The sensitivity differs between the four basic kinds of transport modes; road, rail, sea and air. Sensitivity refers to how much of an impact the surrounding traffic has on the transport mode. The infrastructure, for instance, used in railway transportation is limited which make it more dependant of the surrounding traffic, while road transports are not affected to the same extent. The varying complexity in different unimodal transports is thus obvious. Combinations of transport modes are even more complex due to the additional critical integration on different levels (e.g. documentation, information, required facilities). As illustrated in figure 1., a transport chain consists of four main layers. The illustration is a result from reviews of related beliefs such as the five-layer model of a road transport presented in [7] and empirical studies in the field. The figure is hierarchical ordered, illustrating that the infrastructure is the basic means for transportation; there is a traffic flow of which each transport is a part. The flow of goods is the core of transportation and the information flow placed above refers to that it is not a necessity, but critical for the performance of the transports. Furthermore, each layer is divided into parts. The infrastructure contains rail network, roads, terminals, etc. Traffic flow can be divided into different traffic systems for and within each transport mode and the devoted flows of transports. The flow of goods can be divided into type of goods, type of transport unit used, etc. Finally, the information flow can be divided into technology, systems, format, accuracy, etc. Economic flows are not considered.

Function

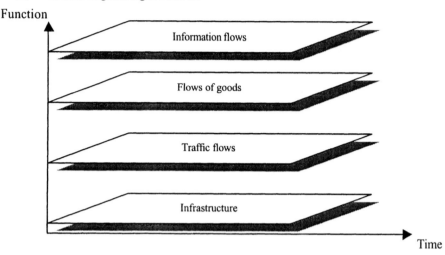

Figure 1. The four main layers of a transport chain.

4 The problem description

Currently, there exist an estimated 15 million containers and this figure is projected to continue increasing for the next 10 years at 8.5% [16]. Ship lines are aware of this growth as can be seen by the huge investments in yard construction of container ships that can transverse the oceans at 25 knots, whilst laden with 8000 or more containers (known in the industry as TEU, twenty foot equivalent unit). The planned container terminal investment in Europe (1999-2001) is approximately 208 million Euros [20]. Container handling systems in in-land and marine container terminals have a substantial impact on waiting time of incoming trucks and trains. Additional waiting time at these terminals directly translates to larger fleet size requirements for ground container transportation, which contributes to traffic intensity, and increased ground transportation capital investment and operating costs. Ship lines are unconcerned if there is a poor terminal productivity, as long as their vessel sails on time. Terminal operators are trying to reduce or stabilize the cost per ton/teu handled and thus maximize profit. Their aim is to efficiently use the resources available during the operating time that the vessel is occupying the berth.

5 Methodology

An intensive literature survey of articles published in journals was conducted. The European projects: IQ, COST330, EUROBORDER, and INFOLOG where analysed. A survey and interviews were designed for 30 port users and port providers of ports in Sweden and in Belgium, in order to establish if the situation of congestion has been resolved. The results from our data collection have shown that the bottlenecks do exist. The results of the survey validate that if port actors can share information with each other through a portal, than they can achieve individual benefits within their business functions. For coordination of information within terminals, portals are considered detrimental to their work. The use of the multi-agent approach in the interface between port terminals and port users is supported from other MAS applications and research [9][4]. The goal is to conceptualise a simulation tool by using a MAS, fed with real data.

6 Multi-Agents System Simulation

There exist several definitions of what agents are and many of them are debatable. In this paper, we use the definition from Davidsson; "an agent can be viewed as an autonomous program that can modify its behaviour based on experiences and is capable of interacting independently and effectively in its environment" [8]. The agent can be alone or embodied, such as in the case of a "Mars Rover." The agent-like technology applications that most are familiar with are web-crawlers, software programs that scan the Internet for information.

A MAS is a collection of agents co-operating with each other in order to fulfill common and/or individual goals [9]. In a MAS, different agents may have different roles and individual goals. The actors or elements in the container transportation system can be viewed and modeled as an information society, where communication, negotiation, and collaboration occur. Agent communication is possible with computer languages such as KQML (Knowledge Query Manipulation Language). The agents are often created by using agent programming, an extension of object-oriented programming. The abstraction level is high in agent programming and facilitates the ability of agents to act in a goal-oriented fashion. The various actors in a system, such as the container transportation system, would be identified and modeled according to their function or behavior. By performing simulations in the agent-based model, patterns and behaviours can be analysed. Through analysis of the complex behaviour of agents representing different parts of the problem domain, (e.g. schedules, operations, and tasks), would provide an opportunity to optimise the resources in the whole terminal interface process.

The MAS simulation of a container terminal interface with a railroad operator is considered feasible since similar use of MAS has been applied (c.f. work by John L. Casti and OASIS air traffic management project at Sydney airport). John L. Casti, a researcher at the Santa Fe Institute simulated the transport system of Albuquerque, New Mexico with the use of agents [4]. A MAS simulation between the actors is helpful in gaining insightful information about a system. An example of a MAS simulation could be a distributed organization of a container transport system.

7 The Railway-Port interface

The interface to other modes of transport lies in this system. The management of the gate consists of obtaining information on containers entering the terminal, leading to the proper physical handling. Controlling the gate to the terminal is important since it affects other parts of the container terminal system. The data that is collected; container number, weight, port of destination, hazmat, reefer, shipper, ship line, and seal number is used when deciding where to place containers for storage and later for loading. The interface also serves the rail operators, as well as other modes of transport with information such as waybills, arrival notices, and dispatches. The rail operators are able to plan and schedule accordingly to the information received from the shipper via a terminal portal.

8 Railway status

As mentioned, the European Commission states its aim of increasing intermodality in order to avoid an increase in road transports and the related problem with congestion and pollution, in the White paper [5]. As many have pointed out, for example in [1], an increase in railway transportation requires an increase in capacity since there are capacity problems already today. In the infrastructure proposition provided by the Swedish government [23] the following is written: *Without efforts for increasing the railway capacity, the transition to environmentally friendly transport modes, which could happen today, will be delayed. The adjustment to a long term sustainable transport system will thus also be delayed* (translation from Swedish). Capacity problems do not only prevent new actors to establish themselves in the transport market for railway traffic, but they also generate bottlenecks, which in turn cause delays in the traffic flow. As described earlier, one deviating train may cause sever disturbances in the whole network depending on how the disturbances are propagating. Problems due to delays in railway traffic in Sweden have been partly studied in a R&D project, *Baninfo,* financed by Banverket, the Swedish National Rail Administrator. The project aimed at identify ways how to increase customer satisfaction at Banverket regarding accessibility to traffic related information, by interviewing several customers on different levels. The results showed that not only punctuality is of interest, but information on deviations and their consequences, i.e. changes in Estimated Time of Arrival (ETA), is also important for the planning of transports. Today, there is no system that has the ability to predict the outcome of changes in the Swedish railway traffic flow. However, as pointed out, the results from the project Baninfo argues for a need of this kind of information at an early stage. Several of the interviewed companies stated the importance of knowing about changes in time, since it is a prerequisite for effective rescheduling.

Prediction of the consequences of a deviation in railway traffic is a complex process, and the factors that affect the final outcome are many. One approach is to simulate the traffic flow in real time and use a distributed system where agents represent the train dispatchers and the transport operators. The *train dispatching agents* are the operative decision makers when handling a disturbance in the train traffic flow, and the decisive measures they take in different situations have to be mapped. The *transport operator agents* also have an influence since when there is a conflict between two trains operated by one and the same company, the company can choose which train the company prioritize. This approach is under development by a group at Blekinge Institute of Technology. For further information, see [19].

This agent-based approach is primarily aiming at increasing the performance in the Swedish train traffic and, further on, the attractiveness of intermodal railway transportation by an increasing punctuality and reliability. The benefits of this approach are dual. Firstly, the simulation will provide a decision-support tool for the train dispatchers to evaluate different counter measures and actions taken when handling disturbances in the railway traffic both in real time and for strategic purposes. Secondly, and most interesting in this context, the simulation will provide all concerned with information on changes in the transports' plans that will affect their business. This information will serve partly as input for ad hoc planning and coordination of resources in terminals such as the ports described below.

9 Port status

The MAS approach is to be considered as a suitable tool in container terminal management due to the complexity, terminals are determined by a variety of inputs, outputs, actors, intrinsic characteristics and external influences. The allocation of resources and scheduling of operations is conducted by several distributed decisions makers. By using agents to optimally schedule and allocate resources to the terminal interface, the rail may be better served and the performance of the container terminal system as a whole may improve. Using the metaphor of an information society, the actors that work through networks and make decisions effecting the daily operations of the port can be properly represented by agents. The use of agents to represent the various actors in a simulation would permit management to better control and coordinate the terminal activities. Ports are demand driven by many customers, and users. Satisfying all actors is very difficult since actors often have *conflicting* interests. Sometimes an actor can even become dominant and his demands can take excessive importance. For the vessel owners it is paramount that the vessel is quickly "turn-around", meaning loaded and discharged as fast as possible. An average container liner spends 60% of its time in port and has a cost of $1000 per hour or more [21]. To shorten the time spent by vessels, terminal operators need to spend special emphasis in resource allocation, receipt of information before vessel berths in order to reduce the $45000 stay of a third generation containership or $65000 of large vessel at port [16]. The terminal operators are providing services that involve much more than loading a ship. Various actors with intrinsic goals, that are often in conflict, in combination with complex coordination of several services, is a decentralized problem area that gives rise to the idea or approach of a MAS.

The MAS approach to the container terminal interface, would allow the terminal interface to be modelled as a *gate agent*. The *gate agent* would receive information of arriving export cargo from a *rail agent*. The information of containers entering the terminal would be communicated to a "yard planner" and "ship planner", which in turn may be modelled as a *yard planner agent* and *ship planner agent*. The *yard planner agent* instructs the *gate agent* to advise the lorry which terminal area to park for loading or unloading. The g *ate agent* communicates with other actor agents (i.e. rail agent or lorry agent) in dispatching containers. The *yard planner agent* would "wrap" an existing software program to optimise the capacity of the yard while minimizing the use of resources. The basic idea is to place wrapping software around legacy code in order for it to appear normal to other agents ~ agentify [9]. The *ship planner agent* is a modelled agent that would "wrap" around an existing ship planning software program. It would allow the ship planner to have decision-making ability and communicate with other agents in order to complete its goal, to load the vessel according to the established scheme. In reversed order, the vessel (modelled as a vessel agent) may communicate via the *yard* and *gate agents* to the rail operator (modelled as a rail agent) the time of arrival and number of containers to be discharged. The information may also include weight, description of cargo, destination, and other data deemed relevant by the *rail agents* in order to optimise and increase the performance of the rail operations. The premise for the agents in the simulation is to identify the relationships between the various elements by mapping them as agents [12]. The use of agents would assist containers or cargo in finding their destinations through the array of networks and systems that make up the container terminal simulation. The simulation tool would be the basis of a DSS.

10 Discussion

According to Parunak, "the use of agent based modeling thrives in situations characterized by a high degree of localization and distribution and dominated by discrete decisions" [18]. Many problems can still be solved using existing methods and the availability of software that has been developed for such tasks (e.g. routing software, stacking algorithms, discrete event simulation). However, in choosing the MAS approach to model the port interface, the actions and functions of the various actors can better analysed than with existing techniques. A holistic model does not exist that analyses the various subsystems, and actors in the container terminal transportation domain. The MAS approach enables the simulation of the various individual actors, processes, and elements to be individually modeled. The simulation allows observation of the behaviours, plans, and co-ordinations between the agents in order to solve a problem. The interesting fact is that before a simulation is conducted, the result is difficult to predict. The simulation of the elements is the basis for an intelligent decision support system, enabling the various actors to plan, schedule and coordinate optimally. Better planning is obtainable with real time data being available for the various agents to analyse and make decisions upon. Technology such as agents may be able to assist terminals by increasing capacity and performance without spending large investments on terminal expansion and equipment. The 'software' rather than the 'hardware' of port development will be the determining factor in future trends in port competition vis-à-vis terminal management [21].

11 Acknowledgments

Due appreciation is given to Prof. Dr. Paul Davidsson at Blekinge Institute of Technology and Prof. Dr. Peter Värbrand at Linköping University.

12 References

1. Aktuellt om Logistik, No. 4, provided by Sveriges transportindustriförbund (in Swedish), 2001.
2. Arlbjorn, J. S., *Logistics knowledge creation: reflection on content, context and processes*, International Journal of Physical Distribution & Logistics Management, Vol. 32, No. 1, 2002.
3. Cardebring et. al., *Summary report of the IQ project*, 2002, TFK Transportforschung GmbH and INRETS for further information or http://www.tfk-hamburg.com/
4. Casti, J.L. *Would be Worlds: How Simulation is changing the Frontiers of Science*. John Wiley & Sons, New York, 1987.
5. Commission of the European Communities, White paper, *European transport policy for 2010: time to decide*. Brussels, 2001.
6. Chow, G., Heaver, T. D., Henriksson, L. E., *Logistics Performance: Definition and Measurement*, International Journal of Physical Distribution & Logistics Management, Vol. 24, No. 1, 1994.
7. D'Este, G., *An event-based approach to modelling intermodal freight systems,* International Journal of Physical Distribution & Logistics Management, Vol. 26, No. 6, 1996.
8. Davidsson, P. *Autonomous Agents and the Concept of Concepts*. PhD. Thesis, Lund University, Lund, Sweden,1996.
9. Davidsson, P. and Wernstedt F., *Software Agents for Bioprocess Monitoring and Control*, Journal of Chemical Technology and Biotechnology, Vol. 77, 2002.
10. Gustafsson, I., Törnquist, J., Källström, L., *Förbättrat informationsutbyte mellan Banverket och dess kunder* , Final report of R&D project financed by Banverket (in Swedish), 2002.

11. Heller, C., *Tracking & tracing in combined road/rail freight transport*, IPTS Technical Report Series, Institute of Prospective Technological Studies, Seville, EUR 18716 EN, March 1999.
12. Henesey, L. Wernstedt F, Davidsson, P., *Market Based Approach to Container Terminal Management*, Agent Technologies in Logistics workshop. The 15th European Conference on Artificial Intelligence, Lyon, France, 2002.
13. Hultén L *EUROBORDER.* European Commission DGVII R&D project-Transport contract no. WA-95-SC.153. Brussels, 1999.
14. Hultén, L., Bolin, H., *Information Exchange and Controllability* (2002), TFK – Transport Research Institute, for further information www.tfk.se
15. Kallstöm L. *Infolog*, European Commission under the Transport RTD Programme of the 4th framework, 2000.
16. Kia, M., Shayan, E., & Ghotb, F., *The importance of information technology in port terminal operation*, International Journal of Physical Distribution & Logistics Management, Vol. 30, No. 3/4, 2000
17. Lumsden, K., *Logistikens grunder*, Studentlitteratur, (in Swedish),1998.
18. Parunak, H., Savit, R., & Riolo, R., *Agent-Based Modelling vs. Equation-Based Modelling: A Case Study and Users' Guide.* Proc. of Multi-Agent systems and Agent-based Simulation, Springer-Verlag: Berlin and New York, pp. 10-25, 1998.
19. Törnquist, J. and Davidsson, P., *A Multi-Agent System Approach to Train Delay Handling*, Agent Technologies in Logistics workshop. The 15th European Conference on Artificial Intelligence, Lyon, 2002.
20. Wiegmans, B.W., Ubbels, B., Rietveld, P., & Nijkamp, P. *Investments in Container Terminals: Public Private Partnerships in Europe*: International Journal of Maritime Economics Vol. 4 no.1, pp.1-19.2002.
21. Winklemans, W., (ed.). *Port Competitiveness.* De Boeck Ltd, Antwerp, Belgium. 2002.
22. http://europa.eu.int/comm/transport/library/marco_polo_summary.pdf Summary of the proposal of Marco Polo project (visited 2002-04-30)
23. http://naring.regeringen.se/fragor/transport/infrastrukturprop2001/bakgr und.htm#jarnvag, Infrastructure proposition 2001 by the Swedish government (in Swedish), 2001.

Port management games

A. W. Veenstra
Erasmus University Rotterdam, The Netherlands.

Abstract

This paper reports some first results on an ongoing project aiming at the development of modern education tools in a Rotterdam based cooperation of schools in the area of transport and logistics. The results comprise a basic definition of such a game and the applicability in the different levels of the school.

Introduction

Rotterdam is historically the maritime centre of the Netherlands. While many see the main reason for this the existence of the largest port of the world, in fact the trade, industry and distribution activity that is relatd to this port is the key factor. Nevertheless, around these activities, a strong maritime infrastructure has been developed consisting of shipping and shipping related technical expertise, maritime and transport education, and enterprises engaged in the physical shipping and transport activities.

Within this context, recently, a cooperation agreement was reached with a number of schools and one university that all teach on topics in transport and logistics. This cooperation was labeled Rotterdam Transport Schools (RTS). The aim of this cooperation is to integrate and streamline educational programmes for the entire logistics chain. For this purpose, RTS contains educational programmes for professional, higher and academic education.

Among its activities, RTS has the improvement of the vertical and horizontal flow of students, the improved storage of knowledge and expertise and the development of educational tools that can be used at all levels of the educational pyramide.

This paper deals with the latter objective. Below, the paper will describe a way to develop a modern port management education tool that could be used throughout RTS. The discussion in this paper is the result of an ongoing process, but the paper will reach some important preliminary conclusions.

For the remainder, some terminology will be consistently used.

Port Management: the purposefull organisation of activities related to the cargo and/or ships in seaports.

Game: learning method whereby a player, through an active attitude other than listening or reading can obtain knowledge and insight and whereby actions of the player can influence the outcome of the game.

Operational management game: By means of a game, the player gets familiarised with operational aspects of a learning object.

Strategic management game: By means of a game, the player gets familiarised with strategic aspects of a learning object.

One of the main questions the paper adresses is: is it possible to develop one tool to cater for all educational objectives? The research in the paper aims to address this question in two ways. First, it describes a number of existing edcuational tools and evaluates them in terms of level and appreciation of students. Second, it sets out to formulate learning objectives throughout RTS and evaluates if these match in such a way that they could fit into one tool.

The paper is structured as follows: the next section describes the Dutch education structure and the structure of RTS. The section after that describes a number of existing port management education tools and evaluates their fitness for use in other layers of the education column. After that the paper sets out the determine learning requirements for education tools throughour RTS. The paper finishes with some closing remarks.

Dutch education structure and RTS

The Netherlands has an education structure that contains secondary school at three different levels: 4 year preparatory professional education, 5 year advanced education and 6 year preparatory academic education. These three levels again lead into three levels of further education as set out in Figure 1. The arrows in Figure 1 depict possibilities for switching between different levels.

The cooperation between schools in Rotterdam teaching in the areas of transport and logistics comprises all levels of further education in Figure 1, including part of the 4 year secondary school (preparatory professional education in inland shipping and port operations).

This cooperation therefore contains a wide range of education levels and students of ages ranging from 12 to 25. The estimated number of students in transport and logistics is 4000 of which 3000 in seconddary school and professional education

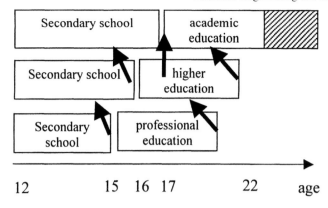

Figure 1: Dutch education system

Justification for the development of port management games

The reason why RTS is interested in the development of modern education tools on port management has two part questions:
1. why develop modern education tools?
2. why focus on port management?

The first question almost answers itself. It is obvious that an institute for learning should strive to dispose of education tools that are in line with a modern educational philosophy and the state of the art technology. This will help prepare students for a position in modern day society, assist students in their development into young professionals and support their education in such a way that they have the skills and knowledge to function according to the expectations of their future employer.[1]

A further question is: what constitutes a modern education tool. Education tools range from reading material to example objects to instruction sets and exam questions. Some of the tools are designed for individual learning, some for group learning. In short there is a huge variety in the type of education tool, and consequently, a large spread in what could constitute a modern education tool.

A way to structure this is to draw upon modern educational philosophy, where constructionist learning is the key. This type of learning is based on the idea that the student should be in charge of its own learning process. The teacher's role is one of assessing, coaching and guiding the student through this learning process. The student, however, takes the lead, determines tempo and reflects on the extent of his or her learning over a certain period. Preferably, the student does this through interaction with other students, teaching staff and practitioners. 'Modern' learning tools should support this type of learning.[2]

This means that the learning tool should be designed in such a way that the student can determine or direct at least part of the learning trajectory. A game particularly fits this objective. It only sets out a starting position and some rules, thereby letting the flow of the game be the outcome of the student's decisions, and it allows interaction between students, who could play different roles in a game. Furthermore, the way the game is introduced and played should allow for a reflection on learning objectives.

The second question is slightly easier to answer. RTS has its focus on transport and logistics. The operations and management of ports is an important part within that theme. A choice for port management as a topic for the development of a new education tool, in parallel to a number of other topics, such as transport chain management and air transport is a natural one.

Overview of existing port management games

After some investigation, it turned out that the schools that are part of RTS already have a number of games and other education tools, details of which may be relevant for the development of a new tool. This section will briefly review these existing tools. This review is relevant because it helps to reveal what learning objectives for these tools are. This section reports also on an evaluation of the multimedia tools by the students for which they were designed. The existing games and some of their aspects are reported in Table 1.

Table 1: overview of existing port management games

	Port of Rotterdam management simulation game	Mainport and manage-ment game	Privatisat ion game	Taco-trans	Business networking game
Environ-ment	Local area computer network	Different rooms, paper	Paper	Inter-net	Internet
Material	Documents, pidgeon holes	Profiles of port functions	Profiles of main actors in privati-sation	none	Oracle database
Execution	12 actors, of which 3 by computer; 2 rounds; game is about order processing	5 groups; game is about tendering for port activities	5 groups; game is about privatisat ion of port compa-nies	Game consists of set of questions; issue is modal split	9 actors, 4 rounds; game is about developing market places
Costs	License is €1,800	Devel: €18,000; no licence	Devel: €2,200 ; no licence	Devel: ?; no licence	Devel: €410,000 Licence applicable
remarks	Game is more or less obsolete				Game is still in development

The games in Table 1 all attempt to modernise the learning environment of the student. They differ in the way they so this. Some of them are really role play games (Mainport and management game, privatisation game), Tacotrans is in fact a multimedia case, while the Port of Rotterdam simulation game is an operational transport chain simulation. The business networking game, on the other hand, is a game about commerce.

The result is that the analysis of these games leads to very different sets of learning objectives. The definition of port management given in the introduction can help us out: port management is the purposeful organisation of activities related to cargo and/or ships in port.

This definition is an operational definition of port management. This is done on purpose. RTS consists of a range of educational levels, as was depicted in Figure 1. If the aim is to develop a learning tool that should work in more than one level, the focus should not be on a purely operational issue, or on a purely strategic issue. The chosen definition of port management represents the middle way.

The games in Table 1 that fit into this definition are the mainport and management game on tendering for transport services in a port, the tacotrans case on modal choice and the business networking game. The simulation game is too operational, the privatisation game too strategic. The problem with the business networking game is that is has a strong commercial business focus with little connection to port management. As a matter of fact, the development now focuses on the automotive industry and not on the port industry as such.

It seems worthwhile to look in a bit more detail at the mainport and management game and the tacotrans case.

Mainport and management game

Learning goal: to gain insight into the complex interaction of the actors in a port that strive to develop logistic chain solutions.

Approach: the game deals with the construction of a response the an Asian tender for logistics services. The quality of this tender document is at the end of the game the basis for the evaluation of the understanding of the participants with respect to the learning goal. This evaluation should be done by the players themselves.

Game play: the game is played with 5 groups. These groups represent (1) a stevedore, (2) a broker, (3) a trucking company, (4) a consultant, and (5) a shipping company. The groups all obtain a profile of their part and the issues they need to address in negotiation. The groups engage in negotiations, where by the result can be individual tender proposals per group, or combined proposals from cooperations that emerge during the game. During the game, the game master feeds the groups new information that results in changes in the proposals.

Evaluation: This game was played as part of an executive course for port managers in Rotterdam in the spring of 1999, and as part of an executive course for port managers in South Africa. As a result, changes were made in the profile documents. The general comment of players was the unexciting game environment.

Tacotrans

Learning goal: to gain insight in complexities of combined transport in a port.

Approach: The internet site provides the students with various links to sources for information on combined transport. These sources are in the form of a reading list, internet sites and video interviews with experts.

Case work: the student or groups of students are asked to explore the internet site and answer all questions aksed.   The result is a written report that can be evaluated by the teacher.

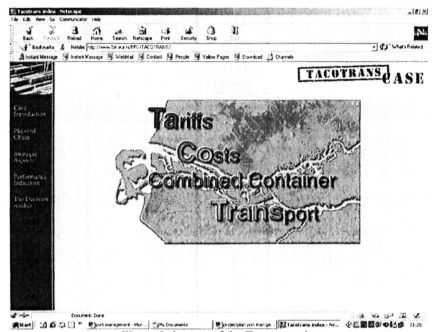

Figure 2: lay out of the Tacotrans site.

Evaluation: The tacotrans case is played regularly at Erasmus University Rotterdam as part of the so-called port minor in the department of business administration. Recently, students were asked to give an evaluation of the usefulness of tacotrans as a learning tool.[3] The main comment was that the case lacked interactivity. The site only contains a calculator that can be used for the comparison of different combined transport solutions. The video interviews are as informative as reading something on paper, when the new experience of the multimedia element wears off. Nevertheless, the multimedia environment was considered to contribute to the attractiveness of the learning tool. One important remark concerned the level of the assignments, which was not challenging for university students. For one, students complained that the calculator, that is part of the site, does not give insight in the structure of the calculations.

This description and evaluation leads to two insights: the construction of a learning tool should address issues of attractiveness, and the development of the tool should somehow allow the playing of the tool at different levels.

Definition of port management game

In broad terms, the port management game this paper envisages is a combination of the above two games/cases. This new game incorporates the level and interactivity of the first game, and the attractiveness and information rich environment of the latter.

A brief first description of the essentials could be:

Learning goal: to gain insight into the complex interaction of the actors in a port that strive to develop combined transport solutions.

Approach: the approach of the mainport and management game to base the game on a fictitious tendering process is useful for the level graduate higher and academic education. The game will probably be less useful for lower year students in higher education and professional education.

The game should be presented in a multimedia environment. This environment offers links to sources of information and evaluation tools that are part of the decision making process, and supports the interaction between the different groups that take part in the game. The game should preferably be constructed in such a way that a varying number of groups can take part in the game.

The game environment should allow the game master to play with the information the different groups have at their disposition. In a computer environment, this could be implemented straightforwardly.

Game play: the playing of the game is a combination of gathering information and fitting this info in the tendering document. As part of this process, calculation tools such as the one provided in the tacotrans case may be useful. Simulation tools are shown to be very useful in gaining insight in complex processes (see Verspui et al. 1999). In addition to this work, the game could provide a platform for talks with other groups and tools for the preparation for these talks.

Some remarks should be made at this point. A set up as described above actually exists within RTS. It is called the 'STC Chain Simulator' and is used mainly as support for education in operational tasks that are part of the transport chain. The simulator therefore facilitates the communication between the various parties in the transport chain though the official forms and messages that are used between them. The development cost of this simulator run in the millions of euro's. This is mainly due to the extensive programming required.

Another remark concerns the implicit choice of the level of the students on which the game is focused. One way to develop a tool that could be used in the whole of RTS would start with an all encompassing learning needs analysis. Any similarities in these needs would form starting points for joint learning tools. However, the evaluation of the tacotrans case has strengthened the conviction that even slight mismatches in the level of the game (which are inevitable when combining professional, higher and academic education) and the level of the students leads to the imperfect attainment of the learning goals for groups at different levels.

Concluding remarks

This paper reports some first results on an ongoing project aiming at the development of modern education tools in a Rotterdam based cooperation of schools in the area of transport and logistics. The results comprise a basic definition of such a game and the applicability in the different levels of the school.

The paper describes the dutch education system and the composition of the joint venture Rotterdam Transport Schools. It then provides an introduction into modern learning philosophy and a summary of the most important existing learning tools on port management within RTS.

On the basis of this overview and some evaluation results of the ones that are considered most useful, a basic description was constructed of the port management learning tool to be developed. This tool combines interactivity with attractiveness and fits the definition of port management as set out in the beginning of the paper.

A disadvantage is that the game tends to the strategic level, which makes it less useful at the more operationally oriented levels of education in RTS. However, for these levels, an extensive learning tool, the chain simulator, already exists. It seems preferable to develop the new tool in the already developed environment of the chain simulator. This will result in a considerable reduction of development costs.

References

[1] Bolhuis, S.M. 2000. Towards independent learning, what teachers to and think (in Dutch). Leuven: Garant
[2] Ratering, D. & K. Hafkamp 2000. Selfguided learning, coaching of experience based learning in organisations (in Dutch). Schoonhoven: Academic Service
[3] Verspui, L., R. Eberson & A. van der Wal Bake 1999. Mocobi: inland shipping simulated. In: Simulation and logistics around the port (J. van Nunen and L. Verspui, eds.). Delft: Oberon

Inter-modality in the ports and sustainability of the EU freight transport

B. Kavalov
Institute for Prospective Technological Studies, Spain.

Abstract

Over the past two decades, the intensive economic growth in the European Union (EU) has been accompanied by a strong increase in the freight transport volumes. Apart from the evident positive impact on competitiveness of the EU economy, the latter really questions sustainability of the EU transport industry, because of more and more expanding adverse transport externalities - sharply increased oil consumption, congestion, accidents and environmental pollution. Some of these externalities are due to subjective factors like inefficient use of resources and poor split amongst transport modes. Generally, it is feasible these factors would be corrected by various technical, market and regulatory means. In this connection, the potential, offered by the inter-modal transport chains with participation of waterborne transport for surmounting of these disadvantages, should be assessed carefully. However, switching of the freight transport demand to inter-modal transport solutions with participation of waterborne transport could be feasible only when the aggregate quality of the inter-modal transport service is higher than the aggregate quality, supplied by other transport alternatives. The key pre-condition for this suggestion is availability of fair rivalry amongst transport modes.

1 Introduction

Over the past two decades, the intensive economic growth in the EU has been accompanied by a significant increase in the freight transport demand. In relative terms, the main share of this transport growth belonged to the road transport, exclusively at the expense of the rail transport and at a lesser extent – waterborne transport. As a result, the current modal split in the EU freight transport consists of 44 % of the road transport, 41 % of the short sea shipping, 8 % of the rails, 4

% of the inland waterways and 3 % of the pipelines. By the year 2010, a new 38 % increase in the EU freight transport industry is expected. The road transport (50 %), followed by the waterborne transport (34 %), is predicted to be accountable for the major share of this growth [1].

2 Main challenges towards sustainability of the EU transport

Apart from the greater covering of transport needs of the EU industry, the above described increase in the EU freight transport volumes results in two main problems. This directly affects and questions sustainability of the EU transport sector. These two main challenges are de-coupling of transport externalities' growth and economic growth [1] and security of the EU oil balance [2].

2.1 De-coupling of transport externalities' growth and economic growth

Increasing of the EU freight transport volumes means that transport needs of the EU industry are covered at a greater extent. On the other hand, such considerable growth in transport activity reflects into an augmentation of the corresponding adverse secondary effects, expressed primarily in congestion, accidents and environmental pollution. Therefore, the main goal of the EU transport policy over the coming years will be to gradually break up the link between economic growth and transport externalities' growth. Objectives of this policy goal are preventing congestion, avoiding as much as possible accidents and decreasing greenhouse emissions and noise. At the same time, reduction of transport externalities is not to be at the expense of lesser quantitative and qualitative coverage of transport needs of the EU industry at all.

2.2 Security of the EU oil balance

The EU transport industry depends entirely upon oil - 98 % of the total transport consumption, representing 67 % of the final EU oil demand. Referring to the prevailing upward trends in the EU transport sector, by the year 2020 the import dependence of the EU upon oil would increase up to 90 % from the current 50 % level. This unfavourable situation is not expected to alter even after enlargement, because the EU-candidate countries suffer similar problems with the oil supply. Such a rate of oil external dependence represents real threat for the security of the EU oil balance, with all ensuing socio-economic consequences.

3 Tools for solving the main problems in the EU transport

There are several policy tools available for surmounting the above mentioned two main problems of sustainability of the EU transport industry [3].

The targeted de-coupling of transport externalities' growth and economic growth, without decreasing the extent of quantitative and qualitative coverage of transport needs, could be achieved by better land-use planning. The expanded application of various information and communication computer-based solutions [e.g. Intelligent Transport Systems] might also decrease the volume of transportation required for covering of a constant size of transport demand, especially by improvement of co-ordination along the transport chain.

In regards to the security of the EU oil balance, the EU-member states have got very limited scope to influence on the oil supply side. However, they could intervene on the oil demand side, mainly by promoting effective and efficient utilisation of fuel in transport.

On the supply side, the main reserve is associated with improvement of the balance split amongst modes. Here, the main target is decreasing the excess share of the road transport by promoting use of other modes, as well as better linking up the transport modes. Actually, the expanded application field of the road transport is the main cause for the synchronised growth of economy and transport (and of transport externalities respectively), as well as for the increased fuel consumption in the EU transport sector. Thus, the main tool for overcoming both main challenges in the EU transport sector is alteration of split amongst transport modes, giving priority to the rail and waterborne transports. As in most cases, the latest technologically is not capable of performing door-to-door transport services, the main emphasis in the coming years should be optimal combination amongst transport modes, i.e. inter-modality, as shown in Figure 1.

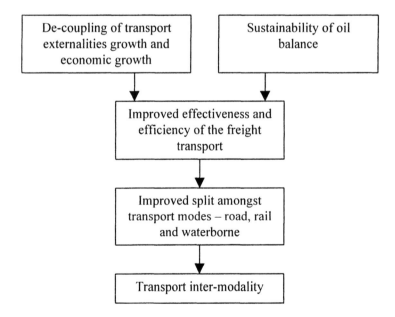

Figure 1: Transport inter-modality and sustainability of the EU freight transport.

4 What the "inter-modality" means

As usual, under the notion "inter-modal transport", it is understood that it is a movement of goods whereby at least two different transport modes are involved into door-to-door transport chain. Taking into consideration reasons given in the previous paragraph 2, this definition of inter-modality could be modified as movement of goods whereby the major part of journey is performed by rail and/or waterborne transport, and any initial and/or final legs, carried out by the road transport, are as short as possible [4].

In fact, inter-modality represents an indication of the extent of integration amongst transport modes. The economic basis for inter-modality is the opportunity to use into integrated door-to-door transport chains individual strong points of each transport mode, while eliminating consequences of their weak sides, in order to improve the overall efficiency and effectiveness of the transport process.

5 Characteristics of the waterborne transport inter-modality

The key question for inter-modality is how to attract freight transport demand. This could be realised only if in the potential customers' concepts the relative aggregate quality of the overall transport service, offered by inter-modal transport chains, is higher than the aggregate quality, supplied by the uni-modal transport opportunities [5]. It means that in the potential customers' mind the inter-modal transport alternative ought to be safer and/or more secured and/or cheaper and/or faster and/or more reliable than the uni-modal transport alternatives available. The relative priority of these criterions defers on case-by-case basis. In regards to the inter-modal transport chains with participation of waterborne transport, their relative competitiveness towards other transport opportunities (including fully terrestrial inter-modal transport options) depends on the following general and mutually related factors:

5.1 Type of the goods

The specific qualitative and quantitative characteristics of the goods could very often pre-determine the choice between uni- and inter-modality. Sometimes it is highly recommended that transportation of some specific cargoes (hazardous, high-value, perishable and etc.) be performed with minimal transhipments. However, this obstruction could be overcome by wider application of containers.

On the other hand, transportation of typical mass cargoes on relatively long distances is better if performed exclusively by waterborne transport, subject to availability of suitable waterways, even if it is accompanied by certain increase in the voyage distance. Therefore, in most cases the inter-modal transport chains could be considered as more feasible for cargoes, carried by the liner shipping freight segment, but not by the tramp one, where the great majority of cargoes are mass ones. However, when inland transportation of mass or dangerous cargoes is needed, the inter-modal transport chains with participation of river or combined sea-river transport, where possible, should be considered as the best transport opportunities.

5.2 Techno-economic characteristics of ports and shipping services

One of the main conditions for successful inter-modal connections in the ports is availability of good links between the waterborne transport and terrestrial modes of transport. Therefore, the rightful and prospective design of ports and terminals, as well as standardisation of loading units and handling equipment, are absolutely indispensable for the effectiveness and efficiency of the inter-modal transport connections in the ports [6]. Finally, the cargo-handling infrastructure in the ports ought to allow secured storage of the goods, safe and expeditious handling and transhipment, adequate information and communication procurement of the transport process, including pre- and end-haulage stages.

5.3 Specifics of the voyage

It is generally assumed that the inter-modal transport chains are competitive on distances not less than 500 km. However, the combination amongst good co-ordination amongst elements along the inter-modal transport chain, adequate and well developed port infrastructure and high-quality management over the waterborne part (voyage and stays in the ports) of the inter-modal transport process could earn competitive inter-modal transport solutions even on considerably shorter distances.

5.4 Partners involved in the transport chain

Peculiar characteristics of parties in the transport process could also favour or prevent utilisation of inter-modal transport chains. For instance, very often relatively small cargo consignors and shippers prefer to use uni-modal transport alternatives even if the aggregate commercial conditions (prices, duration of the voyage and etc.) are worse than those ones of the inter-modal transport opportunities. As usual, this phenomenon is due to lack of knowledge, as well as to unawareness, respectively - fear of the inter-modal and waterborne transport procedures and regulations.

5.5 Rivalry with terrestrial transport modes

The level of rivalry with terrestrial transport modes could considerably influence customers' choices between uni- or inter-modal terrestrial transport alternatives and inter-modal transport options with participation of waterborne transport. Others things being equal, if a well developed terrestrial infrastructure and/or competitive prices of terrestrial freight transport services are available on routes, where inter-modal opportunity with involvement of waterborne transport is presented as well, the relative competitiveness of the latter would be questioned seriously.

6 Key problems associated with the waterborne inter-modality

The most frequent problem, met by the inter-modal transport chains with participation of waterborne transport, is the lack of co-ordination amongst different transport modes involved. As a result, all parties in the inter-modal transport chain suffer significant losses, risen by high-cost time delays. As usual, the lasts are incurred by unsynchronised working hours of inter-modal terminals in the ports with schedules of the terrestrial transport modes, uncoordinated and unproportional - in terms of speed and time - handling of cargoes, consequent congestion, poor punctuality of terrestrial pre- and after- waterborne haulage legs and etc. Therefore, the unwillingness to use inter-modal transport alternatives with participation of waterborne transport sometimes is due to a previous bad experience, no matter whether that experience has been directly suffered or has only been reported by someone.

At some extent, the problem with delayed handling of cargoes could be partially solved by broader utilisation of standardised loading units and means of transport. Unfortunately, apart from containers, common standards of many other loading units are still missed. For instance, presently there are several different kinds of pallets, standardised on country-by-country basis only.

The time delays in the ports could also result from lack of proper communication and information exchange. Sometimes the former is prevented by the fact that the relatively small truck operators, involved in the inter-modal transport chain, are not willing or do not have enough financial resources to invest in communication network required. The misunderstanding of the corporate confidentiality usually causes the latter.

At the end, but not at the last, the question of the internal mutual rivalry amongst different independent operators could also prevent the successful functioning of the inter-modal transport chains. The problem becomes more complicated especially in the case of the presence of many relatively small road transport operators and/or in periods of low business activity and falling freight transport demand.

7 Main reserves for improvement of waterborne inter-modality

7.1 Improved management of inter-modality in the ports

Apart from the measures, logically ensuing from the above described problems with inter-modality in the ports like intensification and better co-ordination of handling of vessels and cargoes, a flexibility of the suppliers of the waterborne transport services towards customers' needs is also essential. At least this means that a market, i.e. seller's approach towards the existing and potential customers ought to be perceived, but not an employee's one. On the other hand, the role and importance of the in-land agency offices and freight forwarding representatives ought to be noticeably risen, in order to attract more potential cargoes and customers to the inter-modal waterborne transport services [7].

7.2 Fair pricing in the waterborne transport

A wider application of fair pricing for the complex waterborne transport service has to be introduced as soon as possible by its suppliers - liner freight forwarders and ships' operators. It means that in order to shift more cargoes and customers from the uni-modal terrestrial transport alternatives to the inter-modal waterborne transport opportunities, a pricing much closer to the actual transport costs incurred plus a reasonable risk premium ought to be applied. The reason for this affirmation is related to some of the peculiar characteristics of the liner shipping, like availability of various freight alliances of ship owners and/or operators, and relatively lower extent of speciffic chartering knowledge by the typical customers of the liner shipping services. Therefore, some liner operators and freight forwarders sometimes are tending to gain an extra-income and profit at the expense of customers by offering them higher freight rates than the realistic ones and/or by inserting in the transport contracts quite unfavourable clauses, being sometimes even in breach with usual established shipping practice. In short-term aspect, such kinds of actions could potentially ensure some benefits. However, in long-term perspective, this most probably will reflect in a loss of customers, who would switch to the terrestrial transport alternatives, because of the unfair pricing and/or contractual behaviour.

7.3 Rising of awareness and dissemination of "best practice"

Due to various factors, a great number of cargo consignors are used to call uni-modal terrestrial transport alternatives and especially the road alternatives. As a result, even when the inter-modal waterborne transport opportunity offers better complex transport service in terms of prices and/or safety and/or security and/or speed and/or reliability, very often it is equally difficult to explain to and to be understood by the potential customers. The key problem here is that such understanding requires changing their minds, which could not be done as quickly as the intention. Therefore, the wider dissemination of the "best practice" and of the awareness about successful practical cases could be considered as one of the main factors for enhancing the waterborne transport inter-modality. In addition, the increase of knowledge about advantages, principles and rules of the waterborne transport - both liner and tramp shipping sectors – via various training courses, is also essential for the broader use of inter-modal waterborne transport chains.

8 Key pre-conditions for the waterborne inter-modality

There are two main pre-conditions for development and enhancement of the waterborne transport inter-operability: the fair and efficient pricing in all transport modes [8] and the inter-operability [9].

8.1 Fair and efficient pricing in all transport modes

Under the notion "fair and efficient pricing in transport", it is understood to be a pricing approach where all transport modes are paying for the full socio-economic cost they incur. In most cases, the last includes infrastructure, congestion, accidental and environmental costs. Presently, the most undercharged mode of transport is the road one because of the prevailing inadequate pricing system in use. The implementation of such kinds of pricing, which take into consideration the impact of transport externalities, is suggested to improve present unfair rivalry amongst transport modes, ensuing from the undercharging of some of them and respectively – overcharging of others. The key consequence from this process is expected to be a considerable amendment in split amongst transport modes, especially with increasing the relative share of the inter-modal transport chains, including wider use of both short sea and inland shipping.

8.2 Inter-operability

The inter-operability is a process, where at least two different operators and/or systems are functioning efficiently and effectively, despite various technical, physical, geographical, legislative, organisational and socio-economic barriers. In the case of inter-modality, the significance and importance of inter-operability is related to the ability of communication systems involved for safe and secured exchange of data, information and services. Due to the great dependence of the effective and efficient work of the inter-modal transport schemes on the accurate and punctual information flows, the availability of high degree of inter-operability along elements of the inter-modal transport chains becomes indispensable for the competitiveness of inter-modality in comparison with uni-modality.

9 Conclusions

The factors of success for the inter-modal freight transport chains in general and especially for transport chains, which include waterborne transport, could not be defined in broad terms like type of goods, distance of transportation and etc. In fact, the choice of cargo consignors is governed by the aggregate quality of the complex transport service supplied, which includes various parameters as prices, safety and security, speed, information procurement, punctuality and etc. Therefore, the relative competitiveness of various freight transport opportunities available - uni-modal, fully terrestrial inter-modal or inter-modal with involvement of waterborne transport - defer on case-by-case basis. However, competitiveness and customers' choices are also governed by the market and rivalry conditions, which are not always fair and efficient by definition. Thus, sometimes market and institutional measures are needed in order to secure fair rivalry amongst transport modes in the EU freight transport sector. The impact of these measures would be improvement of the split amongst transport modes.

On its part, the last would significantly make for the sustainable development of the EU transport sector, by contributing to the de-coupling of transport externalities' growth and economic growth and to the security of the EU oil balance.

References

[1] *European transport policy for 2010: time to decide*, EC White paper, COM (2001) 370, Brussels, 2001.

[2] *Towards a European strategy for the security of energy supply*, EC Green Paper, COM (2000) 769, Brussels, 1998.

[3] Integrated policy aspects of sustainable mobility (Paper 1 of 10), *Thematic Synthesis of the Transport Research Results*, EC Transport RTD Programme, Fourth Framework Programme, Brussels, 2001.

[4] Freight intermodality (Paper 10 of 10), *Thematic Synthesis of the Transport Research Results*, EC Transport RTD Programme, Fourth Framework Programme, Brussels, 2001.

[5] Efficiency and Quality (Paper 6 of 10), *Thematic Synthesis of the Transport Research Results*, EC Transport RTD Programme, Fourth Framework Programme, Brussels, 2001.

[6] Branch, A.E., *Economics of shipping practice and management*, Chapman & Hall, London and New York, 1995.

[7] Van Berkum, J.M., Schuring, W., *Shipping agency practice*, Stichting Vervoer- en Havenopleidingen, Rotterdam, 1981.

[8] *Towards fair and efficient pricing in transport*, EC Green Paper, COM (95) 691, Brussels, 1995.

[9] Interoperability (Paper 9 of 10), *Thematic Synthesis of the Transport Research Results*, EC Transport RTD Programme, Fourth Framework Programme, Brussels, 2001.

Institutional reforms in Lebanon's commercial ports: opportunities and challenges

M. Hadi Baaj
Department of Civil and Environmental Engineering,
The American University of Beirut, Lebanon.

Abstract

On December 31, 1990, the concession contract signed between the State and a private company for the Port of Beirut operation expired. The State (just coming out of a prolonged 15-year civil war) elected to take a "temporary" measure. It appointed a temporary commission to operate the port under the rules of the expiring concession. The legality of this measure, however, has since always been questioned, while the temporary commission underwent three major personnel changes which clearly prevented any long-term thinking or planning. In 1998, the temporary commission entered into a USD 200 Million 20-year joint venture for the establishment of a container terminal Thus, the need became urgent to develop a permanent institutional framework for the port of Beirut. Meanwhile, Lebanon's three other ports were inefficient public institutions and it was desirable that the model proposed for Beirut could also be applicable to them. This situation provided an opportunity for the Government to concurrently rethink its role in the maritime transport sector. There was a clear need to initiate institutional reforms that would ensure the clear separation of Government policy-making from economic and social regulation of the sector (while assessing the need for an independent regulator), and port operation and service delivery. This paper presents the port organization models that were investigated, the multiobjective decision making approach that guided the model selection, the institutional reforms, and the proposed implementation plan.

1 Introduction

Since 1887, the Port of Beirut had been operated by a single private company under a concession contract which awarded the company exclusive rights for port management, operation, and development, subject to conditions and to royalty fees paid to the State. In 1960 (in the midst of a rising tide of nationalizations in the Middle East and following Government complaints that the concessionaire did not invest sufficiently in port expansion and upgrading), the State terminated the concession agreement. Thus, a 30-year contract management agreement was signed which provided for the private company to manage and operate the port on behalf of the State with a fee participation in the revenues arising. The contract downgraded the previous 1887 concession after a buy-out by the State of the Company's rights of exploitation and development, and of the majority interest previously held by the company in the revenues arising subject to a royalty fee for Government.

On December 31, 1990, the contract expired, and the State (just coming out of a prolonged 15-year civil war) elected to take a "temporary" measure. It appointed a temporary commission (Gestion et Exploitation de Port de Beirut, GEPB) to operate the port under the principle of continuity (i.e., under the rules of the expiring concession). The legality of this measure has since always been questioned, while GEPB underwent three major personnel changes which clearly prevented any long-term thinking or planning. In 1998, GEPB entered into a 20-year joint venture agreement with Dubai Port Authoruty, DPA of The United Arab Emirates. GEPB invested USD 150 million (100 million of which were obtained through a loan from the European Investment Bank, EIB) in the infrastructure for a new container terminal, while DPA was to invest about USD 50 million in the container terminal superstructure (including the purchase and installation of 3 gantry cranes). Thus, the need became urgent to end the temporary status of GEPB and develop the most suitable permanent institutional framework for the port.

To that end, The Ministry of Public Works and Transport contracted with High-Point Rendel, a specialized British firm, to propose a permanent institutional framework for the port of Beirut while studying its applicability to Lebanon's three other ports (that were functioning as public institutions, following Law # 4517). In addition the institutional reforms provided an opportunity for the Government to rethink its role in the maritime transport sector, ensuring the clear separation of its policy-making function from economic and social regulation (preferably through an independent regulator), and port operation and service delivery.

Section 2 presents the objectives of institutional reform in the Port of Beirut and identifies the stakeholders and their interests. Section 3 overviews the 9 port models that were proposed for evaluation, while section 4 presents the 16 attributes that these models were evaluated against, utilizing a multi-objective decision making approach to guide the model selection. Section 5 presents the preferred port model and the proposed institutional reforms for the maritime transport sector. Section 6 concludes with the proposed implementation plan.

2 Objectives of reform and the stakeholders' interests

The primary and overriding objectives of introducing institutional reforms in the Port of Beirut were to enable it to: 1) provide a safe haven for ships, 2) achieve cargo-handling efficiency, 3) satisfy customer requirements, 4) provide for the needs of the national economy, 5) achieve an adequate return on the assets committed and on capital investment, and 6) unlock the value of assets in terms of land, people, and capital [1].

Stakeholders were divided in two groups: the first consisted of stakeholders with a "Higher Level" Interest, while the second group consisted of a different and lower level of interested stakeholders who may need to see their rights protected or to be compensated if these rights were to be removed in the interest of the higher level of stakeholders. The first group consisted of the State, the Lebanese people, the port community, the port customers, and the environment. The second group consisted of GEPB, the three Ministries of Transport, Economy, and Finance, Beirut Municipality, the existing private operators, shipping agents, and DPA [1].

3 Alternative port organization models

There are several organizational models for seaports, including a municipal model (common in Northern Europe), a state model (common in Southern Europe and South America), and a private model (common in countries with a British tradition) [2]. A thorough discussion of seaports' reform is provided by Trujillo and Nombela [3]. For Lebanon, the following 9 port organization models were evaluated: 1) "Stay Where We Are" or SWWA (Do-nothing), 2) Full Nationalization Model, 3) Full Privatization Model, 4) Public Institution Model (in accordance with Law # 4517, currently applicable to the ports of Tripoli, Sidon, and Tyre), 5) State-Owned Corporation Model, 6) State/Private Sector Joint Venture Model, 7) Concession Model (similar to the 1887 Beirut Port Concession Model), 8) Contract Management Model (similar to the 1960 Beirut Port Contract Management Model), and 9) Port Autonome Model [1]. The pros and cons of each model have been detailed in Baaj and Issa [4]. Following is a brief overview of each model, as adapted from High-Point Rendel [1].

"Stay Where We Are" or SWWA Model: describes the current situation of GEPB which has been operating on the principle of continuity, as if it were the immediate successor to the previous company which operated under the 1960 concession contract and all those powers remained in place. GEPB has been operating without clear legal powers other than those granted under successive governments since December 31, 1990, as temporary expedients. GEPB's Chairman who is also the General Manager reports directly to the Minister of Public Works and Transport. GEPB has private sector employees and carries out its activities through subcontracting to private operators. It is substantially self-financing and its annual financial surplus is drawn down by the Government. It carries out the planning and development of the port and has established consultative procedures with its principal port users. However by its very status

as a "temporary" body it cannot continue to exist, and to make it permanent would require a new law.

Full Nationalization Model: is where the State not only owns, but also carries out all the planning and development of the port and all the port operation and maintenance activities. In effect the port is under the direction and full control of the State and there is no private sector activity.

Full Privatization Model: is where the ownership of the port and the conduct of all activities within the port lie in private hands. The system is driven by a desire to make profit from such ownership.

Decree 4517 Public Institution: is a public sector entity established primarily to manage, operate, and develop a State-owned public utility within the context of proscribed procedures as not financial authorities and freedoms to act independently. It has a Board appointed by the sector Minister in accordance with a statutory constitution. Its employees are not considered as civil servants however their employment is monitored by the Civil Service Council and approved by the Tutorship Minister. Currently, Lebanon's three other ports of Tripoli, Sidon, and Tyre, operate as public institutions subject to the 4517 decree. There was a clear desire on the part of all Board members of these ports to reform their own ports, along the model proposed for the port of Beirut.

State-Owned Corporation: is a public corporation established in the first instance by the Government which owns the majority of its shares. It is largely subject to the laws, rules and disciplines of companies. Initially, but not necessarily, the State holds 100% of the shares in the company but it may sell some or all of these at a timing of its choosing. Government may hold a "golden share" to prevent the sale to and ultimate control by other parties if there is an overwhelming issue of national interest at stake.

A State/Private Sector Joint Venture: whereby a state sector entity (typically a 100% state corporation) and a private sector company form a joint venture for a specific purpose and for a fixed and renewable term (if the parties agree). In ports it is particularly effective in the development of major port projects such as container terminals. The state sector often develops the terminal's infrastructure while the private sector provides equipment, know-how and sources of private capital and finance. It is normal for this to be either a 50%/50% shareholding or with one party (normally the state sector company) having nominal control under a 51%/49% shareholding structure. A shareholder's agreement can settle powers of decision and dispute procedures, and provisions concerning sale of shares and pre-emption and valuation rules. A management contract for the entire operation is often awarded to the private sector partner. This structure has been used to great effect in China. A joint venture company could be granted a Beirut style concession over land owned or leased by the State or the state sector entity.

The 1887 Beirut Port Concession Model: From 1887 to 1960 a single concession holder enjoyed exclusive rights of management, operation and development subject to conditions and to royalty fees paid to the Government. This was almost like the modern BOT agreements. The detail and duration of the agreement was remarkably robust and worked well. The concession was let by the State and supported by a series of statutes. The operation was wholly within the private sector and the finance for development was raised without reliance on State funds. There therefore remains open a major opportunity to let a new long-term concession or contract to manage and develop the Port of Beirut through a modern revival of the original model dating back to 1887.

The 1960 Beirut Port Contract Management Model: In the 1970's and 1980's many ports in the Arab World were managed under contract by specially formed international port management companies such as Gray Mackenzie at the Dubai Port Authority and at Jeddah. The 1960 Beirut Port contract provided for a private company to manage and operate the port on behalf of the State with a fee participation in the revenues arising. The contract downgraded the previous 1887 concession after a buy-out by the State of the Company's rights of exploitation and development, and of the majority interest previously held by the company in the revenues arising subject to a royalty fee for Government. The Commission Provisoire has managed the Port of Beirut as if the former management contract made with the original concession company in 1960 were still in effect. It has used the "principle of continuity" to do this. In effect the State's interest in this contract has been managed with the State collecting all the dividends. Many of the pros and cons of the 1960 contract model are similar to those of the concession model described above. However some of the points pro are conspicuously absent in the contract model.

The Port Autonome Model: is seen in part in the major French ports and provides for the management and development of State-owned ports on a substantially autonomous basis. Chairmen and Board Members are appointed for a fixed term by the Minister in accordance with a statutory constitution after first considering the representations from the interested parties of the port business activities and from wider sections of the community. The model envisaged here would also draw on the provisions seen in the Law for the Central Bank of Lebanon that was established in 1963 for the regulation of the commercial banking sector. The law has been effective for this purpose and has endured with only one or two amendments since that date. The model replicates substantially the internationally accepted models of the USA/German/French/and British central banking systems which have afforded substantial financial and administrative independence within a high-caliber ethical system operated on commercial lines rather than within a civil service structure or culture.

4 Attributes of the alternative models

A set of 16 key attributes was developed for the evaluation of the 9 alternative models. The score of each attribute was on a scale of 1 to 10 (low to high). It was desirable that the preferred model should score well overall, with consistent scores of at least 5 for each of the attributes. The goal was to maximize a multiobjective function of the 16 attributes expressed as the summation of the product of the score of each attribute by the weight of the attribute. Assuming equal weighting for all attributes, the model's final score was obtained by summing the scores of its attributes. The attributes were the following [1]:

1) Degree of freedom from Government interference (with rights to subcontract)
2) Ability to buy, sell and lease, and rent lands and enjoy property title
3) Degree of financial independence to borrow and lend and be self-financing without reliance on the Government
4) Ability to be commercially pro-active and responsive to market forces and to develop and project a favorable public image
5) Ability to carry out and engineer development works within its port limits and to appoint all necessary consultants and advisors for this purpose
6) Ability to set independent administrative procedures both at the Board level and for the conduct of the day-to-day business of the entity
7) Degree of freedom in determining its own recruitment and other personnel policies (with complete freedom to hire and fire, carry out training and establish pay and conditions of service on the basis of merit)
8) Ability to achieve bankability through the ability to pledge and assign the assets and revenues of the port without recourse to sovereign guarantee
9) Degree of accountability
10) Probability of timely legal implementation
11) Degree of being in tune with the Lebanese Free Enterprise Spirit
12) Degree of being in tune with global trends
13) Degree of compatibility with previous models applied in Lebanon
14) Ability to reduce the end user costs
15) Ability to reflect the national interest
16) Ability to retain inherent asset value

Note that the higher stakeholders' interests were represented through attributes 14, 15, and 16 (end user costs, national interest, and retention of inherent asset value). It was clear that the alternative institutional models would differ substantially in their ability to achieve high scores on all attributes. However, as the attributes were seen as desirable goals, the preferred model would be one which would enhance and achieve the points pro while eliminating, protecting from, or diminishing the influence of the points cons. There would naturally be preferences exercisable according to the standpoint of each accredited assessor. There would also be a political preference to be exercised towards the end of the evaluation process. The evaluation of the 9 models against the 16 attributes (which was meant as a guiding tool in the selection of the preferred option) have been detailed in High-Point Rendel [1].

5 The proposed reforms

Based on the results reported in High-Point Rendel [1], the State Corporation Model emerged as the highest scoring followed by the Concession Model as a close second. In all of its attributes, the State Corporation Model scored consistently above the halfway mark and had no difficult low scores (as can be seen in the Nationalization Model and also in so far as the inability to achieve timely implementation in the Full Privatization model). Thus it was recommended that a 100% State-owned commercial corporation (Beirut Port Corporation, BPC) be set up, which would lease from the State all port premises and equipment for 99 years (State retains ownership of all assets). BPC would immediately seek to sell about 25% of its shares to a strategic partner. The strategic partner would be the management contractor, a private firm specialized in port operation and management, which would operate under a contract with BPC. The remaining 75% shares would be progressively sold by the State in tranches over a 10-year period, thus completing the eventual full privatization of BPC. There would still be a provision for the State to keep a "golden share" to protect the national interests, similar to the U.K. privatization models [5]. Lebanon's three other inefficient commercial ports would also corporatize, in a manner similar to the Port of Beirut (with the possibility of eventual privatization).

With any shift to increased freedom of ports to set their own tariffs and to enable the introduction of market forces, there occurs a need for independent regulation. Thus, a National Maritime Council (NMC) is proposed to be set up to carry out economic and social (safety, health, and environmental) regulation in addition to strategic planning. NMC would be a light-handed regulator with the main desirable characteristics of: 1) independence with a reasonable amount of discretionary power, 2) autonomy and expertise, and 3) accountability [2]. NMC would be in charge of the following functions [1]:

1) Review the nature and level of port charges, hear representations, and hold such inquiries in respect of these charges (so as to ensure their fairness and competitiveness).

2) Advise the Minister of Public Works and Transport on matters of strategic investment planning (generally for all projects having a value in excess of USD 50 million).

3) Facilitate the coordination and integration of maritime transport within the total transport chain.

4) Ensure that the Ports of Lebanon make adequate plans for investment to accommodate the demands of shipping and cargo, thus avoiding unnecessary congestion costs to the national economy.

5) Prepare, establish, and administer the scheme for compensation and the provision and management of pensions of the former personnel of the GEPB when the provisions of vesting date for the BPC come into force.

6) Carry out each three years a performance audit of the activities of BPC and its appointed management contractor.

7) Recover the costs of independent regulation of the ports sector through a scheme or schemes imposed on the ports and the traffics passing through the ports.

Figure 1 shows the current and proposed institutional arrangements. The reforms, when successfully implemented, imply the separation of policy-making (kept with the Minister), regulation and planning (kept with the NMC), and operation (kept with the contract management/strategic partner). The Ministry of

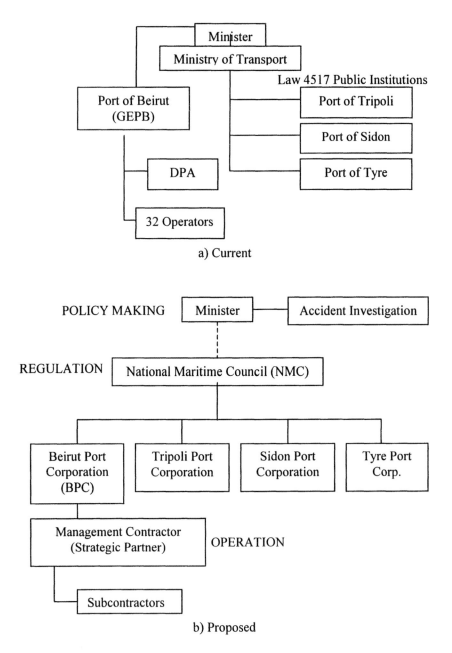

a) Current

b) Proposed

Figure 1 : Current and proposed institutional arrangements

Public Works and Transport has approved of the proposed reforms, as broadly consistent with the philosophy for reforming other transport sub-sectors [4, 6]. Such philosophy is based on the separation of policymaking (kept with the Minister), operation and service delivery (by the private sector only, where possible, otherwise via corporatized State Enterprises) and economic and social regulation (by an independent authority). A Steering Committee has been formed and entrusted with preparing the Draft Law establishing the BPC and the NMC, so as to proceed to the next step that involves seeking the approval of the Council of Ministers then the Parliament.

6 Implementation plan for the sector's reforms

The proposed implementation plan for the sector's reforms integrates two major elements: the establishment of the overall legal framework and the implementation of the institutional framework. The implementation of the institutional reforms is a major multi-year program of work that will require a significant level of resources. The work plan consists of four major work streams:

1) Program Management and Oversight. This work stream is concerned with the management of the overall program, ensuring that all program elements are performed in a coherent manner, noting the interdependencies that will occur, and reporting progress to the Minister of Public Works and Transport, the Council of Ministers, and Parliament.

2) Establishing the Overall Legal Framework. This work stream is concerned with establishing the legal framework necessary to implement the overall reforms. The activities include the drafting of the primary legislation, the secondary legislation, and the repeal and amendment of existing legislation.

3) Establishing the Institutional Framework. This work stream covers all activities that will result in the creation of the two separate entities: the Beirut Port Corporation (BPC) and the National Maritime Council (NMC).

4) Awarding of the Port Management Contract. This work stream covers all activities that will result in BPC's successful awarding of a port management contract to a professional contractor.

Acknowledgement

The author would like to acknowledge the International Bank for Reconstruction and Development (IBRD) for providing the Administrative Reform Loan to Lebanon, which was used to fund the development of the reform plan.

References

[1] High-Point Rendel, *Port of Beirut Institutional Reform Study*. Final Report submitted to the Ministry of Public Works and Transport, Beirut, Lebanon, 2001.

[2] Estache A. and De Rus G., (eds). *Privatization and Regulation of Transport Infrastructure: Guidelines for Policymakers and Regulators*. World Bank Institute publication, The World Bank, Washington, D.C., 2000.

[3] Trujillo L. and Nombela G., *Privatization and Regulation of the Seaport Industry*. Policy Research Working Paper no. 2181, World Bank, Washington, D.C., 1999.

[4] Baaj M. Hadi and Issa, J., Institutional Reform in Ports of Developing Countries: the Case of Lebanon - Part I: The Plan. *Maritime Policy and Management*, Vol. 28, No. 4, pp. 393 – 407, 2001.

[5] Guislain, P., *The Privatization Challenge: A Strategic, Legal, and Institutional Analysis of International Experience*. World Bank Regional and Sectoral Studies, The World Bank, Washington, D.C., 1997.

[6] Baaj, M. Hadi, The Land Public Transport Sector in Lebanon: From Chaos to Sustainable Reform and Organization, Part I: the Plan. *Journal of Public Transportation*, Vol. 3, No. 3: pp. 87 – 108, 2000.

Methods of comparative plotting of the ship's position

A. Stateczny
The Institute of Marine Traffic Engineering, Maritime University
Szczecin, Poland.

Abstract

In recent years the problem of position plotting in navigation has been dominated by satellite systems, the GPS in particular. These systems are used both at sea (maritime navigation) and in the air (aerial navigation) as well as on land (terrestrial navigation). With the application of satellite systems the position can be plotted within very short spaces of time, in the range of a few or a dozen seconds.

Relying exclusively on satellite systems, however, exposes to the danger of losing information in case of average, intentional switch-off, disturbance and possible encoding of information reaching the user. This results in the necessity of having yet another, autonomous system at one's disposal (independent of external information sources) making possible the plotting of position in an autonomous way.

These requirements are met by methods of comparative navigation. The object of interest of comparative navigation is plotting the ship's position by comparing a dynamically registered image with a pattern image. The pattern images can be numeric radar charts, sonar or aerial, suitably prepared for comparison with respectively radar, sonar or aerial images. Yet the most frequently registered images at sea will be radar images; the pattern, on the other hand, will be a numeric radar chart generated on the basis of topographic and hydrometeorological data or previous radar observation.

The article presents methods of computer ship's position plotting by means of comparative methods.

1 Introduction

The main source of image information in comparative navigation at sea is the marine navigational radar compared with the marine radar chart, generated on the basis of topographical data and constituting a layer of the marine numerical chart. Another source of information is the sonar, whose image can be compared with a sonar chart generated on the basis of a sea bottom shape model. Fig. 1 presents a concept of the vessel's comparative position plotting. This position is plotted on the basis of both overwater (radar) and underwater (sonar) information. Owing to this approach the ship's plotted position is tied to potential navigational obstacles.

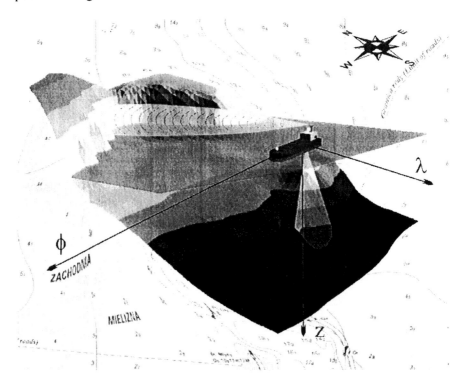

Fig.1. The concept of comparative position plotting [1].

The so-far applied methods of analytical comparison of digitally recorded radar pictures and the sea chart are based on complex and time-consuming calculation algorithms requiring the computer's large memory. What is sought for in these algorithms is the part of the chart most similar or least dissimilar to the analyzed radar image. In order to obtain the ship's position hundreds or even thousands of images are compared. In the course of comparisons particular image elements are analyzed. A number of interesting conclusions relative to analytical methods have been included in [2], [3], [4]. Among analytical methods the best results were obtained by applying the logical product method [5], which consists in examining the conformity of respective elements of the images compared. Due to the large number of calculations performed while using the analytical methods, the results obtained are likely to become outdated. Therefore, other methods are sought for which could be applied in comparative navigation. The new approach to the problems of plotting the ship's position by comparative methods consists in using artificial intelligence methods, which are artificial neural networks.

There are two basic concepts of the vessel's comparative position plotting using artificial neural networks. The first consists in making use of previously registered images, the second in generating a chart of patterns.

Every time the position plotting algorithm is selected, the problem of image compression or reduction should be considered

2 Plotting the ship's position using logical product

For images registered in matrix form, as an ordered set of elementary surfaces, their best matching can easily be calculated by applying the logical product method. In the image analyzed pixels corresponding to the coastline, the land pixels and possibly some characteristic points should be sorted out. Before starting to plot the vessel's position by this method, the possibility of reducing the analyzed images should be considered.

One of the simplest methods of decreasing the amount of information indispensable for plotting the ship's position is reduction of the analyzed images (radar image and the numerical marine chart). In the first stage of seeking for the vessel's position reduced images can be compared (e.g. up to 50% or 25%) by reducing the number of pixels in the images. Reducing the number of pixels consists in calculating the value of the 'substitution' pixel on the basis of value of a few (say, four) neighbouring pixels of the analyzed images. In this way we perform a kind of generalization of the analyzed images, losing in accuracy, but considerably accelerating the initial search for the point of best matching. The substitute pixels can be determined according to the following algorithm:

- ❏ when there appears a characteristic point in four of the replaced pixels, then the substitute pixel assumes the value of the characteristic point;
- ❏ when there appears a coastal point, then the substitute pixel assumes the value of the coastal point;
- ❏ when only land points appear then the substitute pixel assumes the land point value;
- ❏ when only zeros appear – zero (the sea).

And so, for instance, four pixels corresponding to elementary surfaces with a side of 25m are replaced in the first stage of searching by a pixel with a side of 100m.

Naturally, after determining the initial position of best matching of the images, a search on complete images should be carried out, but only in the closest neighbourhood of the position found.

An algorithm that fully takes into consideration the nature of the radar image is the logical product. As already mentioned, in this algorithm land points, coastline and characteristic points have been sorted out in the analyzed images. According to the above-mentioned assumptions the dependence for determining the image-matching coefficient is as follows:

$$kw(k,l) = ws \cdot ns(k,l) + wb \cdot nb(k,l) + wl \cdot nl(k,l) \tag{1}$$

where:
ns(k, l) – the sum of characteristic (special) points conformable on the chart and on the radar image;
nb(k, l) – the sum of coastline points on the chart conformable with the coast points of the radar image;
nl(k, l) – the sum of conformable land points;
wl, wb, ws – weight coefficient of the land, coastline and characteristic points.

The weight coefficients should be determined each time for a particular radar image in accordance with the equations:

$$wl = \frac{SR \cdot ml}{ll}, \quad wb = \frac{SR \cdot mb}{lb}, \quad ws = \frac{SR \cdot ms}{ls}, \tag{2}$$

where:

$$SR = ll + lb + ls \tag{3}$$

ll, lb, ls – the sums of all points of respective kinds on the radar image (when any of the sums equals zero, then the respective weight becomes zero too);
ml, mb, ms – coefficients determining the proportional share of particular image points.

Numerical experiments have shown that best results are obtained when:

$$ml = mb = ms = 0.333 \tag{4}$$

and when

$$ll, lb, ls \neq 0 \tag{5}$$

then

$$wl \cdot ll = wb \cdot lb = ws \cdot ls \qquad\qquad (6)$$

that is, the matching of all land points will have the same weight as the matching of all coastal points and of all characteristic points.

The matching of radar images with the sea chart by this method gives very good results in the process of plotting the ship's position. What may become a problem is only the defining by the operator of, e.g., the characteristic points on the radar image and their accurate marking. The restructuring of radar images before starting the matching process may slightly delay the moment of plotting the ship's position. A more comprehensive description of the method presented with results of numerical experiments is contained in the monograph 'Comparative Navigation' [6].

3 Neural ship's position plotting using previously registered images

A new approach in comparative navigation is the use of artificial neural networks for plotting the ship's position. In the positioning process there can be used previously registered images and their positions determined by e.g. the GPS system or by geodetic methods. The registered images correlated with positions constitute the teaching sequence of the artificial neural network. The teaching process is carried out earlier and can last freely any period of time. In the course of using the taught network the dynamic registered images are passed currently to the network input, and the network interpolates the position on the basis of recognized images closest to the analyzed image. A merit of this method is teaching the network by real images with their disturbances and distortions. So, the teaching sequence includes images analogous to those that will be used in practice. The basic problem of this method is the necessity of previous registration of numerous real images in various hydrometeorological conditions.

Analogous to the case of analytic methods the process of positioning is inseparably bound with compression of input data. One of the ways of image reduction is to determine its invariant and then the discrete Fourier transform. As a result of assembling the above transformations we obtain n – the element vector corresponding to the analyzed image. On the input side, a vector of established number, say 200 of the first transform elements, is the teaching sequence of the neural network, and on the output side the ship's position is registered at the moment of recording the image. Results of applying the above combination of transformations have been given in [7].

Another approach is the use of artificial neural networks for image compression. The Kohonen network is the one most frequently applied for the purpose. In work [8] an original method of image compression is suggested using the Kohonen network and the General Regression Neural Network (GRNN). In the method presented in work [8] the images are first subjected to the process of segmenting, and then to compression. The process of segmenting has the task of dividing the logically analyzed area into sub-areas, considerably accelerating their further treatment. Compression by means of neural network consists in assigning a number to each image segment. The assembling of all numbers for each segment of the image gives us a vector that is the compressed form of the image given at the input of the neural network (or group of neural networks). The Kohonen network has a limited set of values, which it is able to return to us; it is a set of indexes or numerical values associated with each neuron. When the network picture appears at the network output, it will return to us the value connected with the neuron most similar to this image. It will make a certain generalization; the more neurons there are in the network, the smaller the generalization, and the compressed image closer to the original.

An alternative is provided by the GRNN network Instead of the value associated with the most similar neuron we can return the value adequate to the degree of input image similarity to all remembered images in the network – approximate it on the basis of information included in Kohonen network. The value returned by the GRNN will be closer to the truth than the one from Kohonen network. In this way, without increasing the amount of information remembered, we obtain a more accurate transformation of the image into its compressed form. When applying this method, the output vector of the Kohonen and GRNN network pair along with the ship's position registered at the moment recording the image, will constitute the teaching sequence of the neural network that determines the ship's position.

After compressing the analyzed image a teaching sequence of the neural network designed for plotting the ship's position is constructed. The task of the network will be to construct a mapping function associating the analyzed picture with the position. Numerical experiments have shown the advantage of the network dedicated to interpolation tasks [9], which is the GRNN. For plotting the ship's position it is necessary to apply a pair of networks, as each network will determine one of the ship's position coordinates. After the network teaching process is finished, the currently registered image is passed to the network pair input, and the networks return the interpolated ship's position coordinates.

4 Neural ship's position plotting using a generated chart of patterns

Another way of approaching the problem of plotting the ship's position is making use of a generated map of patterns. It may be a radar, sonar or aerial chart. A map of patterns is generated on the basis of a spatial terrain model and takes into account the specificity of observing the terrain by means of particular measuring instruments (radar, sonar or optoelectronic devices). The pattern method consists in generating images that could be registered from selected vessel positions with assumed distances between successive positions. In this method, no previous registration of real images is required; only in the course of preparing the system for working in a particular water area or terrain is it necessary to generate simulated images. These images are simulated so as if the vessel was in successive positions in the water area. A data neurobase of its kind is constructed where any obtainable images are remembered.

In the process of preparing the teaching sequence a set of simulated images is prepared and compressed, and next the network is taught in image – position pairs. The network teaching process takes place while the system is prepared for work and is usually not limited temporally. After the network teaching process is finished, as in the method with real images, the current image is passed to the network input, and the network interpolates the ship's position on the basis of similarity of this image to the patterns contained in the teaching sequence. In the course of the system's work the response from the network (fixing the ship's position) is almost instantaneous.

As in the method with real images, the best results were obtained by applying a pair of coupled GRNN networks taught by the teaching sequence after compression by Kohonen network. Each of the GRNN networks determined one of the ship's position coordinates.

5 Sum-up

The article presents selected methods of comparative ship's position plotting based on registered images and corresponding patterns. Two of these methods used artificial neural networks. The application of GRNN network pairs, each of them determining one coordinate of the ship's position, allowed to obtain satisfactory positioning results. Numerical experiments showed considerable resistance of the method to disturbances of registered pictures. The method presented proved its usefulness for working in real time, as the delay time of the system is insignificantly small.

References

[1] Stateczny A., A Comparative System Concept of Plotting the Ship's Position. Proceedings of International Conference on Marine Navigation and Technology "MELAHA 2000" Alexandria Egypt 2002.

[2] Austin G. L., Bellon A., Ballantyne E., Sea Trials of a Navigation System Based on Computer Processing of Marine Radar Images. The Journal of Navigation 1987 Vol. 40.

[3] Austin G. L., Bellon A., Riley M., Ballantyne E., Navigation by Computer Processing of Marine Radar Images. The Journal of Navigation 1985 No 3.

[4] Hayashi S., Kuwajima S., Sotooka K., Yamazaki H., Murase H., A Stranding Avoidance System Using Radar Image Matching - Development and Experiment. The Journal of Navigation May 1991 Vol. 44 No 2.

[5] Stateczny A., Problemy komputerowego wyznaczania pozycji okrętu metodami porównawczymi. *(Problems of Computer Plotting of the Ship's position by Comparative Methods. Scientific Papers. Naval Academy of Gdynia.)* Zeszyty Naukowe AMW 107A/1990, Gdynia 1990. (in Polish)

[6] Stateczny A., Nawigacja porównawcza. Gdańskie Towarzystwo Naukowe. *(Comparative Navigation. Gdansk Scientific Society).*   Gdańsk 2001. (in Polish).

[7] Stateczny A., Wąż M., Neural Algorithm of Fixing the Ship's Position. Annual of Navigation 2000 nr.2

[8] Stateczny A., Praczyk. T., Artificial Neural Networks for Radar Image Compression. Proceedings of International Conference EXPLO SHIP 2002. Szczecin Poland – Kopenhagen 2002. (in Polish)

[9] Specht D.F., A General Regression Neural Network, IEEE Transactions on Neural Networks, Vol. 2. No. 6, 1991.

Implementation of marine regulations in decision support systems for vessel traffic services

Z. Pietrzykowski, M. Narekiewicz
Maritime University of Szczecin, Poland

Abstract

The paper presents a concept of a description of international and local marine regulations for vessel traffic supervising and management within approaches, fairways and harbour areas. Linguistic variables based on the fuzzy set theory are used. The goal is to support decision process in VTS centres. Methods and tools of fuzzy inference are used for that purpose.

One example of this can be an interpretation of vessel's safe speed in a specified area. To comply with COLREGs, many factors must be taken into account while specifying a vessel's safe speed. These are, among others, vessels parameters, visibility, traffic density, manoeuvrability of the vessel, state of wind and sea. The local regulations most often define only maximum and minimum admissible speeds. On this basis the operator recommends or orders a safe speed for ships covered by a VTS station. Most of the factors are described linguistically, e.g. good visibility, high intensity of vessel traffic. From this point of view it seems essential to use such notions in decision support systems employed in VTS centres.

Examples of rules are discussed and analysed. On this basis fuzzy inference systems for these rules are built. These inference systems represent regulations, accounting for navigators' knowledge and experience. The results are presented.

The processing of information, described by linguistic variables, is referred to as computing with words. The realisation of the presented concept may make the operation of VTS personnel more effective. Linguistic interpretation of the rules may be also used in vessel traffic management through planning and optimisation of vessel passages. A similar approach using a linguistic description can be applied as well in the optimisation of other port tasks.

Introduction

At present numerous systems of vessel traffic control are in operation throughout the world. They cover heavy traffic areas and/or areas difficult to navigate in. As a rule, these systems are supposed to monitor vessel traffic. Currently introduced vessel traffic management services (VTMS) are information systems based on specialised computer systems. Their characteristic feature is the use of special navigational equipment supporting the processes of data collection, processing and presentation. To enhance the effectiveness of their performance, they are supplemented by additional modules for information management and supporting the operator's decisions. The systems in question are aimed at such tasks as traffic organisation in the fairway, traffic surveillance and control, navigational assistance. Their implementation requires that international and local regulations be appropriately interpreted. This task is by no means, particularly in cases where the regulations refer to the so called good marine practice. Hence it seems purposeful to provide assistance in regulations interpretation to VTS operators, ship masters and pilots.

1   Regulations

The principles of safe navigation can be derived from a number of regulations. The International Maritime Organization (IMO) strives for the standardization of regulations concerning international shipping all over the world. The issues of safe navigation are mainly comprised in two conventions: COLREGs (International Regulations of Collision Prevention at Sea and the SOLAS Convention – Safety of Life at Sea) [1, 2].

Besides, national and local regulations are in force. These regulate problems of navigational safety in particular areas accounting for their specific character. While international regulations often refer to the good marine practice, local regulations precisely control traffic rules in a given area. The term 'precisely' means detailed rules with numerical values specifying e.g. maximum length, beam or draft of the ship.

In restricted areas, where traffic is rather intense, VTS systems are often employed. These systems are operated in accordance with the SOLAS Convention and national legislation of the country where the system functions.

A Vessel Traffic Service system is considered to be a system put in operation by a coastal state administration in order to provide for safe navigation, effective traffic and marine environment protection [1].

The primary objective is to ensure safe navigation and the safety of the environment within the system operation. The principal functions of the system are as follows:
- traffic organisation in the fairway
- traffic surveillance and control
- navigational assistance
- co-ordination of rescue operations in the case of accidents and disasters
- securing and supervision of navigational systems operation

- provision of data for port and regional services
- collection of data for administration, research and planning.

2 Organization and control of ships movement in VTS systems

Traffic organization on a fairway, surveillance and control of traffic as well as navigational assistance calls for access to information on vessels including data on ship movement, sailing area, hydrological and meteorological conditions, regulations in force, dangers to navigation. The necessary information in the case of port approaches comprise port traffic, free berths etc.

An example of a functioning VTS system is the one covering Szczecin-Świnoujście fairway, with approaches to the ports of Szczecin and Świnoujście (Poland). The system operates according to local regulations [3]. The regulations of Szczecin-Świnoujscie Port Authorities divide the range of ship traffic control and management into two areas: Świnoujście Centre - north of Fairway Tower 1, and Szczecin Centre, south of Fairway Tower 1 (Fig. 1). VTS operators at both centres are capable of complete assessment of a traffic situation and are supported in making decisions concerning the area covered by their centre. The operators can also monitor the situation in the other sections of the fairway. Decisions concerning vessel traffic crossing either of the covered areas are co-ordinated between operators of the centres.

The system makes it possible, *inter alia*, plotting the areas of hazards defined by the operator, prediction of target position for pre-set vessel courses, speed and time, and the prediction of system status in the pre-set time.

The operator determines the time a ship can join the fairway traffic on the basis of available information and his/her knowledge. S/he assumes that the vessel will proceed at the maximum speed defined by the regulations. The operator informs passing vessels of their expected encounters with other vessels and defines point at which the encounters should take place. Having this information, ship's master monitors and controls his ship's speed.

3 Examples of regulations interpretation

A number of regulations in force on the Świnoujście-Szczecin fairway have to be interpreted requires that prevailing conditions are taken into account.

Safe distance between vessels in traffic flow. Under the regulations, the minimum distance between vessels equals 370 metres. Besides, ship commanders are obliged to maintain a safe distance. In an extreme case that would be a stopping distance. This distance in most cases is far greater than the values specified in the regulations.

Safe passing. The ship passing manoeuvre is allowed along the entire length of the fairway for ships of specified size. The regulations do not account for external conditions, i.e., mainly, hydrological and meteorological conditions. In many cases the VTS centre does not allow the manoeuvre which might threaten navigational safety in prevailing external conditions.

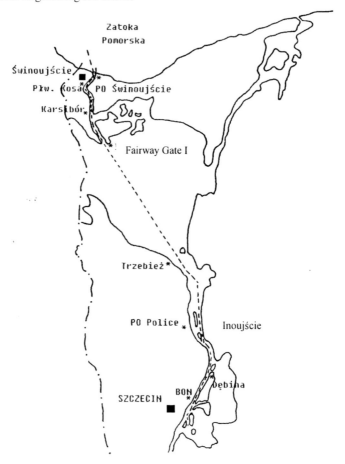

Figure 1: Świnoujście-Szczecin fairway.

Safe overtaking. The manoeuvre of overtaking a vessel is allowed by the regulations only along designated sections of the fairway for vessels with specified maximum size. An additional requirement to be satisfied is a large difference in speed between the overtaking vessel and one being overtaken. In this case, too, the regulations do not take into account external, mainly hydrological and meteorological conditions. In many cases the VTS centre issues no consent for an overtaking manoeuvre due to high risk for navigational safety, resulting from external conditions.

Safe course crossing. The regulations allow a ship to cross the trajectory of vessels on the fairway, moving along the main traffic lane, at a distance of not less than 500m. In reality the distances are longer on account on ensuring the safety of such manoeuvres. The distances are different and depend on ship size, external conditions, whether crossing is to be ahead or astern of a vessel on the fairway.

Maximum size vessel. Vessels allowed to enter the fairway must have parameters specified by the regulations. However, it often occurs that other vessels are stopped due to hydrological-meteorological and other conditions (wind, water level, dangerous cargo on board).

Safe speed vs. maximum permitted speed. The regulations set forth maximum admissible speeds which depend on vessels size and vary depending on a fairway section. The given speed values result mainly from the necessity of assuring the safe operation of the fairway and prevention of bottom damage and washing of the shore and other hydraulic structures located along the fairway. There is differentiation accounting for other external conditions affecting the navigational safety level, such as visibility, wind, current, or internal conditions, e.g. type of cargo on board.

The interpretation of the fairway regulations rests on VTS operators, pilots and vessel masters. The interpretation by operators essentially affects traffic organization. It is vitally important for the safety of vessels and environment alike and has to be allowed for in systems equipped with optimising tools of traffic management.

It is of vital importance from two points of view: safety and economical criteria, the latter being essential for all business organisations, mainly shipowners and port authorities. Therefore, it seems worthwhile to design advisory systems supporting VTS operators in the area of regulations interpretation.

4   Interpretation of regulations in inference system

The interpretation of regulations entails the use of inference rules appropriate for given problems. It is characteristic of the human to use linguistic variables described with linguistic values in inference rules [4]. In the case of safe speed estimation, visibility is one of them. It can be described using the following linguistic values: very good , good, bad, very bad. Taking into account only two factors: visibility VIS and the ship's draft in relation to available depth of water DW, inference rules for determining the safe speed V_s could have the form

$$\text{If VIS good and DW small, then } V_s \text{ is high} \qquad (1)$$
$$\text{If VIS very bad and DW small, then } V_s \text{ is low.}$$

The realization of inference rules in this form will require the use of suitable mathematical apparatus. Methods and tools of fuzzy logic are used for such tasks. The notion "good visibility" is an example of a fuzzy set, defined in the universe of discourse X, of possible values of visibility. The set is described by the membership function $\mu(x)$, which assigns to each element x its degree of membership to this set:

$$VIS_G = \{x, \mu(x)\}, \qquad \forall x \in X \qquad (2)$$

Such an approach to build the inference system requires the defining of inference rules, linguistic variables and their membership functions [5, 6, 7, 8]. The structure of such a system is presented in Figure 2.

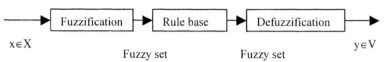

$x \in X$ Fuzzy set   Fuzzy set $y \in V$

Figure 2: Structure of a fuzzy inference system.

Different types of fuzzy inference systems can be implemented: Mamdani, Sugeno and fuzzy-neural networks. These systems use crisp values at the input, realize processes of fuzzification, fuzzy inference, and estimate an answer, that after the defuzzification determines a crisp (non-fuzzy) value at the output. In case of imprecise input values it is possible to use fuzzy numbers, e.g. with reference to visibilities: visibility „about 2 Nm". Defining input values in the form of linguistic variables can supplement the system at present, or be an alternative in the future. This of type of information processing, based on linguistic descriptions, can be qualified as computing with words.

5   Safe speed - investigations

Expert /questionnaire/ research has been performed with the participation of pilots handling vessels on the Świnoujście-Szczecin fairway. The research concerned the criteria for determining safe vessel speeds and the speed values. The group was selected for their long sea service, the knowledge of local conditions, vessels and regulations binding on the Świnoujście-Szczecin fairway.

The analysis focused on the criteria of safe speed, used by the experts. A number of factors affecting the determination of safe speed were distinguished. Table 1 presents these factors together with the priorities assigned to them by the pilots. According to their suggestions, these factors were classed into three groups describing a vessel, the area and hydrological and meteorological conditions.

Table 1: Factors affecting the safe speed determination and their priorities (Mean values of priorities for the examined group of pilots)
(1 – highest priority)

	Vessel	Priority	Area	Priority	Hydro-meteorol. conditions	Priority
1	Length	2	Width	1.25	Visibility	1.5
2	Beam	2	Depth	1	Wind force	3
3	Draft	1.25	Navigational difficulties	2.75	Wind direction	3.25
4	Manoeuvring ability	1.5	Vessel beam / area width	2.25	Current direction [*]	2.25
5	Cargo on board	4.33			Current speed	2.75

[*] currents: inward (Świnoujście-Szczecin), outward (opposite)

The analysis of the results leads to a conclusion that the area parameters are the most vital factor in determining safe fairway speed, the others being vessel size and some hydro-meteorological parameters (visibility). This may result from the fact that the Świnoujście-Szczecin fairway is not a uniform waterway. It consists of canals and dredged stretches of rivers (Odra, Świna) and Zalew Szczeciński.

The pilots' task was to define a safe speed for different values of the parameters describing the particular factors. Three fairway sections were distinguished: 1) breakwater heads at Świnoujcie to Gate I, 2) Gate I – Inoujście, 3) Inoujście – the Port of Szczecin. At the same time the regulations account for the division into vessel groups by their length, beam and draft, time of day and - not incorporated in the regulations – visibility, wind force and direction, current direction and speed. The gathered data have embodied the knowledge of expert-pilots.

6   Acquisition and representation of expert-navigators' knowledge

The collected facts have been used in designing a knowledge base for an advisory system of safe speed determination. Fuzzy logic neural networks were used for knowledge representation. They constitute a universal approximating system which represents multi-dimensional data sets and is able to learn and adapt to changing environmental conditions. There are difficulties in applying them connected with, among others, a selection of an optimal network type and structure. Besides, it is not possible to interpret the rules due to the covert form of knowledge, hidden in the structure and weights of connections between neurones.

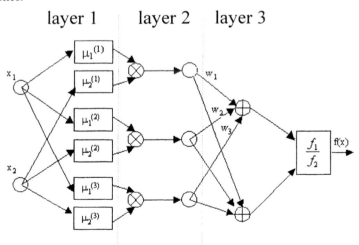

Figure 3: A structure of a fuzzy logic artificial neural network for two input data and three rules.

Fuzzy logic artificial neural networks may be classed as hybrid systems, using positive properties of fuzzy systems and artificial neural networks. Like neural networks they have a layer structure and additionally utilise fuzzy logic systems which enable the execution of accepted fuzzy rules. Learning algorithms can be used in the learning process as they are in the case of typical artificial neural networks. An example of its structure is shown below in Fig. 3.

Neurones of layer 1 transform an input data set x into a fuzzy set F described by membership functions $\mu_i^{(j)}(x)$ (process of fuzzification). Layer 2 executes the fuzzy rules of inference. The fuzzy sets of inference results are transformed in layer 3 into a determined output value. The process is referred to as defuzzification.

The application of the network makes it possible to use, in designing, its structure of knowledge related to basic principles of interference used by experts in a given scope. It also allows to attribute initial values to parameters describing the network. Moreover, it accelerates the network teaching process

7   Results

The gathered data on determining safe vessel speeds were utilized in the process of teaching of fuzzy logic neural network designed for the purpose. Input data were the parameters of the factors presented in Table 1. Examples of the results are shown in Figures 4 and 5.

Expert navigators considered visibility as one of the most essential factors

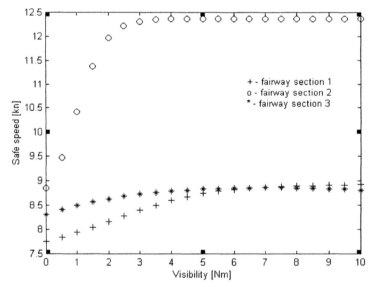

Figure 4: Ships safe speed for different visibilities, ship length 120 m, beam 17 m, draft 7 m; good manoeuvring ability, no dangerous cargo on board, no wind, no current, daylight; fairway sections No 1, 2 and 3.

affecting the determination of safe speed (Table 1). Increased visibility results in an increase of safe speed only to a certain value (Fig. 4). The value equals three Nm for the examined fairway section. This leads to a conclusion that the ability to determine a ship's position from observations of visible aids to navigation assures better feeling of safety than in the case of position being determined by navigational instruments (radar, GPS). The differences in maximum speeds at the three fairway sections result from the different character of the fairway itself. Sections 1 and 3 are parts of dredged river stretches or man-made canals, while section 2 runs through Zalew Szczeciński.

The influence of other essential factors, such as the length and draft of a ship, on its safe speed is illustrated in Figure 5. The influence of these factors manifests itself only after certain boundary values, are exceeded, the values close to allowable values set forth by the regulations.

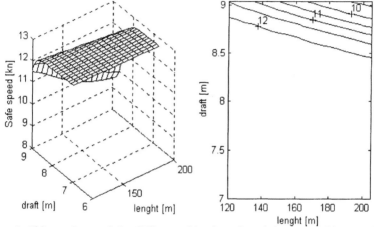

Figure 5: Ships safe speed for different ships length and draft; fixed beam 17 , good manoeuvring ability, no dangerous cargo on board, no wind, no current, daylight; fairway section No 2.

The use of such a tool as fuzzy logic neural network enables to account for the influence of individual factors on the safe speed value without analytical description of the relationships.

Summary

Navigators may find it difficult to comply to the regulations and maintain the principles of good navigational practice in relation to safe navigation. This fact is due to a large number of diversified factors that have to be accounted for. An appropriate decision-supporting system may be of assistance in this respect. This type of system must utilize the knowledge and experience of navigators. These may be represented by methods and tools of artificial intelligence. Such methods and tools have been used in a decision-supporting system for the determination of ship's safe speed in a restricted area. An inference system has been built on the basis of navigators' knowledge and experience. The system uses elements of the fuzzy sets theory.

The use of knowledge and experience of navigators – experts in the field herein described appears to be purposeful. The basic difficulty lies in acquiring and representation of the knowledge and experience. Practical use of such a system calls for the extension of the acquired knowledge and its verification.

It seems purposeful to supplement the system with interpretations of other regulations, including those mentioned in point 3. This will make it easier for VTS operators to assess a navigational situation of a proceeding vessel. It can also be applied in planning, vessel traffic optimization and surveillance. The introduction of linguistic variables frequently used by the man may enhance the effectiveness of the communications between the navigator and VTS system.

References

[1] *Convention on the International Regulations for Preventing Collisions at Sea*, (COLREGs), International Maritime Organisation, 1972.

[2]   *International Convention for the Safety of Life at Sea (SOLAS)*, International Maritime Organisation, 1974.

[3] *Port Regulations No 1/2000 28.04.2000*, Official Bulletin of West Pomeranian Voivodship, 2000, No 20 item 227.

[4] Kacprzyk J., *Fuzzy sets in systems analysis*, PWN Warszawa, 1986 (in Polish).

[5] Driankov D., Hellendoorn H., Reinfrank M., *An Introduction to Fuzzy Control*, Springer Verlag, Berlin Heidelberg, 1993.

[6] Osowski S., *Neural networks in algorithmic formulation*, WNT Warszawa, 1996 (in Polish).

[7] Pietrzykowski Z., Applications of neuro-fuzzy networks for identifications of distress situations in vessel traffic in restricted areas. *Proc. of 7th International Scientific and Technical Conference on Sea Traffic Engineering*, Szczecin, pp. 131-142, 1997 (in Polish).

[8] Dziedzic, T, Pietrzykowski, Z., Uriasz, J. (2000). Knowledge-based System for Evaluation of Ship's Navigational Safety. *Proc. of Ist Conf. COMPIT 2000, Potsdam*, pp. 132-140, 2000.

Analytical models for Ro-Ro and Lo-Lo terminals in a multipurpose port

F. Russo, A. G. Cartisano
Department of Computer Science, Mathematics, Electronics and Transportation, "Mediterranea" University of Reggio Calabria, Italy.

Abstract

Freight transport plays an important role in the transport system, insofar as it is a fundamental element for the economic development of an area and a country in general. In Italy over 80% of freight travels by road, despite the country's 7400-km coastline which is particularly suited to short-sea shipping. The ports are organized as freight interchange centres: they are equipped to integrate with road transport for the initial and final links, and use sea and rail routes for long distances.

The elements that form an integrated freight transport system, whether it be multimodal (freight transfer by two or more transport systems), "complex" monomodal (freight transfer that uses only one mode of transport but with different vehicles) or intermodal (freight transfer that uses more than one transport mode but using the same container) or combined definited also piggy-back transport (intermodal transport by means of container, swap body or semi-trailer, and using road for final haulage, and rail or sea for the intermediate leg), can be aggregated into three categories: Loading Unit (UL); Movement Units (UM); Transportation Units (UT).

The freight transport systems that use more than one mode have acquired greater importance as they lead to a total reduction in costs. One of the main hubs of the intermodal system is the port because of the modal change involved. It is thus necessary to have a supply model that allows, in the planning phase, cost and performance of the specific hub in the transport system to be estimated.

1 Introduction

Nowadays, freight transport plays an important role in the transport system [2] [8], insofar as it is a fundamental element for the economic development of an area and a country in general [6]. Knowledge of the effect of the various factors upon freight transport times and costs is essential in different sectors [9]. In the context of strategic planning, such knowledge allows us to appraise different development policies of the various modes, analyzing their respective economic benefits. In operational context, knowledge of the various factors allows us to determine cost and performance functions.

In Italy over 80% of freight is transported by road although the country has over 7400 km of coastline that are well suited to short-sea shipping [3]. The most promising area of development is the tendency to view the Mediterranean as a fulcrum in the world maritime scenario. In particular, container traffic through the port systems of southern Europe have seen a much higher growth rate (+80%) than in those of northern Europe (27.6%) in the period of reference from 1995 to 1998. Ports and freight villages are viewed as centres of transport and freight interchange, equipped to integrate traditional road transport, using sea and rail for long routes [7] [13].

The freight transport systems that use more than one mode have acquired greater importance as they lead to a total reduction in costs. One of the main hubs of the intermodal system is the port because of the modal change involved. It is thus necessary to have a supply model that allows, in the planning phase, cost and performance of the specific hub in the transport system to be estimated.

In this paper a method is introduced to model the road-sea intermodal system (Section 2). The connecting infrastructures, namely the port systems, are analysed, using a method proposed in literature. Finally (Section 3) performance functions are specified and calibrated in relation to the different types of terminals.

2 Problem definition

The elements that make up an integrated system of freight transport, whether it be:

- multimodal: freight transfer by at least two transport modes;
- "complex" monomodal: freight transfer that uses only one mode of transport but with different vehicles;
- intermodal: freight transfer that uses more than one transport mode but using the same container;
- combined defined also piggy-back transport: intermodal transport with container or swap body that uses road for final haulage, and rail or sea for the intermediate leg;

can be aggregated into three categories:
> Unit of Load (UL);
> Unit of Movement (UM);
> Unit of Transport (UT).

In relationship to such elements the system examined, intermodal transport or combined road-sea, can be divided into three subsystems (fig.1):
① subsystem in which the ULs travel on UT ship;
② subsystem in which the ULs are transfered by UMs;
③ subsystem in which the ULs travel on road UT.

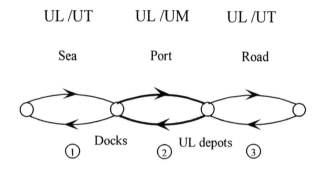

UL /UT   UL /UM   UL /UT

Sea   Port   Road

Docks   UL depots
①   ②   ③

Figure 1 Diagram of the road-sea system

Subsystems 1 and 3 have been described in the literature [10] [4]. This study is related to the specification of subsystem 2, represented by a graph by which some performance (percept and unperceptive cost) functions for the simulation are defined. The method used is that proposed in Russo [11]: in this paper an interchange general cargo terminal is analysed, with reference to Ro-Ro (Roll on, Roll off) and Lo-Lo (Lift on, Lift off) transfer types.

The total transport time is hypothesized as deriving from a linear combination of three quantities, related to the subsystems:
> time of access/egress;
> time of docking and freight transfer at terminals;
> time of port-to-port trip.

As regards the time of access/egress (subsystem 3), stop times on road are to be excluded, given the short distances between the ports and zone centroids.

The time of docking and freight transfer depends on terminal organization the technique of transfer, the load unit and ferry type used, as well as the frequency of the crossing.

On short routes the service is usually high frequency and is effected with double-access Ro-Ro ferries (horizontal transfer of the vehicles). The loading units are the complete set of Heavy Good Vehicles (HGV). In general the Ro-Ro ferries load also Light Good Vehicles (LGV) and cars. On long routes the service is usually scheduled with low frequency and is effected with single access Ro-Ro ferries with horizontal transfer of the vehicles. The loading units are HGV and LGV, but can be also semi trailers and single containers loaded by trucks.

In the Mediterranean basin, besides the short-sea shipping services with the transport of load units through ferries, other services are also used to transport containers with the use of Lo-Lo transhipment techniques (vertical transfer using special port crane). Services may be of the following types:

➤ Feeder services (common);
➤ Line shipping services (owners).

The feeder service is the service by which containers are loaded/unloaded in a transhipment port by/from an ocean-going ship.

To determine the cost functions, we proceeded to specify and calibrate linear statistical relations.

3 Analytical models for terminals

In freight transport increasing importance is being attached to systems that use more than one transport mode. Transfer functions between different modes take place in specialized terminals.

In the road-rail case there are special terminals called freight villages or *interports*, equipped both for the vertical and horizontal handling of the ULs. Russo [11] proposes a general model to represent intermodal nodes, with a specification for the road-rail case. For road-sea intermodal transport a similar scheme may be used to that proposed for road-rail.

In the case of specialised ships, in multipurpose ports, the transport system may be represented according to the type of ship using graph theory. Representation of a multipurpose port is not as straightforward as for a specialised container terminal, given the great variety of freight involved. Indeed, a specification of operations conducted in the port may be associated to each type of ship, and hence of good.

In this paper different types of ships are considered: those that support transport with trucks or semi-trailers, namely Ro-Ro ferries with single and double-access, and Lo-Lo feeder or liner ships.

Data were gathered from the port of Catania [1] [12], with subsequent surveys in the ports of Palermo and Villa San Giovanni (Straits of Messina).

The port of Catania covers a land surface area of 268,000 m^2 and about 870,000 m^2 on water. The docks at the port extend for around 5,000 m. It lies at the centre of the Mediterranean basin, equidistant between Suez Canal and Gibraltar, situated between European and African ports.

The port of Palermo has an intermodal terminal that covers a surface area of around 15,000 m^2 and a container terminal, with an area of about 150,000 m^2 allowing ships up to 300 m of length to operate.

The port of Villa San Giovanni is protected by a straight dock which has areas reserved for Ro-Ro ferries; it links the isle of Sicily to the Italy by means of high frequency service of ferries (on average ten minutes between two departures of ferries).

The shipping traffic observed concerns tree types: Ro-Ro ferries (short and long routes) and Lo-Lo feeder ships. As regards the former, the times were recorded for each manoeuvre (2,548 in all) of loading and unloading of vehicles for 38 ferries arriving in port, while 2,692 times were recorded for 29 feeder ships arriving in port. The calibrations have been performed by means of linear regression [5].

3.1 Ro-Ro terminals

In general the Ro-Ro ferries used in long routes are equipped by single access, while the Ro-Ro used in short routes are equipped by double access. In the following we treat at first the long route services and then the short route.

In the case of long routes and scheduled services with low frequency, large-capacity multi-deck ferries are generally used (at least 1500 meters of vehicles are on board), in which the loading units are mainly trucks and semi-trailers. The graph corresponding to all the operations concerning access to the port, unloading, loading and egress of a ferry is schematized in figure 2.

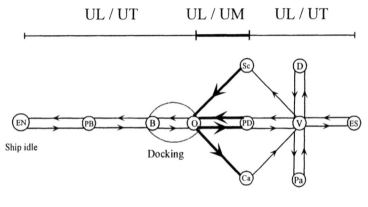

EN	= in/out ship	ES	= in/out road
PB	= pilot on/off board	PD	= depots of UL
BP	= docking approach	O	= end mooring, beginning
DP	= customs		loading/unloading
Sc	= unloading	Ca	= loading
VP	= internal road	Pa	= parking

Figure 2 Graph of UL port operations with Ro-Ro ship

The same graph allows us to analyze all transfers that the loading units, in this case trucks and semi trailers, can undergo in the port in question. The bolder lines concern the transfers, eventually through UM, inside the terminal.

It is hypothesized that the transfers of the semi-trailer happens only with specialized truck tractors (donkeys).

The manoeuvres effected when a ship enters port, of whatever type, are divided into three different categories:
➢   Access manoeuvres;
➢   Loading and unloading maneuvers;

> ➢   Egress manoeuvres.

For access and egress manoeuvres average in/out times and their variances, are as follows:

$$T_{access} = 0.47 \quad [h] \qquad Var\,(T_{access}) = 0.38$$

$$T_{egress} = 0.41 \quad [h] \qquad Var\,(T_{egress}) = 0.09$$

The access time was estimated from the moment the pilot boarded the vessel to the conclusion of mooring operations with the opening of the hatches; the egress time was estimated from the beginning of sailing to the pilot's departure. The cost functions related to the single links crossed by UM are determined according to UL location.

In this case the transfers times (viewed by the user) depend on the times of acceptance and delivery required by the shipper. In general, it may be assumed that trailers have to arrive at the port terminal at least 1.5 hours before the scheduled departure of the service, while for delivery to the recipient a value of 2.5 hours can be assumed from the docking of the ferry at the port of destination. Such values include transhipment times for loading and unloading from ferries.

For ferries that transport semitrailers on long routes and that are loaded and unloaded by dedicated truck tractors, the transhipment time of movements for loading T_{ml} and unloading T_{mu} can be evaluated as follows:

$$T_{ml} = \beta_{l,tr}\,NT + \beta_{l,s/tr}\,(NS/NT)$$

$$T_{mu} = \beta_{u,tr}\,NT + \beta_{u,s/tr}\,(NS/NT)$$

in which:

NT   = is the number of truck tractors effecting the operations;
NS/NT   = is the relationship between the number of loaded or unloaded semi-trailers and the number of truck tractors that perform the transhipment.

Table 1 reports the parameters of a model calibrated for large ferries with a single loading/unloading hatch. The model supplies the times in hours.

Tab. 1   Times of loading/unloading for long route Ro-Ro ferries

Parameter	unloading		loading	
	$\beta_{u,tr}$	$\beta_{u,s/tr}$	$\beta_{l,tr}$	$\beta_{l,s/tr}$
Coefficient	0.09	0.16	0.29	0.12
t-student	0.42	3.78	1.32	2.49
Rho^2	0.82		0.67	

On short routes the service can be, more usually, high frequency and in this case it is effected with Ro-Ro ferries with double access, loading units being trucks. In this case the time of standstill and movimentation to the embarkation T_{em} can be considered inclusive of two quantities, the first related to the service wait and the second related to the embarkation   procedures;   time   at unloading T_{di} concerns   only disembarkation procedures.

Hence:

$$T_{em} = T_{\varphi} + T_{ml}$$

$$T_{di} = T_{mu}$$

where T_{φ} is the average waiting time for loading to start; if the arrival of ferries can be simulated with a Poisson variable and the arrival of heavy vehicles is uniformly distributed in the time slice considered, it can be assumed that T_{φ} is equal to the inverse of frequency. T_{ml} stands for the average transfer time for loading and T_{mu} for unloading.

The relationship holds in the case in which present levels of service demand do not exceed service supply. If in certain time slices demand exceeds supply (due to changes in demand and/or in supply) the overall time at the terminal must be calculated taking account of embarkation waits. In this case, to determine T_{φ} it is necessary to use flow theory.

In some specific cases with particular terminal lay-outs different functions should be specified for loading and unloading times. In general, however, we may assume the following type of function:

$$T_{ml} = T_{mu} = \Sigma_c m_c N V_c$$

in which c is the generic class of vehicles that can be embarked, NVc is the number of vehicles of class c, and m_c is the relative parameter.

Table 2 reports the values of a model valid both for the manoeuvres of get on and for those of get off from ferries Ro-Ro, that allows the exit of one truck at a time. The model supplies the time in minutes and considers the presence of cars.

Tab. 2 Time of loading/unloading for Ro-Ro ships with two entrances

Vehicle	Car	LGV	HGV	Bus
Coefficient	0.16	0.43	0.91	1.68
t-student	2.88	1.72	1.38	1.28

3.2 Lo-Lo Terminals

For Lo-Lo ship the operations performed in a multipurpose port are identical to those of a specialized port. The difference lies in container storage capacity on the land. Operations may be represented by the graph reported in fig. 3.

The overall access and egress times, with definitions given, in terms of average value and their variances are as follows:

$$T_{access} = 0.40 \quad [h] \quad Var(T_{access}) = 0.20$$

$$T_{egress} = 0.37 \quad [h] \quad Var(T_{egress}) = 0.04$$

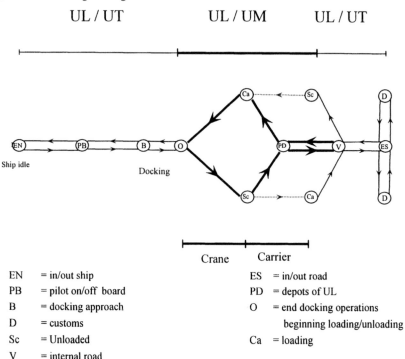

Figure 3 Graph of UL port operations with Lo-Lo ship

EN   = in/out ship   ES   = in/out road
PB   = pilot on/off board   PD   = depots of UL
B   = docking approach   O   = end docking operations
D   = customs   beginning loading/unloading
Sc   = Unloaded   Ca   = loading
V   = internal road

The feeder ships database consists, besides the general data similar to those of Ro-Ro ferries, of all times measured in each operation during the unloading of the containers (hook up, lifting, transfer, lowering, unloading). The specificated and calibrated models are as follows:

$$T_{ml} = T_{mu} = \beta_{cont} \cdot N_{cont} \qquad [h]$$

N_{cont} = number of containers that are unloaded and loaded.

In table 3 the parameter values obtained from the calibrations are reported.

Tab. 3 Times of Loading/Unloading for Lo-Lo ships

	unloading	loading
Parameter	β_{cont}	β_{cont}
Coefficient	0.08	0.07
t-student	38.49	55.32
Rho^2	0.75	0.98

It is worth noting that on average the times required for loading and unloading Ro-Ro are at least double those required for Lo-Lo.

References

[1] Cartisano A. G. (2000), "Analisi dei Sistemi di Offerta di Trasporto Multimodale   Terra-Mare: Specificazione e Calibrazione di Funzioni di Utilità", Tesi di Laurea, Dipartimento Informatica Matematica Elettronica e Trasporti, Università degli Studi di Reggio Calabria

[2] Cascetta E. (2001), "Transportations systems engineering: theory and methods ", Kluwer Academic Publishers

[3] Cascetta E., Iannò D. (2000), "Calibrazione aggregata di un sistema di modelli di domanda merci a scala nazionale", Metodi e Tecnologie dell'Ingegneria dei Trasporti, G. E. Cantarella and F. Russo (Eds.), Franco Angeli

[4] Gattuso D., Musolino G., Modafferi F.,(1998), "La formazione del costo di trasporto marittimo containerizzato" Trasporti Europei no. 8/9

[5] Judge G. G., Hill R. C., Griffiths W. E., Lutkepohl H., Lee T. C. (1988), "Introduction to the Theory and Practice of Econometrics", Wiley, New York

[6] Kesic B.,Mrnajavac E., (1996), "Defining of port gravitational areas as a function of port development", in Trasporti Europei no. 3

[7] Musso E., (1998), "I porti, costi interni ed esterni, pianificazione del territorio, ruolo dei sistemi locali", Trasporti Europei no. 8/9

[8] Nuzzolo A., Russo F. (1997), "Modal split at international level: a system of models for italian -based freight", Proceeding of 25th PTRC, European Transport Forum, PTRC, London

[9] Regan A. C., Garrido R. A. (2000), "Modeling Freight Demand and Shipper Behavior: State of the Art, Future Directions", Preprint of IATBR Conference, Sydney

[10] Russo F. (1997), "Un sistema di modelli per il calcolo di tempi e costi delle spedizioni di merci su strada e su ferrovia", Modelli e metodi dell'Ingegneria del traffico, G. E. Cantarella and D. C. Festa (Eds.), Franco Angeli

[11] Russo F. (2001), "Trasporto intermodale delle merci", Introduzione alla Tecnica dei Trasporti e del Traffico con Elementi di Economia dei Trasporti, G. E. Cantarella (Ed.), UTET, Turin

[12] Russo F., Cartisano A., Comi A. (2001) "Modelli per l'analisi degli anelli finali della distribuzione delle merci" Metodi e Tecnologie dell'Ingegneria dei Trasporti, G. E. Cantarella and F. Russo (Eds.), Franco Angeli

[13] Russo F., Gattuso D. (2002) "Progetto AMI: Il ruolo dei trasporti nella prospettiva della Zona di Libero Scambio Euro-Mediterranea" (Eds.), Franco Angeli

System simulation for the evaluation of the oil barge operation in Kaohsiung harbor, Taiwan

Yang-Chi Chang & Chin-Chuan Chen
Department of Marine Environment & Engineering, National Sun Yat-sen University, Taiwan.

Abstract

The oil barge operation in Kaohsiung harbor is a typical system of resources allocation problems in a complex and dynamic environment. Such system is far more difficult to deal with than a static and deterministic system, and often depends on experienced human experts for the oil barge assignment. This research has developed an integrated system for assessing the overall performance of such port operation. Both expert system and system simulation techniques are applied in this analysis. The role of the expert system is to translate the current heuristic of assignment into a rule-based knowledge for the human-like reasoning. To further evaluate the schedule arranged by the expert system, the system simulation model of the oil barge operation has been formulated using the software AweSim®. This model is capable of quantifying the service quality under various assignment scenarios to support the management of the oil barge operation. With the help of such an integrated system, it is expected to facilitate the evaluation of the oil barge operation in terms of efficient resources allocation in Kaohsiung harbor.

1 Introduction

Kaohsiung Harbor, located at the southwest coast of Taiwan, is the largest international port in Taiwan, and the fourth largest container-handling harbor in the world. Excellent geography and port environment contribute to its prosperity. It is located right between the Taiwan Straits and the Bashi Straits, and it has a long and narrow shoal as her natural barrier. The Taiwanese government is planning to make Taiwan a HUB port in the Asian Pacific area. The Port of Kaohsiung will be the best candidate for the trans-shipment center. According to Statistics of 2001, Kaohsiung Harbor Bureau (KHB), the number of inbound vessels has increased 40.1% from 12,888 in 1993 to 18,162 in 2001. In light of this trend, it is necessary to consider the demand for development of the entire port in advance. As part of this, the logistic operation of fueling service, provided by the Chinese Petroleum Company (CPC), has a serious impact on the future development of the port. Any delay in the oil barge operation would postpone the schedule of outbound vessels. This would not only cause the carriers to incur extra charges for port service fees, but also create a risk of losing the increase in business potential for KHB and CPC.

The oil barge operation in the Port of Kaohsiung is a typical system with resources allocation problems in a complex and dynamic environment. Such system is far more difficult to deal with than a static and deterministic system, and often depends on experienced human experts for the oil barge assignment. The system manager is confronted by the major dilemma of not knowing the management efficiency under the current dispatching mechanism. Besides, if the dispatching rules need to be modified due to a future resource variation, how would the changes affect the system and how to deal with such development effectively? Currently the system manager lacks a solid tool to assess the system performance, and as such has no appropriate resources improvement plan when the Port of Kaohsiung becomes the trans-shipment center in the future.

This research, supported by the National Science Council of Taiwan, has proposed an integrated system, using both the expert system and the system simulation techniques for evaluating the oil-barge operation in the Port of Kaohsiung. To accommodate the human expert's role in the current oil barge dispatching mechanism, an expert system has been utilized as the replacement of the real expert in the entire modeling process. The heuristic regarding the current schedule arrangement is collected at the beginning through several interviews with the CPC engineers who would set up the oil barges operational plan for the following day, based on the orders from the ship's agents. Such experience is then transformed into a digital form of knowledge base, and stored in the expert system for further reasoning. The results acquired from the expert system will provide the input as the pre-defined schedule for the simulation model, which will represent the complete oil-barge operations, including the transportation and fueling processes. With the embedded statistical process the simulation model is capable of generating significant long-term statistic reports as the system performance indices under the designated resources assignment rules. This will make it clearer and easier to show the decision makers how well the current dispatching mechanism performs. It allows a comparison between various adjustments on assignment rules, and shows the appropriate response plan to meet the future need when the Port of Kaohsiung becomes the trans-shipment center.

2 Methodologies

"Expert systems" are sophisticated computer programs that are equipped with knowledge and inference mechanisms to solve problems efficiently and effectively in a narrow problem domain. These systems evolved from artificial intelligence (AI) systems using symbolic logic and heuristic to find solutions just like real human experts. There are several excellent reasons to justify why people develop an expert system rather than rely on human experts as was done in the past. The advantages of such systems over human experts are that it is permanent, consistent, easy to transfer and document, and cheaper. A number of different application areas, for instance agriculture, engineering, medicine, and military science, have enjoyed benefits from using such technique [1]. To allocate oil barges for the fueling service is a complex decision-making process affected by several factors that are closely interrelated. Such an arrangement always relies on the expert, and fits in with the "planning" category of expert system applications because they decide on an entire course of action before acting.

One of the major differences that makes expert systems differ from conventional programs is that the expert system manipulates knowledge while conventional programs process data. Knowledge represents information which an expert system needs before it can function intelligently, and this usually takes the form of rules. Rules provide a formal way for recording strategies, or recommendations, developed through years of problem-solving experience. The "IF condition, THEN conclusion" statement is the general expression of rule-based knowledge, indicating the fact that when the condition is satisfied, the conclusion is in effect. By means of direct interaction with domain experts, heuristic could be acquired, and should be organized systematically into a knowledge base. System developers are then required to choose one type of building tool from either the expert system shells (e.g. EXSYS) or programming languages (e.g. LISP). There are pros and cons for both types of tools. Programming languages offer more flexibility but require more effort to design the knowledge base and construct the inference engine that accesses the knowledge. After carefully comparing the functionality of various products, the choice of the expert system tool should primarily depend on the application requirements in the research.

Although the heuristics may provide a feasible approach to solve the current problem, it does not guarantee that it will generate a good solution when something changes in the future. One of the inherent limitations of expert systems is that they are incapable of refining and improving the knowledge base. Unless some experiments can be conducted to show the system performance, the decision makers have no way but to trust the expertise acquired from the so-called expert. Furthermore, as the status of the problem changes in the future, it will be time consuming for the expert to adjust the heuristics. To do an actual real-time test would require a tremendous amount of resources and effort, and is the least cost-effective option. A better alternative would be to resort to formulating some type of mathematical or statistical models that simulate the original problem. Such model building process provides the insights into problems and is widely used to assist in the design, management, or development of policy relative to natural or constructed systems [2].

The oil barge and tugboat services are similar port logistic operations, which require more information than the Queuing theory can provide to support reasonable planning [3]. In order to thoroughly explore inter-related components over a long period of time, and to evaluate various planning strategies based on reliable forecasts, the technique of system simulation is appropriate to deal with the similar problems [4]. In particular, the characteristics of an oil barge operation is the combination of transportation and fueling service with a variable data element, which lends itself to the application of stochastic simulation.

System simulation is a powerful tool for analysis and design. By establishing a set of structural and procedural elements that represent the real system, it would help to conduct the designated experiments, to identify the system behavior, and then to evaluate the overall system performances based on various design or operating strategies [5]. A simulation model itself cannot determine an optimal solution; rather it can produce experimental outcome from which an alternative can be selected. It is therefore applicable for simulation models to answer "What if" questions in the scenario analysis with the specified candidate list. Such analysis is the typical usage of system simulation to support decision-making.

Many dedicated simulation languages have been developed to replace the earlier FORTRAN language as the efficient model-building tool. These languages, such as GPSS, SIMSCRIPT, and SIMAN, use statements specifically designed for representing the state of a system, and moving the system from state to state. However, a complete problem-solving process requires more than just a model by itself. Additional tools and techniques, such as data management, scenario generation, output analysis, documentation and the presentation of results, are necessary to support total simulation projects [6]. In recent years, software engineering has made it possible to develop a multi-functional and user-friendly simulation support system. Among them, AweSim® developed by Symix Systems Inc., provides an integrated problem solving environment for an interactive and graphic modeling process. Meanwhile, this software maintains its flexibility by incorporating independent components, which can be created using other computer languages, with the simulation model. This capability allows the current research to connect the expert system with the simulation model for effective and efficient oil barge management in the port of Kaohsiung.

3 System constructions

In order to build a realistic system, a full awareness of oil barge dispatching mechanics and all aspects of the operational procedures is necessary. At the highest level of the system, the headquarter of CPC in Taipei receives orders from local ship agents, and at the end of a day the CPC will notify the Storage & Transportation Station (STS) in the Port of Kaohsiung regarding the complete orders for the next day. After acquiring such information, the senior engineer in charge of dispatch will arrange the work schedule for each oil barge based on some implicit rules learned from long-term experience. The last stage of the system is to carry out the orders through the oil barge operation, which includes the trip from the STS wharf to the vessel's docking berth and the fueling process. The captain of the barge needs to check the invoice on-site before the fuelling operation begins. The fueling operation requires connecting the oil tube, unloading the oil, closing the valve, and disconnecting the oil tube. For a large order that exceeds a single oil barge's capacity, the first barge will wait for the supply from another barge to finish the required service. Otherwise the barge will either travel to the next vessel, on condition that there is enough oil for the service, or travel back to the STS wharf preparing for the next trip. Figure 1 shows the flow chart of the oil barge operational system.

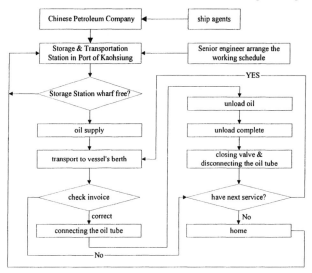

Figure 1: Flow chart of oil-barge operational system

In light of the discussion above, the schematic diagram of the model is illustrated as Figure 2. There are three model components based on the partition of the system flow in sequence. The first module will randomly generate the preliminary information regarding the inbound vessels that need the fueling service. Such vessels are treated as the entries in the system simulation model, which associates the attributes of the oil type, the amount of the order, the berth, and the schedule of arrival and departure. The second module will collect the information generated in the previous process and allocates the oil barge for each entity, using the pre-built expert system. Each vessel entity is assigned the resources of the oil barge as specified by the oil-barge's name, assigned a priority for using the assigned resource, and the content of delivery by the oil barge. The last component is to run the system simulation model for the evaluation of the oil-barge operation under the current dispatching mechanism as represented by the expert system. Information regarding the attributes of entities (vessels) and the allocation of resources (oil barges) forms the foundation for this stochastic analysis that will calculate the service time of each oil barge and the related statistics to generate the performance indices.

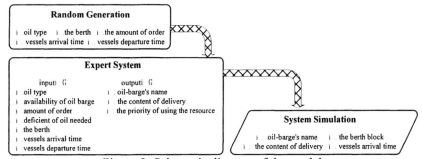

Figure 2: Schematic diagram of the model

3.1 The knowledge base of the expert system

Modeling the oil barge allocation is the most crucial element, and is driven by the expert system, the knowledge base of which is derived from the heuristic. Through face-to-face communication, this research has taken the required information from the CPC engineer in two stages. In the first phase, applying a non-structural interview guides the researchers to the broad view of the domain knowledge. To further extend these initial results, the researchers take part in a constructive dialogue with the human expert in order to elaborate on the dispatching mechanism. The result of this knowledge-acquisition process discloses several factors affecting the oil barge assignment. They are: the vessel's arrival and sailing schedule, the geographic location of the berth, and the amount and type of oil that has been ordered. A detailed discussion on the impact of each factor is listed in the following:

1. Vessel's arrival and sailing schedule: The oil barge operations can only be conducted during the time interval between the vessel's arrival and sailing, and the fueling has to be completed no later than the sailing schedule. These two factors pose immediate constraints for the oil-barge assignment in terms of the resource utilization priority.

2. Geographic location of the berth: The natural formation of the Kaohsiung harbor is like a long strip spanning from North to South with deep-water berths located at the southern side. An inbound vessel will dock at a specific berth based on its tonnage, length, and draught. Logically, an oil barge should be allocated to serve the vessels in the neighboring berths for efficient transportation. In addition, the oil barges with large capacity tend to serve the heavyweight vessels docked at the southern side, where higher fuel demand is common. However, there is an exception when the smaller oil barges cannot handle the service on the northern side, the large ones will then take over the deficiency. To effectively address this issue in the model, the neighboring berths have been aggregated into five clusters each in the northern and southern sides as shown in Figure 3. The vessels within the same cluster will have the same priority for the resource allocation.

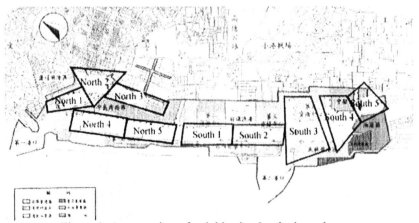

Figure 3: Aggregation of neighboring berths into clusters

3.   <u>Amount and type of oil ordered</u>: The variety of oil barges in the STS has made these two factors the essential parts of the dispatching mechanism. The capacity of the barges ranges from 220 to 1500 tones, and the storage tank of a barge carries either diesel oil or fuel oil. The general principles of dispatch are that the oil barge with the larger capacity will be assigned to serve the vessel with the higher demand, and the order of either diesel or fuel will be fulfilled by the corresponding barges as shown in Figure 4.

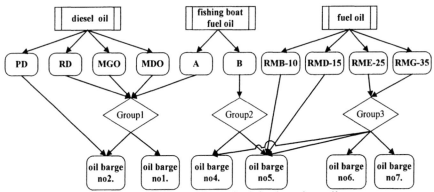

Figure 4: General dispatching principles based on oil types

After thorough interviews, the heuristics of the human expert are carefully translated into the rule-based knowledge using the "IF-THEN" form. The impact factors listed above are associated with the "IF" statement as the prerequisite for the oil barge assignment. To define further complex situations, the "IF" statement may accommodate several conditions joined by some logical operators such as "AND" and "OR". Once the conditions are validated, the "THEN" statement will be fired to describe the consequence, which is the assignment of the oil barge. One specific example of such rule-based knowledge is illustrated as follows, and is equivalent to the experience that: given a type of oil, insufficient amount of oil after the first fuelling process, and oil barge number 2 is available, the CPC engineer will assign the oil barge #2 to serve this vessel.

> **IF**   *Type of oil= MGO, MDO*
> > **OR**   *Type of oil=A*
> > **AND**   *Insufficient amount of oil= 0-220*
> > **AND**   *Working situation of oil barge number 2= 0*
> **THEN**   *Barge name= number 2*

3.2 System simulation

Through the experiments on simulated oil barge operation, the long-term statistics (including average service time of barges, mean waiting time of vessels, utility rates of barges, and the efficiency of wharves utilization in the STS) can be derived effectively. Consequently such information can support assessments on the current heuristics of dispatch embedded in the expert system, and helps to identify bottlenecks in the entire oil-barge operation. If the evaluation shows a deficiency in the system performance, any revised strategy, such as a modification of the dispatching rules, or the addition of new barges to the fleet, can be investigated through the same modeling procedure. Without actually implementing anything, the system manager is able to foresee the outcomes of the proposed strategies and is able to select the most appropriate strategy under all constraints. The same approach can also be applied to deal with strategic planning to meet the future challenge from a highly increased number of inbound vessels.

Three conceptual elements, including workstation, queue, and entity, constitute a simulation model, which can be represented as entities flowing through a network of nodes (queues) and activities (workstations). The first step in the construction of such a model is to define the entity, which is any object with variables representing the system state. In this study, the vessels treated as entities in the model use the system variable to indicate the status of service to their vessels (completed or incomplete). The next and most creative step is to develop a network model whose sequential process is similar to the oil-barge operation as mentioned earlier. The software "AweSim" has been used for the model development through the synthesis of network elements using the graphic form. Using the graphic symbols as a logical and visual medium facilitates the process of conceptualization and communication. Once the graphic representation of the network model is complete, AweSim will transcribe the simulation model into the proprietary script for the model execution.

The framework of the network model in the current study is demonstrated in Figure 5 using the graphic symbols. At the beginning of the model is the "create node" in order to randomly generate the entities, which are the inbound vessels, based on a probability distribution function (PDF). During the creation of the entities, the attributes, such as the amount and type of oil ordered (associated with each vessel) will also be produced following certain patterns. The information from the create node is exported to the external expert system component for the allocation of oil barges. The results are then sent back to the network model by inserting the ASCII file into the second node. Once all required information is available, the next section of the model simulates the oil-barge operation. At first the vessels have to wait for the service from the assigned oil barge in the "await node". When the oil barge is available to serve the vessel, it will fetch the information regarding the upcoming service by means of the "assign node" and will also try to allocate a STS wharf for oil supply in the "await node" if the remaining oil is not enough for the next service. As soon as the action of oil supply is completed, the oil barge will free the resource of the STS wharf by the "free node", and the status of oil

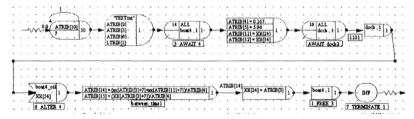

Figure 5: Graphic presentation of the simulation network model

barge usage will be changed by the "alter node". The following activities, including transportation from the STS wharf to the berth of the vessel and fueling process, require variable time periods that will be calculated in the "assign node". After the service is completed, the model will release the resource of the oil barge by the "free node" and the entity of the vessel will be dismissed from the system by the "terminate node".

There are several activity durations in the simulation model that have to be estimated correctly in order to justify the integrity of the model. First, the oil supply on the STS wharves has to pump the designated type and amount of oil to the oil barges. Such activity duration is primarily based on the size of the tube, amount of supply, and the pumping rate that is relevant to the viscosity of the oil being pumped. Secondly, the transportation to and from the STS wharves and the berths of the vessels requires a different time span for each oil barge. Logically, the activity duration for the transportation depends mainly on the speed of the barge and the distance of the trip. The speed of the various oil barges is variable owing to the difference in the horsepower of each oil barge, the weather condition, the degree of crowdedness in the harbor, and the amount of oil loaded. Nevertheless it is too complicated to consider all these circumstances, and therefore the average speed of an empty oil barge is used for calculating the time to travel back to the STS wharves, and 70% of this speed is used for calculating the transport time to the berths for a loaded barge. The service distance is fixed at each pre-classified cluster of a vessel's berth. Thirdly, the activity of the fueling process involves both an oil barge and a vessel. Three influential factors can be identified, which are: the diameter of the oil intake into the vessel, the amount and type of oil required, and the pumping rate ,which is decided through negotiation between the captain of the oil barge and the chief engineer of the vessel. According to interviews with senior captains, the model would take 80% of the full pumping capability as the average pumping rate for the simulation. While making the calculation, additional attention has to be paid to the unit conversion from metric ton (MT) to kiloliter (KL). This study applies the standard conversion, that is to say: one(1) MT of fuel oil is equal to 1.06KL, and one(1) MT of diesel oil is equal to 1.2KL.

4 Results and discussion

After the development of such integrated system, model verification is necessary to justify the results from simulation. The expert system has been examined by comparing the simulated reasoning with the real oil-barge schedules using the whole year records. The analysis of discrepancy in both schedules shows 90% of similarity, which is to demonstrate the knowledge base extracted from the human expert can function well to replace the role of the human in the whole modeling process. As for the simulation model, the time for the last oil barge to finish the fueling operation in a working day has been collected and analyzed under the control of using the same schedule. The time deviation between the simulation and the real data is found less than 10%, indicating good quality of the simulation model.

With the solid proof, various experiments can be conducted to evaluate the performance of the oil-barge management system. Under the current dispatching mechanism, it is obvious to identify from the simulation report that the oil barge number 1, 2, and 4 have longer working time than the others, while the oil barge number 6 and 7 take up lower ratio of the service activities. Presumably, according to the current low growth rate of inbound vessels in the Port of Kaohsiung the fleet of the oil barges in STS should be enough to handle the fueling service until the year of 2004. Based on the researcher's heuristic, several revised programs for the current dispatching rules have been proposed including "multi-barges assignment", "the most economical resources allocation", and "additional new resources allocation". The knowledge base of the expert system has been modified to accommodate these revised programs. The results from the simulation model show the "the most economical resources allocation" program would further reduce the utility of the oil barges number 6 and 7, but the time for the last oil barge to finish the work is even later. The rests of the proposed revision are not as good as the current one.

5 Conclusions

The integration of expert system and system simulation provide a valuable approach in terms of mapping out the complex system operations in a whole. Yet, the degree of sophistication in such modeling process depends on how complete the knowledge base and the operational procedures had been set up. The current study accumulates the daily working schedules and reports of the oil barges in the entire year. With more than sixty thousand records available for the analysis, the intensive information has laid the strong foundation for building the trustworthy system as shown by the model verification. In consequence, this integrated model is capable of quantifying system performances not only for the current environment but also for the future developments when the Port of Kaohsiung becomes the transshipping center. The embedded decision-support function of the system allows the system manager to easily test the revised programs or strategic plans and to adopt the most appropriate scheme to enhance the overall managerial efficient for the oil barge operation.

References

[1] Waterman, D.A., *A Guide to Expert Systems*, Addison Wesley, pp. 32-39, 1986.
[2] Revelle, C.S., Whitlatch E.E. & Wright J.R., *Civil and Environmental Systems Engineering*, Prentice Hall: New Jersey, pp. 1-6, 1997.
[3] Wang David, *Simulation study on the application of pilots and tugboats - case of Kaohsiung Harbor*, Master Thesis, Dept. of Transportation and Communication Management Science, National Cheng-Kung University, Tainan, Taiwan, 1999.
[4] Julian A.S., Simulation of an inland waterway barge fleet distribution network, *Proc. of the 1998 Winter Simulation Conf.*, eds. D.J. Medeiros, E.F. Watson, J.S. Carson & M.S. Manivannan, pp. 1219-1221, 1998.
[5] O'Reilly, J.J. & Lilegdon W.R., Introduction to Awesim. *Proc. of the 1999 Winter Simulation Conf.*, eds. P.A. Farrington, H.B. Nembhard, D.T. Sturrock & G.W. Evans, pp.7-13, 1999.
[6] Pritsker, A.B. & O'Reilly J.J., *Simulation with Visual SLAM and AweSim,* John Wiley and Sons, NY, pp. 81-84, 1999.

Section 2
Environmental aspects

Marina development and environmental impact assessment requirements - the case of Lefkada Marina

G. Polychronidou, K. Liolios & B.S. Tselentis
Department of Maritime Studies, University of Piraeus, Greece

Abstract

Increased tourist trade and pleasure boat activities in the Ionian Sea have led to new constructions and expansion of existing marina facilities. The site selected for marina development on the island of Lefkada is near the main town, on location "Alykes". This shallow and protected area was not maintained after the closure of the salt work activities and the area was flooded by sea water, creating an ecosystem characterized by high primary production and depths not exceeding 70 cm and as shallow as 20 cm. Salt work activities, as well as materials used for recent land fill efforts, have increased concern about the physicochemical characteristics of the seabed sediments and dumped land fill soil. Marina development dictated extensive dredging in order to obtain operating depths for pleasure boats ranging from 4 to 8.5 meters. Previous studies performed as required by the Environmental Impact Assessment (EIA) procedures in order to obtain planning and construction permits, described in great detail environmental indicators of the marine and coastal pre-construction environment. Dredged materials were also analyzed in order to assess the quality and therefore the management/disposal strategies in order to avoid the dispersal of potentially contaminated sediments. The paper presents and compares the environmental data obtained before and after marina construction, the objective being to quality review the Environmental Impact Assessment process and investigate the degree to which a linear system such as an EIA is adopted and applied to a dynamic environment such as a marina. Based on these findings, conclusions and proposals as to how the EIA process might, more effectively, highlight and therefore mitigate significant environmental impacts due to marina construction and dredging are made.

1 Introduction

For most of the Greek islands, tourism is becoming the main driving force for economic and commercial development. Lefkada Island has lagged behind compared to other Ionian Islands such as Corfu, but recent trends in overnight stays for the island over the last decade, indicate that Lefkada is becoming a favourite and promising tourist resort in the area. As shown in Figure 1 overnight stays in Lefkada island have increased steadily during this period attaining the highest yearly average increase, compared to the other Ionian islands, the Ionian islands totalling about 4.500.000 overnights per year for this period. It has become apparent, that such increases may undermine tourist development especially when the hotel sector is not able to provide adequate and high quality accommodation, unless other developments leading to an upgrading of tourist services are also instigated on the island. In this context, it is believed that the Marina development plan will be a serious asset for the island.

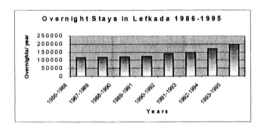

Figure 1: Overnight stays in Lefkada for the period of 1986-1995 [1]

In designing the layout and facilities of any marina (floating docks, canal, bunkering stations, repairs and maintenance area, hotel), many parameters have to been taken into account and particularly the specific characteristics of the physical and anthropogenic environment. Some of the most important elements in choosing the site in Lefkada Island to develop and build this marina were the following:

✓ Boaters are usually of medium or high income and are prepared to spend in order to enjoy their holidays, either at sea or land, thus enhancing tourism in Lefkada

✓ Most of the potential activities associated with boaters and yachts, can be found in and around the town of Lefkada

✓ The town is connected with mainland Greece by airport and road utilizing a bridge

✓ The demand for building marinas around Greece is increasing due to the competition of Mediterranean countries as far as pricing and the quality of their services is concerned

✓ The excellent natural protection of the region provides an ideal mooring area

✓ The town of Lefkada has become one of the most famous "bases" for cruising in the Ionian Sea, due to the fact that the island is centrally placed [1].

The new marina in the town of Lefkada will also have the following advantages and benefits for the town itself:

✓ Immediate economic benefits (through foreign exchange) arising from marina facility development and usage

✓ Invigoration of commercial business in the town and increase of employment opportunities in the area, since there will be a need to staff operations at both the construction, as well as for the operation phase

✓ Development of tourist businesses associated with the operation of the marina, such as fuelling, catering, brokerage, etc. [1].

As the owners of the marina declare, "The marina's construction philosophy is the welfare of people and the environment. The high quality specifications, for the areas of public use as well as for the entire marina, are founded on stringent rules governing health, aesthetics and environmentally friendly development."[1]. Thus, measures have been made in both phases and are being presented. This paper presents the environmental data collated before and after construction of the marina. Based on the declaration of the owners and the fact that environmental considerations should be integrated into the construction and operational phase of the marina, an attempt is made to assess the impacts due to the construction process, as well as assess the conclusions and recommendations of the EIA, performed before construction.

2 Environmental impacts

The coastal sea zone of the marina is 165,000 m^2 and total berthing capacity 630 yachts of various categories. On the land area of 72.000 m^2 an wintering area will accommodate 285 vessels, as well as offer maintenance and repairs facilities. The marina also provides safe moorings, electricity, water, phone, bunkering, sewage and waste oil reception facilities, and easy hauling/launching through travelift and ramps. Additionally, there are information desks, administration offices, medical desks, showers and toilets, bank branches and ATM's, chandlery, shops, car parking, restaurants, a small hotel, and boat renting stores.

This region served as a salt works area till the late 50's. Reports indicate intensive salt production, utilising several hundred pits, which the calm seawater of the narrow passage between the island and mainland Greece flooded regularly. Salt work activities, as well as materials used for recent land fill efforts, have increased concern about the physicochemical characteristics of the seabed sediments and dumped landfill soil. On the other hand, during the construction, dredging was necessary in order to increase the depth, as well as to build a canal through the marina that will enable the recycling of the water.

Dredged materials were also analysed in order to assess the quality, and therefore the management/disposal strategies (land or sea).

Generally, marinas are potentially significant sources of pollution in coastal waters often being hot spots for coliform bacteria and other pathogens, aliphatic and aromatic hydrocarbons (PAH) and heavy metals. The use of antifouling paint and other chemical preservatives, used mainly during operational phase, are toxic to numerous organisms. Benthic communities usually incur the most acute effects, with significant changes occurring in species composition, abundance and diversity at marina sites. Operating craft frequently lack onboard sanitation devices and release raw sewage to coastal waters. Oil and fuel leakages, as well as engine exhausts are sources of PAH's. Such pollution input degrades water quality, especially in shallow estuaries and coastal embayments with poor water circulation [3].

It is, therefore, recognised that environmental considerations are of outmost importance to any coastal development interventions involving marine constructions such as pleasure boat marinas, as well as during operational phase. Nevertheless, differences still exist as to the extent and type of this integration. In most countries the implementation of Environmental Impact Assessments (EIA), is enforced by legislative and administrative regulations, whilst others integrate it as part of general planning schemes. EIA's aim is to mitigate significant impacts, including the minimisation of undesirable impacts.

2.1 Environmental impact assessments

Although EIA systems are comprised of many significant, integrated and interrelated parts, one of the most important sections that not until recently has been sufficiently investigated, is the post-auditing methodologies. As Wilson [4] states, "an environmental impact assessment (EIA) audit evaluates the performance of an EIA by comparing actual impacts to what was predicted". Several authors [5,6] have identified four basic auditing types focusing on post-project appraisal:

1. Implementation audit, that examines whether mitigation measures and/or any other imposed conditions have been established.

2. Project impact audit that serves to highlight all the environmental impacts that have been taken place due to the development of the project.

3. Predictive techniques audit, that compares and reveals the accuracy and utility of various predictive methods used in EIA.

4. EIA procedures audit, that evaluates the overall efficiency of the EIA system at a macro-level.

The efficient and systematic use of post development auditing, especially in the case of a marina development, can result in a number of significant benefits and advantages, the most important of which are [6,7,8]:

❖ The results from post auditing can be used as an effective tool for sustainable environmental management over the life of the project.

❖   By revealing some special, as well as unpredicted impacts caused by a specific type of development (such as a marina development) post auditing can provide a basis for improving the existing predictive techniques.

❖   Finally, post auditing can be used as a feedback to the entire EIA system. In this way, the "reinvention of the wheel" is avoided and improvement of future practice by "learning through experience" can take place.

On the other hand, several researches have highlighted the fact that post-auditing studies based on various project types, are still very limited, inconsistent and not at all widespread. Carrying out a post-auditing study can be hindered by a variety of problems:

•   First of all, as Dipper *et al.* [9] states, the availability of pre-existing monitoring data is a pre-requisite for any post-auditing study. In many cases, the almost absolute lack of any kind of impact monitoring data is acting as a prohibited factor to the conduction of a post-auditing research.

•   Secondly, the EC Directive 85/337/EEC (as amended by 97/11/EC) does not require any mandatory monitoring and auditing program in a case of a proposed development. Consequently, the majority of the developers seem unreluctant to establish any monitoring schemes, mainly due to the increased cost of monitoring activities. Therefore, a lack of perception among EIA participants is established. Even when monitoring data can be located it is frequently inaccurate, inadequate and biased.

•   Moreover, many impact predictions found in the Environmental Impact Statements (EISs) are presented in a rather vague and ambiguous way, thus hindering the efficient interpretation and usage of this data.

•   Lastly, another vital problem is the potential existence of impacts that had not been predicted and therefore stated in the EIS, as well as several project changes that may take place in a rather late stage of the EIA process and therefore, the impacts caused by those modifications are not examined whatsoever.

Having stated the most important problems often associated with post-auditing in EIA, it is subsequently rational to anticipate that numbers of case studies focusing on post-auditing is rather limited. Even though search of the literature reveals some examples most of these case studies investigate big project types, such as power stations, chemical plants, incinerators, but not marina developments. A possible reason for this, may be the fact that proposals for leisure activities usually account for a small minority of all project proposals, while the construction costs, as well as the time and effort invested, are relatively small compared to the project categories mentioned above.

However, although a marina does not occupy relatively large areas, is situated at the land-sea interface, "in the heart" of very dynamical and fragile environments with substantial biodiversity, which are susceptible to rapid degradation due to human development. Moreover, studies on marina developments have highlighted many integrated, distinctive and irreversible impacts to the nearby environment. In this paper we attempt to apply the principles of the post-auditing process to Lefkada island marina, since we were involved with the estimation of all the relevant environmental data before the construction, as well as taken an active part in the prediction and recommendation processes.

3 Environmental data and results

Sampling positions are shown on Figure 2. Positions remained constant for the pre and after-construction sampling regime. At these positions, water and sediment samples were collected. The samples were transported to the laboratory and analysed following well-established environmental chemistry methodology and techniques. The data presented in this paper represent the pre-construction (**Before**) environmental indicator (column B) and the post-construction condition (**After**) (column A).

The microbiological condition of the area seems to have changed to the better, since E. Coli and Enterococci levels are reduced, in most cases being within the levels specified by the Directive on bathing water quality and the Directive on shellfish water quality levels. It must be mentioned that due to the construction process many streams and rainwater drainage outlets, that inevitably accept illicit waste waters from nearby urban areas, were diverted away from the area. The post-construction picture is however, not clear as yet, since the sampling was performed in spring (March 2002), the marina only accommodating 40 – 50 vessels. Table 2 provides information on basic nutrient concentrations of the seawater before (column B) and after most of the construction activities have taken place (column A).

It is obvious that there is no statistically significant change to the trophic state of the sea, even though the dredging process removed the top layer of the sea bed (shallow depths of 0.5 m) that was composed of algae, seaweeds and a microcosm that was involved in biological degradation, a process that potentially could lead to the provision of some basic nutrients to the sea. Further sampling is required to describe the effects on these nutrients, probably highlighting a decrease, due to the restriction of fresh water streams to the area

As far as the basic oceanographic parameters are concerned (Table 3), the study showed that the results are as expected, normal, stable and with no fluctuations after the construction of the marina.

Figure 2: Location of samples

Table 1. Analysis of sea water samples for microbiological contamination

Samples	E-Coli/ 100 ml		Enterococci/ 100ml	
	B^1	A^2	B	A
I 3	$>10^6$	41	300	<1
III 2	100	20	10	<1
IV 3	35	131	10	10
I 1	$>10^6$	285	200	<1
Γ	$>10^6$	203	$>10^6$	20

B^1 = Before construction A^2 = After construction

Clarity has increased due to the increase of the depth in the area and salinity data are almost stable for the entire sea area. The area was studied intensively for sediment heavy metal concentrations, as it is a well-known fact that sediments represent the sink of all elements entering the sea. A series of analysis were performed as previously stated in accordance to EIA requirements before the construction as well before dredging.

The data in column B (Before) represent averages of at least four samples at each sampling point. Column A data, represent one sample at the same positions (see Figure 1). The surface sediment in most of the study area is composed of clay and in areas close to the docks it is fine-grained, in contrast to areas around the north breakwater, where it is muddy, black and coarser. This is to be expected, since during the construction phase a lot of grab dredging has been done and the process has affected the consistency of the sediment.

The concentration of the metals in the area is low, indicating that there are no significant anthropogenic inputs of heavy metals to the coastal ecosystem. Table 4 sums up the heavy metal concentrations before (column B) and after (column A) for the most toxic metals, of interest to all environmental impact assessment studies.

Table 2. Concentrations of basic nutrients at selected sampling points

Samples	Phosphate µg-at / l		Nitrates µg-at / l		Nitrites µg-at / l		Ammonium µg-at / l	
	B[1]	A[2]	B	A	B	A	B	A
III 2	0,49	0,25	0,76	0,89	0,12	0,05	0,98	0,78
I 3	0,12	0, 37	0,92	0,81	0,05	0,03	0,23	0,62
I 1	0,22	0, 44	0,38	0,17	0,15	0,05	0,42	0,55
Γ	0,22	0,39	1,72	1,13	0,18	0,07	0,35	0,88

B[1] = Before construction A[2] = After construction

Tributyl tin (TBT) is also included, since it has been associated with pleasure boat activities. Although the area had limited pleasure craft, it is believed that these data will act as a good background reference in order to assess impacts due to antifouling paints, when the marina is in full operation. Results concerning the other metals represented in Table 4, although statistically not significant (due to limited sampling points), indicate a reduction for most metals in most of the surface sediments analyzed. Some positions with higher levels than pre-construction values, could be due to the fact that the dredging process (grab) resuspended the fine sediment and allowed the transfer of the adsorbed heavy metals to areas of the marina where sedimentation rates was high. It is obvious, however, that further sampling and analysis of sediment samples must be performed in order to assess in a more precise way the environmental effects of the construction process. The organic carbon content of the post-construction area is significantly lower that the pre-construction ones, a fact to be expected, since the dredging process removed the surface sediment layer where most of the previous organic matter decomposition activities deposited their products. It must be pointed out that biological monitoring was not performed in the area, since the species inventory of the pre-construction area was not detailed and long-term enough, to perform comparative studies.

In conclusion, it is evident that the construction process has not seriously altered the environmental indices that were selected for the study, following EIA methodology. Any small alterations observed, seem to be in the direction of improving the environment, and in this respect we can state that the conclusions and recommendations that followed the environmental assessment before the construction, were withheld to a high degree. It is obvious, however, that further measurements and a systematic monitoring regime must be implemented, as it is important to monitor with extreme care both the impacts arising from the construction process, as we may still be expecting delayed effects, but also more importantly the effects during the operation of the marina. The marina is expected to be fully operational in 1-2 years.

Table 3. Basic oceanographic parameters

Samples	pH		Temperature °C		Salinity ‰		Clarity (m Secci)		Dissolved oxygen (ml / l)	
	B1	A2	B	A	B	A	B	A	B	A
K	7,98	8,36	16,1	16,3	36,3	38,2	<15	1,9	5,01	-
III 2	8,1	8,33	21,5	16	37,0	38,2	-	2	5,13	5,0
I 3	8,22	8,32	19,2	15,4	30,2	38,4	-	2	4,05	3,1
I 2	8,02	8,3	22,2	15,4	36,7	38,5	-	2,6	4,28	4,8
I 1	8,18	8,27	23,8	15,4	38,3	38,4	-	2,5	3,81	6,3
Γ	7,9	8,34	23,2	16,2	37,9	38	-	2,2	3,97	-

B1 = Before construction A2 = After construction

Table 4. Metal concentrations and organic content of sediments

Samples	Ni ppm		Pb ppm		Cr ppm		Cd ppm		Zn ppm		Hg ppm		TBT ♣ ppb		Organic content %	
	B1	A2	B	A	B	A	B	A	B	A	B	A	B	A	B	A
K	43	37,5	15,4	32,5	62,3	23,2	ng ♦	ng	151,1	221,3	ng	ng	ng	ng	5,1	3,2
III 2	62	75,2	24,3	72,3	56,7	19,4	ng	ng	140,4	185,2	ng	ng	ng	ng	6,1	2,9
B	49	68,1	20	22,2	44,2	35,2	ng	ng	135,7	98,3	ng	ng	9,1	ng	5,3	3,5
I 3	86	22,2	33,3	13,5	77,3	72,3	ng	ng	187,9	93,8	ng	ng	5,4	ng	4,1	2,2
Γ	56,7	56,7	29,7	42,7	45,9	28,3	0,11	ng	48,6	105,7	ng	ng	ng	ng	6,6	2,8

♣ tributyl tin   ♦ non detectable   B1 = Before construction A2 = After construction

References

[1] Florios N., *Lefkada Marina; Environmental Impact Statement*, Prefecture of Lefkada, 1998.

[2] *The Lefkada Marina*, Lefkada Marina Brochure, 2002.

[3] Kennish M. J., *Practical Handbook of Marine Science*, CRC Press, pp. 636-637, 2000.

[4] Wilson L., *A Practical Method For Environmental Impact Assessment Audits*, Environmental Impact Assessment Review, 18, pp. 59-60, 1998.

[5] Wood G., *Post-Development Auditing of EIA Predictive Techniques: A Special Analytical Approach*, Journal of Environmental Planning and Management, 42(5), pp. 672, 1999.

[6] Bailey J. and Hobbes V., *A Proposed Framework and Database for EIA Auditing*, Journal of Environmental Management, 31, pp. 164, 1990.

[7] Glasson J., *The First 10 Years of the UK EIA System: Strengths, Weaknesses, Opportunities and Threats*, Planning, Practice and Research, 14(3), pp. 367, 1999.

[8] Wood G., *Is what you see what you get? Post-Development Auditing of Methods Used for Predicting the Zone of Visual Influence in EIA*, Environmental Impact Assessment Review, 20, pp. 538, 2000.

[9] Dipper B., Jones C. and Wood C., *Monitoring and Post-auditing in Environmental Impact Assessment: A Review*, Journal of Environmental Planning and Management, 41(6), pp. 735, 1998.

Critical aspects in the application to ports of directive 96/82/EC

F. Altavilla, S. Berardi, P.A. Bragatto
ISPESL National Institute for Occupational Safety and Health, Italy.

Abstract

Tank containers are a modern and efficient transport mode for many hazardous goods. They are suitable both for liquids and for liquefied pressurised gases. A serious damage to a tank container, with sudden loss of most content, is a highly improbable event; but it has anyway to be considered, in order to obtain a safety report compliant with precautionary criteria, as required by the Italian recent regulation on chemical hazard in port areas. Some accident scenarios have been simulated using TNO EFFECTS2 software code. Release of a very toxic liquid; release of a toxic liquid and release of liquefied pressurised gas have been considered, assuming different atmospheric conditions. Consequences of worst cases, as considered in this paper, could affect a quite large area, but anyway could be fronted by prepared and trained operators.

1 Introduction

Safety is an essential and necessary element of the sustained economic activity of port areas and should be an integrated part of the management of port areas, rather than an "add-on", as well as environmental protection. On this basis, Italian Legislator, decided to implement Directive 96/82/EC[1] on the control of major accident hazards involving dangerous substances also for industrial and petrol ports. Article 4 of Directive excludes from application ports and marshalling yards, even if in premises (whereas 12) provides the State Members may adopt appropriate measures also for transport related activities at docks, wharves and marshalling yards, in order to ensure a level of safety equivalent to that established for industrial installations. Decree of Environment Ministry 16 May 2001 n.293 [2], requires Port Authorities, as defined in Italy by Law 28

January 1994 n.84, to prepare an integrated port safety report, based on items and information provided by:

1) operators of establishments inside the port areas, where dangerous substances are present in quantity equal or in excess of the quantities in Annexe I of Directive 96/82/EC

2) enterprises authorised to load, unload, tranship and store dangerous cargoes

3) public and private owned service agencies relevant for port safety.

Assessment of risks deriving from dangerous cargoes handling is the first step in preparing integrated safety report. All measures for chemical risk control and mitigation derive From this assessment, as well as emergency planning.

It is to be remarked that Decree n.293 aims just at dangerous substances, as defined in mentioned Directive 96/82 and does not consider other safety issues, regulated by previous laws.

2 Vulnerability issues in ports

Application of Decree n.293 is a big challenge, and a research effort is necessary to provide port authorities and operators with technical guidance. For a long time, research community had been developing and proving methods and procedures for chemical risk assessment in industrial sites. For chemical safety purposes, ports could be considered like large and complex industrial installations. Anyway there are deep differences between ports and industrial plants that have to be well understood in order to transfer safety experiences to port field [3]. Among these differences the following ones have been stressed for the purpose of this study:

i.   In ports is difficult to control accesses, surveillance cannot be so tight as at fixed installations and fraudulent actions cannot be excluded at all, as well as terrorism.

ii.   Casual labour is much more usual than at fixed installations and it is difficult to assure a minimal training level for occasional workers.

iii.   A lot of companies handle dangerous goods. They can have different organisations and different safety procedures and harmonisation may be a difficult job.

iv.   Of course there is much more water than in any industrial plant. Substances that react with water and produce toxic gases or flammable gas require major cares in port than on land. Furthermore, some substances, not relevant for human health, may be dangerous for marine environment and require special precautions.

v.   Many different hazardous substances may be stored in the same warehouse, as well as on the same freight container ship. In case of an accident, effects of different substances may sum up.

vi. People presences are usually higher in industrial-commercial ports than in any other industrial plants. Furthermore in Italian ports often industrial areas are contiguous or close to passenger terminals, where, occasionally, thousands of people may concentrate.

vii. Large and very populated historical centres stay usually behind major Italian ports, whereas industrial installations are usually set in dedicated areas, far from populated neighbouring.

viii. Lorry drivers are required by international transport laws to own a special authorisation to carry dangerous goods, but a lot of other different vehicles may enter and circulate in ports and may deal, directly or indirectly, with dangerous goods handling.

ix. Maritime accidents in port areas could involve chemicals and hazardous substances.

x. A tremendous variety of chemicals may be loaded unloaded and stored, depending on market demand. Among such goods, just a few may be dangerous and personnel happen just occasionally to deal with hazardous substances.

xi. In Italian ports, number and quantities of different chemicals and hazardous goods traffic is expected to increase also considering the governmental program named "Sea Highways".

xii. Transport modes (ship, rail and road) are subject to different laws, standards and authorities so that competence conflicts may occur.
For all these reasons, ports are more vulnerable than industrial plants and a precautionary approach should to be adopted for risk analysis and safety report. From a conservative safety report, a more careful chemical safety policy and a better preparedness for chemical emergencies will derive.

3 Dangerous cargoes

Most port accidents deal with oil products and other liquid chemicals carried by special tank ships[4]. Procedures and methods for facing such a risk are already well known and operators of large bulk chemical storage with ship loading-unloading facilities are well prepared as they for long time had been subject to industrial risk directives and laws. Further chemical risks, instead, may be underestimated. Among these risks, the present paper focuses risks dealing with hazardous goods freighted in containers. This is the suitable transport mode for most chemicals. Bulk transport, in fact, is feasible just for huge quantities and requires special ships, while freight containers are much more flexible and safe. There are tank containers designed for flammable, toxic and corrosive liquids as well as special tank container for pressurised gas like ammonia or hydrocarbon. Tank containers are designed for multi modal transport and, thus, have to comply with many maritime, rail and road regulations. ISO, IMDG, ADR, RID, IMO and International Convention for Safe Containers, set standards and procedures for safe tank containers design, production, maintenance, cleaning and acceptance[5].   Tank-containers have usually the overall dimensions of a standard 20 feet freight container. Tanks are usually protected from static electricity, can stay in extreme temperature conditions (-50°C to +50°C), and can hold not less than 60 minutes in conditions of fire. Depending upon material and design features (valves and rupture disks), tanks may also allowed to transport pressurized gas.

Tank containers are undoubtedly the safest transport mode for many dangerous substances. Untidy applications of procedures and voluntary acts of sabotage could anyway happen, for any of the previously mentioned reasons. As regards to ports vulnerability issues, major accident as consequence of slovenliness or sabotage cannot be excluded in risk analysis.

4 Worst cases and consequences assessment

In risk analysis, as worst possible case, consequences of a serious damage to a tank container, with sudden loss of most content, have to be considered, in order to have a safety report compliant with precautionary criteria. For this purposes, the present paper considers a 20 feet, 24.7 cubic meters, tank containers, meeting the requirements of Italian national and ISO standards, international conventions and agreements on tank containers.

In this paper just three have been considered: very toxic liquid, toxic liquid and toxic liquefied gases. For each considered category of dangerous substances a characteristic substance has been selected in order to carry out simulations. Table 1 present the representative substances selected per category of dangerous substances. The consequences for these categories are expressed in terms of maximum distances at which persons might have immediate danger for life or health. The consequence distance of a toxic cloud is the maximum distance at which, on a height of 1.5 m above the ground level, a concentration is calculated with the ability for a person to escape without loss of life or irreversible effects in case of an exposure duration of 1800 seconds (IDLH). In determining IDLH (Immediate Dangerous for Life or Health) concentration, the ability of a worker to escape without loss of life or irreversible health effects is considered along with deleterious effects that could prevent escape. The concentrations for IDLH are derived from [6] and are presented in table 2.

Table 1: Representative substances

Category	Liquid	Liquefied pressurized gas
Very toxic	Acrolein	-
Toxic	Acrylonitrile	Ammonia

Table 2: Toxic concentrations for representative substances

substances	IDLH [mg/m3]
Acrolein	4.7
Acrylonitrile	188
Ammonia	350

EFFECTS2 software code [7] has been adopted for simulations. To calculate the consequences for the substances as presented in table 1, the following types of release are distinguished: 1) release of liquid; 2) release of liquefied pressurised gas. Each items will be described in more detail below.

4.1 Release of liquid

A liquid release from a tank through a hole has been considered. Liquid release had been supposed produce a pool whether on land surface or on water surface. Toxic vapour releases from both water and land have been evaluated in order to analyse the different consequences.

4.1.1 Outflow
As mentioned above, this assessment is focused on the maximum consequences of a portable tanks leakage, thus only the outflow due to a full bore rupture of the tank is considered. As for the calculation of the mass flow rate in case of a tank rupture it is assumed an unlimited release. Table 3 presents input parameters for outflow simulation.

Table 3: Outflow simulation input

Filling degree [%]	90	Leak size [m]	0.1
Pressure [atm]	1	Height leak [m]	1.3
Temperature [K]	293	Discharge coefficient [-]	0.62

The outflow of a liquid is calculated with the liquid release from vessel through hole. For this model it has been assumed that the pressure above the liquid level inside the vessel remains constant. The model is described in [7]. Table 4 presents simulation output. As far as it concerns the aim of this work, it has been assumed nobody could stop in time the flow.

Table 4: Outflow simulation output

	Acrolein	Acrylonitrile
Time of release [min]	11	13
Total mass released [kg]	5983	6064.5

4.1.2 Slick evaporation from water surface

It is assumed that the release of liquid results in a slick over the water surface. Table 5 presents input parameters for slick evaporation simulations. In table 6 simulations output are shown.

Table 5: Slick evaporation input

Assumed ambient and water parameters			
Water temperature	288.15 K	Water depth	9 m
Ambient temperature	293 K	Water velocity	0.01 m/s
substances characteristics			
-	solubility at 20°C (% weight)		boiling point
acrolein	20%		52,8°C
acrylonitrile	7%		77,5 °C

For following simulation purposes, it has been assumed that in the first hour, nobody is able to remove the sick from water. The resulting evaporation rates are the input for the dispersion model.

Table 6: Slick evaporation output

	Acrolein	Acrylonitrile
Slick diameter [m]	56.20	41.00
Average evaporation rate [kg/s]	0.09	0.02

4.1.3 Pool evaporation from land surface

It has been assumed that the release of liquid results in a pool formed on the ground surface of a pier. It is assumed that in about twenty minutes from the first tank damage some emergency measures could be adopted. Thus atmospheric release has been studied for just ten minutes from outflow end (flow ends about 11-13 minutes after tank boring). A 20°C ambient temperature and a 30°C soil temperature have been assumed. Roughness of the subsoil determines the minimum layer thickness of a spreading pool and it has been assumed 0.5 cm. The evaporation from pool and the atmospheric dispersion depend on the atmospheric stability class and on the wind velocity. A windy weather with wind velocity 5 m/s, with neutral atmospheric stability (class D) is a typical condition for Italian coastal areas. A very stable atmosphere (class F) with weak wind (1 m/s) is anyway possible, and it is usually considered the most unfavourable for natural dilution. A very unstable atmosphere (class A) with very weak wind (1 m/s) is instead typical of hot summer days. These three atmospheric conditions (F1, D5, A1) have been selected as representative of reasonable meteorological scenarios. For toxic substances the evaporation rate is calculated as the average over the first 10 minutes. Table 7 presents simulation output values. The resulting evaporation rates are the input for dispersion model.

Table 7: Pool evaporation output

	Acrolein			Acrylonitrile		
	F2	A1	D5	F2	A1	D5
Max. pool area [m2]	1400	1426	1426	1502	1502	1502
Mean evaporation rate [kg/s]	3.04	2.87	4.38	1.77	1.54	2.67

4.1.4 Atmospheric dispersion

To evaluate the maximum consequence distances, the evaporation rate, as calculated above, has been linked to the atmospheric dispersion model, within EFFECTS2. For acrolein and acrylonitrile, the neutral gas dispersion model has been used to calculate the dispersion, assuming weather classes F2, D5 and A1.
The neutral gas dispersion model is based on the Gaussian plume model. This model must only be used for gases with a density approximately the same as air. Besides, the direction of the release is taken as horizontal in the wind direction.
For simulation purposes, an industrial area with obstacles which are not too high has been assumed.

Both length (L) and width (W) of toxic cloud are given for the consequence distance. Table 8 present consequence distances for different liquid spill scenarios. Figure 1 shows toxic cloud from an acroelin pool, under different weather conditions.

Table 8: Consequences Distances

	Weather class	A1	F2	D5
		L x W (meters. X meters.)		
Acrolein (very toxic)	Evaporation from water	93 x 46	680 x 37	n.a.*
	Evaporation from land	733 x 387	1624 x 171	3543 x 457
Acrylonitrile (toxic)	Evaporation from water	n.a*	n.a.*	n.a*
	Evaporation from land	280 x 81	1275 x 88	837 x 66

* In no points IDLH concentration had been reached

4.2 Release of liquefied pressurised gas

In case of liquefied pressurised gas, outflow is much faster than a liquid and result soon in a gas cloud in the atmosphere.

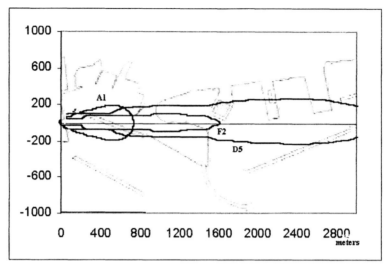

Figure 1 Toxic cloud form an acrolein pool, on the pier surface, with
different weather conditions (A1 D5 and F2)

4.2.1 Outflow

The outflow of a liquefied pressurised gas is calculated considering the following
situation: tank containing pressurized liquefied anhydrous ammonia with a hole
in the vessel below liquid level in the liquid phase. In the tank a vapour-liquid
equilibrium holds, with a pressure equal to the pressure at given temperature.
Table 9 presents simulation input parameters.

Table 9: Release of liquefied pressurised ammonia simulation input

Filling degree [%]	90	Leak size [m]	0.1
Temperature [K]	293	Height leak [m]	1.3

Table 10 presents simulation output. After 90 seconds, the mass of liquid into
the tank is 820.8 kg, the mass of vapour is 119.31, the tank filling degree is 5 %
and the height of the liquid into the tank is 0.27 m.

Table 10: Liquefied pressurised ammonia simulation output

Maximum mass released [kg/s]	147
Time of release [min]	1.5
Total mass released [kg]	12730

4.2.2 Atmospheric dispersion

Also for ammonia, the neutral gas dispersion model is used to calculate the
dispersion of the substance for weather classes F2, D5 and A1. For terrain
roughness length class and the ambient temperature refer table 9. The

atmospheric dispersion is calculated as the average over the first 10 minutes. Within that time a natural partial abatement of the cloud is assumed, due to dilution and to dry or wet deposition. Table 11 presents results from model simulation. As usual cloud length and width are presented, as well as cloud minimum and maximum distance from release point. Figure 2 presents toxic cloud from an ammonia release, under different weather condition.

Table 11: Release of liquefied pressurised gas: simulation output

Weather class	A1	F2	D5
Maximum concentration [mg/m3]	2601.7	31250.0	456.4
Distance maximum concentration [m]	600.0	1086.4	2715.4
L Maximum length of vapour cloud [m]	313	921	558
W Maximum width of vapour cloud [m]	267	136	151
Max. distance to IDLH concentration [m]	757	1573	2999
Min. distance to IDLH concentration [m]	443	652	2445

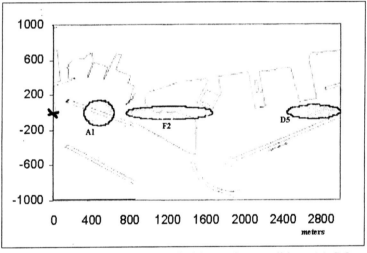

Figure 2 Toxic cloud after a release of with weather conditions A1, D5 and F2

5 Discussion and conclusion

Some of the parameters used for the calculation of the consequence distances might be pessimistic. For liquefied pressurised gas, typical tanks for this kind of transport are made by special steel thick sheets and just a very energetic hit could bore them [8]. The probability of occurrence of a large bore rupture was not evaluated, but it is very low indeed. For liquid release it has been assumed that in fifteen minutes, nobody has managed to stop the liquid spilling. This assumption might be too pessimistic. Also leak height and dimensions have been assumed favourable to liquid spilling.

Other parameters, instead, might be too optimistic. For liquid release on soil it has been assumed that in half an hour emergency, team neutralizes toxic pool emissions; it might take some more time to detect leakage and to organize first actions. For liquid release in water damage to livings was not taken into account at all, but it could be relevant and require complex remediation activities. For liquefied pressurised gas, presented results consider just the first ten minutes after complete gas release, assuming in that time a natural abatement of the cloud. After ten minutes, anyway, toxic cloud might advance again and affect a larger area. Assuming the time for natural abatement thirty minutes, results could be much more bad, specially with very stable atmospheric condition.

At the end loss of hazardous substances from a tank container inside a part area cannot be excluded in a precautionary risk assessment. Consequences of worst cases, as considered in this paper, could affect a quite large area, but anyway could be fronted by well trained operators[9]. Preparedness is thus vital to manage chemical risks and to assure higher safety levels in ports.

References

[1] Council Directive 96/82/EC *Official Journal of the European Communities* No 10 pp. 13-34
[2] Decreto 16 maggio 2001 n.293 *Gazzetta Ufficiale Repubblica Italiana* N.165
[3] Guidance concerning chemical safety in port areas *OECD Environment Monograph* n. 118 1996 63 pp.
[4] *www.rempec.org/accident-analysis.html* 2000
[5] Gill,M. Rawlison,J. May,T. Carbonnier,J. Smith,M. Acceptable Container Conditions *International Tank Container Organization* n.1 May 1998
[6] NIOSH Pocket guidew to chemical hazards *National Institute for Occupational Safety and Health.* 1994
[7] Yellow Book Methods for the calculation of physical effects CPR-14E 3rd ed. 1997
[8] Lees F.P. Transport Containers *Loss Prevention in the Processes Industries* Butterworths London 1980 pp. 788-790
[9] IMO/UNEP Consultation Version *APELL for port areas 1996: Preparedness and response to chemical accidents in ports 83 pp.*

Environmental management of port oil terminals

D. G. Prokopiou and B. S. Tselentis
Department of Maritime Studies, University of Piraeus, Greece.

Abstract

Bunkering is considered an environmentally high-risk process as international statistics on accidental pollution incidents indicate. The process is highly complicated, often involving several partners and many procedures and protocols. Procedures on board ship are well structured and well described in documentation provided by the manufacturers as well institutions such as IMO (MARPOL 73/78 clauses and Annexes), ISM auditors and others. It is also an area where much research has provided a good insight as to the factors involved, as well as many practical solutions to problems inherent to these processes. Another area where further research is needed, concerns oil refinery terminals, which, at least for Greece, play a major part in the transportation network of both crude as well as refined oil products. This paper presents the findings of research work, concerning the quality of oil terminal and bunkering procedures followed by refineries and oil terminals in Greece. The results are based on personal interviews with top ranking executives from the refineries, the Hellenic Coast Guard, Port and Local Authorities, Research Institutes and Health and Safety Bodies. All four major oil refineries were studied (three in the greater Attica area and one in Thessaloniki) as well as smaller oil terminals situated on many islands (mainly serving and operated by the National Electricity Board) and smaller oil terminals serving oil storage tanks mainly situated near or on the coastline. Data presented are discussed in relation to oil terminal environmental management procedures, highlighting practices and processes pertinent to the bunkering industry which is striving to establish safety and environmental protection issues as its top priorities.

1. Introduction

Recent data from the US Coast Guard [1], concerning the time period between 1973 and 1993, indicate that the percentage of total volume of oil spilled in U.S. waters by source comprises of 18% from pipelines and by 18% from facilities in general. The same source [1], estimates that, by operation, cargo transfer amounts to 23%, tanker facility operations 2%, bunkering 1% and pipeline 1%, of the total volume of oil spilled in U.S. waters.

It is also a well-known fact that around 75% of all pollution incidents involve oil either as crude or as refinery products [2].

Greece is a major bunkering centre in the Mediterranean, the market being large enough to sustain eleven physical suppliers, eight of which are independents and three representatives of oil majors. There are also 60 traders, which mainly deal with the worldwide market rather than in Greece alone. The annual bunker sales for Greece are estimated to be around 2.5 million tonnes and on average 30% of the imported and domestically produced oil is sold as marine bunkers, compared to the OECD average of less than 15%.

Although the market has been stable in recent years, there are signs of growth in the near future. The abolition of the cabotage restrictions in the passenger sector and the expected appearance of American and European cruise lines [3], coupled to the national programme of port development throughout the country [4] and especially the cruise terminal of the port of Piraeus connected to the 2004 Athens Olympic Games, will mean more ships and ship movements, and increased demand for bunkers. Along the same lines, commercial traffic is showing sighs of increasing, Piraeus Port reporting an increase of 19% in container traffic for the year 2000 [5], Thessaloniki, taking advantage of its strategic position in the Balkans, has increased its transit cargo and Patras is already accommodating a constant stream of new ferries added to the fleets of companies operating between the port and Italy. Finally the competitive prices of bunkers in Greece attract numerous ships, which deviate from their course to benefit from the low prices, even though during the summer months delays and shortages are experienced due to increased demand from the tourist industry.

Recent developments concerning the building of a 300 kilometre pipeline that will run from Burgas on the Bulgarian coast to Alexandroupoli on the Greek Aegean coast, transporting around 35 million tonnes of oil annually, is expected to increase tanker traffic and bunker sales, since there will be ample amounts of low cost Russian oil arriving on the north-eastern part of Greece in close proximity to the Dardanelles. Storage tanks (with a capacity of 1 million m^3) and floating oil terminals for oil loading, are planned for the area.

Another peculiarity to Greece is the number of small and isolated islands, which although ideal places for tourist development, nevertheless still require an energy source to power their electricity generators. Thirty six oil terminals, mainly managed by the National Electricity Board of Greece (DEH), operate on nearly all the islands that are situated at distances that do not, as yet, permit an underwater electricity link to other islands or mainland Greece. These are an important link in the oil chain from oil production and transportation system.

2. Greek oil terminals

In Greece four major refineries operate reaching a combined capacity of approximately 19 million tones a year. Three reside in the Greater Attica area, and one in Thessaloniki. Two (one in Attica and one in Thessaloniki) are operated by Hellenic Petroleum (HP) the country's largest industrial and commercial enterprise, amounting to half the nation's refining capacity. The other two, Motor Oil and Petrola Hellas, both privately owned by shipping families, reside in the capital area, and plan further expansions of both industrial processes and new products. All the above-mentioned refineries have an extensive coastal oil terminal infrastructure, since all crude oil supplies arrive by sea. In addition smaller oil terminals are situated on many islands, as mentioned previously, serving and operated by the National Electricity Board, as well as smaller oil terminals serving oil storage tanks situated near or on the coastline. Two of the three largest oil terminals serving the National Electricity Board are in Crete and the third is on Rhodes island. Main bunkering terminals are situated in all main Greek ports, such as Piraeus, Elefsis , Thessaloniki, Patras and Volos. The Ministry of Industry, Energy and Development is responsible for granting planning and operation permits as well as special licenses for an oil terminal. Such certification provides the basis for compliance to health and safety standards and considerations laid out by Greek and International law. The Hellenic Coast Guard and the local Prefecture also play an important role in assessing preparedness and local contingency planning including regular safety exercises. Staff training, equipment maintenance and readiness are also controlled and certified. The law governing oil refineries, oil trading installations, and the industries, which use petroleum fuels, states that the above mentioned are obliged to install oil reception facilities, as well provide and maintain the appropriate equipment in order to deal with pollution accidents/incidents [6].

2.1 Refinery Terminals

Refineries in Greece are at close proximity with the coastline some with more than one terminals. Vessels visiting Greek refineries range from as small as 500 to 250,000 dwt. Refinery terminals act as independent and self-governing ports, often developing and applying procedures and cargo transfer and handling practices suited to the special characteristics and operations of these installations. These ports are used for loading and discharging crude oil, chemicals, and oil products. Tugs, pilot boats, patrols, anti-pollution boats and small tanker ships all play an important part in the refinery terminal processes. Tankers wishing to load and discharge their cargoes are only allowed to do so at these terminals.
Of the four refineries in Greece, Aspropyrgos refinery has two terminals one at Aspropyrgos and one at Pahi Megaron. The refinery at Ionia near Thessaloniki has two terminals one on the Kalohori coastline and the second on an artificial island at Thessaloniki port.

2.2 Oil product terminals

These installations provide land based industries with oil products, as well as. serve as loading sites for oil products usually stored on land based storage tanks. Light and intermediate fuels are handled at the following terminals :
(1)   Bunkering terminals: most of them are at Piraeus and Thessaloniki and two at Creta (Kali Limenes)and Syros.
(2)   Oil terminals used for local petroleum oil needs: The biggest islands and the main Greek ports have such installations (e.g. Volos, Igoumenitsa, Kavala, Alexandroupoli, Rhodes, Mitilini, Creta, Hios)
(3)   National Electricity Board terminals: These serve as unloading points on the Greek islands, providing fuel to power the electricity generators owned and operated·by DEH
(4)   Terminals serving individual industrial complexes such as steel mills, quarries, grain mills etc.(e.g Volos and Gyali island near Kos)

3. Ship characteristics

Several types of vessels visit the above described specialized terminals .These vessels fall into two categories: (1) Tankers that carry crude oil and oil products to the terminals and for bunkering services and (2) Ships that use terminals to take bunkers.
    It is a well known fact that from the 1st of July 2002 all these vessels, including vessels with carrying capacities of over 500 tones, will have to conform to ISM Code inspections. In the near future, therefore, all tankers approaching oil terminals will be ISM certified, thus minimizing the chances of environmental damage due to accidents. Taking into account that all these vessels are under Port State control and classification society scrutiny, it seems reasonable to assume, that a dramatic decrease in accidents and incidents leading to marine pollution will be observed over the years to come.

Table 1. Extent and frequency of oil terminal accidents/incidents

Areas	Terminals	Tanker calls per year	Accident/pollution incidents (1992-2001)
Northern Greece			
Prefectures of Thessaloniki, Kavala and Evros			
Kavalla central port authority	3		0
Samothraki island port authority	1	2-3	0

Thesaloniki central port authority	2+3	95-115	6
Northern Aegean islands			
Prefectures of Lesbos, Hios and Samos			
Agios Efstratios island port authority	1	0-1	0
Hios island central port authority	2	40-50	
Ikaria island port authority	1	9-10	0
Lemnos island port authority	1	4-5	1
Mitilini island central port authority	3	110	Insignificant amounts
Samos island port authority	1	25-27	1
Central Hellas			
Prefecture of Magnesia and Prefecture of Evia island			
Aliveri port authority	1	24	1
Halkis central port authority	1	1-2	0
Skyros island port authority	1	3	0
Volos central port authority	9	200	4
Prefectures of Piraeus, Western Attica and East Attica			
Antikithira island port authority	1	0-1	0
Elefsis central port authority	3+5	4000	12
Piraeus port authority	4	600-800	-
Lavrio central port authority	1	24	1
Western Hellas - Ionian islands			
Prefectures of Korinthia Patra, Ilia, Messinia and Thesprotia			
Igoumenitsa central port authority	1	40-45	1
Isthmian port authority	1+0	1800	4
Patra central port authority	2		0

Prefectures of Corfu, Zakinthos, and Kefalinia islands			
Corfu island central port authority			
Erikousa island port authority	1	0-1	0
Kefalonia island central port authority	1	0-1	0
Othonoi islands port authority	1	0-1	0
Zakinthos island port authority	1	0-1	0
Aegean Islands			
Prefecture of Cyclades islands			
Amorgos port authority	1	1-2	0
Anafi port authority	1	0-1	0
Andros port authority	1	9-11	0
Donousa port authority	1	0-1	0
Ios port authority	1	3-5	0
Kythnos port authority	1	1-2	0
Milos port authority	1	6-7	0
Mykonos port authority	1	15-17	Insignificant amounts
Paros port authority	1	17	0
Serifos port authority	1	1-2	0
Syros central port authority	2	6-8	6
Thira port authority	1	24	0
Prefecture of Dodecanese islands			
Rhodes central port authority	3	80	0
Kos port authority (including Gyali island terminal)	3	70	0
Karpathos port authority	1	6-9	1
Kalymnos port authority	1	15-20	Insignificant amounts
Patmos port authority	1	4-5	0
Symi port authority	1	2-3	0
Astipalaia port authority	1	1-2	0
Kastelorizo port authority	1	1-2	0
Agathonisi port authority	1	0-1	0

Crete island			
Prefectures of Lasithi, Heraclion, Hania and Rethimno			
Hania port authority	3	232	1
Heraclion port authority	5	150-350	17
Kali Limenes bunkering station	1	10+75	0

4. Conclusions

Data concerning oil refinery terminals, presented in Table 1, have been collated from questionnaires that were completed by personal interviews with high ranking environmental safety managers from Petrola Hellas refinery at Elefsis, Hellenic Petroleum refinery at Aspropyrgos and Hellenic Petroleum Ionia refinery at Thessaloniki, as well as Hellenic Coast Guard officers responsible for these areas (Thessaloniki, Elefsis and Isthmia). From the reported data most of the accidents were caused by human and management miscalculations and errors, such as bad seamanship, shift desertion and understaffing. Interestingly further analysis of the data concerning ship size and incident frequency, indicated that the majority (about 70%)of oil spill incidents involved small vessels (<2,500dwt). It is true however that when large vessels were involved in an incident, the oil pollution was considerable, as in the case at Isthmia involving an oil spill of 520 tonnes of crude oil in 1996.

Data concerning oil product terminals, presented in the table above, have been collated from questionnaires that were completed by personal interviews with managers from the physical suppliers namely: EKO/ELDA, IMS SA, SEKA/SEKAVIN, JET OIL, SHELL, BP, AEGEAN, LID OIL, FAMM, ETEKA, TRANSOIL/IBIA and PETCO. The main cause for accidents experienced at these terminals, according to these suppliers, were the badly maintained oil barges and small supply tankers {<1,200 deadweight tones (dwt)} as well as the untrained crews who, were given the responsibility of performing the bunkering procedures. Our data collected from major Hellenic Coast Guard outposts at Kavalla, Samothraki, Thessaloniki, Lemnos, Mitilini, Skiros, Volos, Elefsis, Isthmia, Patra, Miconos, Paros, Siros, Thira, Kalymnos, Kos, Samos, Rhodes, Hania, Heraclion, Igoumenitsa and Kalymnos, partly confirm the above suggestions, but interestingly highlight further causes. These are summarized as follows: i) Badly maintained pipelines on the piers and on land. A characteristic case is the island of Syros, where an increased number of accidents (6) causing marine pollution, occurred with a relatively small number of tanker approaches (6-8). It is noteworthy to mention that other terminals with much higher tanker calls per annum have much lower accidents (see Hania area). ii) Inadequate port and mooring facilities for ships. A characteristic case is the Linoperamata gulf at Heraclion Crete, where seventeen (17) accidents occurred over a 10 year period, at 4 terminals with a relatively high number of tanker calls (2292 in 10 years). In these cases the ship has to anchor off a buoy and transfer oil products via an underwater pipeline. The usual cause of oil escaping to the marine environment is the movement of the ship due to bad weather and current conditions, with the subsequent breaking of the pipeline.

The questionnaire also noted proposals that key stakeholders made aiming at increasing the safety and environmental protection of the industry. High on the priority list came the need for further education and training of refinery, oil terminal and barge crews, on issues of bunkering and cargo transfer operations, guidelines and checklists concerning safety management and local contingency plans [7].

The issue of restoring the coastline in the Elefsis area, where the operation of two refineries has, inevitably over the years, severely affected the marine environment, could be dealt with by instigating an environmental management plan, based on environmental monitoring and remediation of sea bed sediments. Finally, it is believed that certain areas in Greece face increased traffic and deal with high petroleum oil amounts, increasing the possibilities to accidents that can seriously harm human life and also have a serious impact on the environment. It is proposed that ports and installations in general, be studied carefully utilizing the recently developed methodologies of risk assessment in order to provide reliable scientific data that will provide the basis for management decisions concerning further investments and new developments for the industry.

Acknowledgements

The authors wish to thank the following for their collaboration:
Sublieutenant Startopoulos Isthmia Port Authority, Sublieutenant Bispinas Thessaloniki Central Port Authority, Sublieutenant Kaoutskis Elefsis Central Port Authority, Lieutenant Zarras Volos Central Port Authority, Acting Sub Lieutenant Skiada Rhodes Central Port Authority , Hatzibarba F. Ministry of Northern Greece, Thessaloniki, Metikanis D. National Electricity Board, Athens Christidis A,Thriasio District Development Association, Elefsis and Rafailidis A. Hellenic Petroleum Ionia Refinery,Thessaloniki .

References

[1] US Coast Guard (1995)
[2] Hall K., *Impacts of Marine Debris and Oil – economic and social costs to coastal communities.* KIMO Shetland UK., 2000.
[3] P. Aivatzidis "Greece and Oil" *WorldBunkering,* Issue 6, number 2 May 2001.
[4] Englezou, I., Tselentis, V., Tzannatos, E. and Amanatidis, G., Port Pollution and Exhaust Emissions from Ships, *Proceedings of the 10th World Clean Air Congress*, Helsinki, pp. 229 – 232, May 1995.
[5] Hatzakos S., Chairman Transport Committee ESPO (personal communication)
[6] Dilanas A., :Speculations on Environmental Pollution, (in Greek), Athens 1999.
[7] Papapetrou P. Prefect of Western Attica (personal communication)

Evaluation of beeswax based petroleum bioremediation products

B. Waldron[1] & W.M. Griffin[2]
[1] *Petrol Rem, Inc., USA*
[2] *GMS Technologies, Inc. and The Green Design Initiative, Carnegie Mellon University, USA*

Abstract

PRP® is physically modified beeswax that stimulates the natural microbial population to degrade oil. The focus of this study was to demonstrate the use of PRP in the form of a small boom that can retain and enhance the degradation of the retained oil. Diesel fuel was used as the model oil. The experimentation was performed using a custom designed model bilge reactor in a microcosm study. We demonstrate that the observed accelerated degradation was due to the PRP stimulating the natural microbial population capable of degrading hydrocarbon.

We describe a series of experiments designed to determine the efficacy and mechanism of the commercial product PRP/BioBoom®. Experiments were carried out in specially constructed tanks, which exposed the oil spill response product to near-environmental conditions (mesocosm). We found that: PRP enhanced biodegradation of the model oil compared to the non-stimulated natural population; 97 and 76 percent reduction in measured aliphatic and aromatics, respectively, compared to the non-stimulated natural population which degraded the aliphatic and aromatics 48 and 5 percent, respectively. PRP used as a boom (BioBoom) was observed to absorb free oil and enhance its biodegradation within the boom. Eighty-three percent of the aliphatics and 51 percent of the aromatics were degraded within the boom.

A theory for the efficacy of the material and its potential benefits in marine management and pollution control is proposed.

1 Introduction

The discharge of oily wastes into waterways is a common and global concern. Estimates place United States petroleum consumption at over 290 billion gallons each year. Due to the challenge of transport, refining, distribution, and petroleum product use an average of 13,000 spills are reported annually. Major spills generate public awareness, but the United States Environmental Protection Agency (EPA) has realized that non-point source discharge of oil results in a considerable amount of pollution. The EPA estimates that 150 – 450 million gallons of oil/fuel are discharged into US waterways annually. To put this figure into perspective, the Exxon Valdez accident released approximately 10.1 million gallons, only 1/15th of what the US releases on an annual basis.

Petrol Rem, Inc. is commercializing a series of oil spill response bioremediation products under the name of PRP. PRP has been listed on the U.S. Environmental Protection Agency (EPA) National Contingency Plan's Product Schedule since November 1990 as a biological additive. Melted beeswax is converted into hollow microscopic spheres. The spheres are left loose or encased in oblong fabric bags of various diameters and lengths depending on the intended application. Due to the oleophilic properties of the beeswax, and its overall bulk density, the products float on the surface of the water allowing oil and other petroleum products to bind on contact.

Petrol Rem's product line includes various forms of PRP including their containment booms and bilge socks. The purpose of the products is to contain, absorb and facilitate the biodegradation of the spilled oil. Because both the beeswax and petroleum biodegrade, disposal is limited to the fabric bag.

2 Literature Review

2.1 Bacteria

The details of physiology and ecology of microbiological hydrocarbon metabolism, has been documented [1,2]. Knowledge of how bacteria can use oil as a carbon source, and the metabolic pathways associated with its use has led to the possibility of exploiting these processes to aid in oil degradation. This can be accomplished by stimulating the indigenous microbial population (biostimulation) or by adding specific microorganisms (bioaugmentation), Atlas, Leahy and Colwell, Dietz, and Swannell [1,2,3,4], have all reviewed the practice and techniques of these two strategies.

Most environments contain hydrocarbon-degrading microbes. The most common metabolic pathway for microbial consumption of petroleum is terminal oxidation, and subsequent β-oxidation [6] to permit the microorganism to get the carbon into its intermediary metabolism. Adding petroleum causes the bacterial population to shift to a higher percentage of hydrocarbon-degrading organisms [3,5,7].

Microorganisms are known to exist in both free floating (planktonic) and "bound" states (sessile). According to Kirchman and Mitchell [8] bacteria bound to particles or surfaces provide more than 40% of the heterotrophic activity while only comprising 10% of the population. This is particularly important in the case of PRP, an oleophilic particle. When in contact with oil the wax and petroleum create a semi-solid matrix of oil and wax. The material creates a surface area, allowing bacteria to bind stimulating the bacterial activity [9].

2.2 Metabolism

Metabolic activity is dependent on the concentrations of specific nutrients, and may be sub optimal if one or more are deficient [9]. Bacteria and other microorganisms require phosphorus and nitrogen to perform normal metabolic activities [10].

Other compounds not expressly required for metabolic functions, have been shown to have a stimulatory effect on bacterial metabolism. Research suggests that the presence of fatty acids can actually help to initiate and increase the amount of hydrocarbon degradation [12], which partly explains the positive benefits of beeswax's presence on biodegradation rates.

2.3 Beeswax

Beeswax composition is complex and varies geographically, seasonally and with indigenous vegetation [13,14]. It is composed of primarily a mixture of fatty acid esters averaging carbon chains of approximately 40 carbon atoms [13]. Tulloch [15] further explained composition in 1980 when he determined that the esters were present in both monoester and more complex forms, such as diesters, triesters, and hydroxyesters. In total, there are more than 300 different compounds in natural beeswax, only four are present in an amount more than 5% of the total: C_{40} (6%), C_{46} (8%), and C_{48} (6%) as monoesters, and C_{24} acid (6%). Beeswax is biodegradable [16,17].

3 Objectives

Evaluations by the US EPA demonstrated that PRP enhanced biodegradation of oil but only slightly, and this research sought to confirm product performance in a "real world environment." A previous *in-situ* test verified the ability of PRP to hold and not release oil into the environment, but a true measure of the biodegradative capabilities wasn't determined [18]. A flowing mesocosm test, mimicking a Tier III evaluation as described by NETAC [19], designed to simulate a fresh water stream was used to. The full report covers a review of the product testing methods, a description of both the field and laboratory-generated data, and an analysis (with statistics) of the experimental results.

Following are the objectives the study: evaluate the biodegradation of petroleum hydrocarbons by products manufactured with and without added microorganisms, determine if the product is beneficial regarding biodegradation when compared to a synthetic absorbent boom, and investigate the effectiveness of the loose beeswax product alone.

4 Methods and Materials

4.1 Biodegradation analysis using the Bilge Model Reactor

4.1.1 Bilge model reactor set-up

The bilge model reactor (BMR) as used in the experimentation is shown in Figure 1. The beaker size was 400 mL to accommodate $^{1}/_{4}$ inch glass tubing for the inlet and outlet. To prevent the contents from draining completely when flow was started required the addition of a "siphon break" on the outlet.

Water was sampled from Point State Park located at the confluence of the Allegheny, Monongahela and Ohio rivers in Pittsburgh, PA on the day of the test. The water was immediately transferred to the laboratory and dispensed into the BMR's. Two hundred milligrams of fresh diesel fuel was added to the reactors. BMR's requiring Beeswax products were given 1 gram of

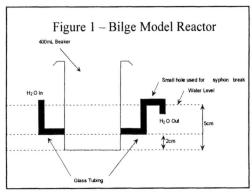

Figure 1 – Bilge Model Reactor

material to each flask. [See results for experimental design.] At this point, time 0 samples were sacrificed for analysis. At time 2 weeks and 4 weeks BMR's were sacrificed for analysis. The BMR's were gently shaken for the appropriate time on a rotary shaker – the rate was below the calibration of the shake table but gently moved the liquid on the glass but did not cause any losses through the opening in the BMR's. All BMR had covers that prevented contamination of the experiment but air could readily enter the reactor.

4.1.2 Extraction methods

The extraction method followed EPA SW 846 Method 3510 – Separatory Funnel Method modified to accommodate our sampling strategy. The liquid from the Bilge Model Reactors (BMR's) was transferred to a 500 mL separatory funnel making sure that samples containing the materials were transferred to the funnel. A 50 mL aliquot of methylene chloride (CH_2Cl_2) was added. The contents were mixed. After extraction, the funnel was permitted to stand and the 2-phases to separate. The organic phase was collected for immediate GC analysis.

The extraction efficiency for the diesel fuel was compared versus a standard curve at various concentration of diesel, which would represent a 90% decrease during the course of the experimentation. The idea was determine if similar extraction efficiencies would occur in the presence or absence of the Beeswax. The efficiencies ranged from for 90 to 103% based on comparison to a 5-point standard curve (25, 75, 100, 150, 200 mg diesel/BMR). Based on the calibration curves and the known concentrations of diesel present in each standard, it was possible to ascertain the new concentration of diesel fuel based on the GC's measurement of the diesel range organic (DRO) compounds.

The extraction process recovered the diesel linearly. However, the presence of the beeswax presented a number of unique problems. A significant amount of time was spent solving the impact of the Beeswax on all of the analytical methodology, particularly recoveries. The impact of the wax on the instrument is reflected in modification of the instrument conditions as described in the methods. Extraction routinely recovered more diesel range organics in the presence of beeswax than without. This is counterintuitive since one would expect due to the hydrophobic nature of the beeswax it would hold on to the hydrocarbon preventing good extraction. Separate standard curves were developed extracting known quantities of diesel fuel with and without Beeswax. In this way extraction efficiency and impact of the beeswax were accounted for during the experiment.

4.1.3 Chemical analysis
The analytical work was done on a Hewlett-Packard 5890 Gas Chromatograph (GC) equipped with a Hewlett Packard 7673 Autosampler, a 30 m, 0.25 μm ID RTX-5 column (Restek Corporation) and a hydrogen flame ionization detector. The salient parameters were as follows: For the Gas Chromatograph: Injector Temperature: 300° C, Detector Temperature: 325° C, Initial Oven Temperature: 50° C, Final Oven Temperature: 320° C, Oven Rate: 5.0° C/min, Helium Carrier Flow Rate: 4 mL/min, Purge Flow Rate: 7 mL/min, and Split Vent Flow Rate: 2.5 mL/min. For the Autosampler: Sample Washes: 2, Sample Pumps: 5, Viscosity: 7 seconds, and Volume: 1 μL.

The oven temperature was maintained at 250° C when not in use. Periodically the oven was maintained at 320° C to remove all the heavy compounds preventing the buildup of PRP components on the column that would degrade the instrument's sensitivity. The auto-injector syringe also had to be removed every 20 samples and cleaned mechanically with cleaning wires and an ultrasonic cleaner. The septum and injector lining were also to ensure that there was no carryover from the previous samples. Two-way analysis of variance (ANOVA) was used to verify results.

4.1.4 Standard preparation
For data interpretation it was necessary to use a calibration curve. There were several different curves that were constructed to demonstrate the relationship between mass and the area value read by the gas chromatograph.

4.1.5 Most probable number calculation
Samples from each experimental vessel were used to calculate the bacterial populations.

Total Hydrocarbon-degrading Organisms: A 6-tube MPN will be performed by dispensing 0.1 mL aliquots of each dilution into 2 mL of Bushnell-Haas broth dispensed into 6 wells/dilution of a 6 row by 4 well micro-titer plate. Twenty μL of filter sterilized diesel fuel will be added to each well and the MPN plates covered and incubated at room temperature. After a 14 day incubation period, 100 µL of a 5mg/mL solution of *p*–iodonitrotetrazolium violet will be added to each well to determine growth. Development of a pink or purple color upon standing for 45 minutes is considered a positive response. The MPN Calculator program will be used to provide the number of microorganisms per mL of the sample.

Total Heterotrophic Organisms: Microbial analysis was performed using MPN determination. A "6-tube MPN" was set up by dispensing 0.1 mL aliquots from each dilution into 1 mL of Trypticase Soy Broth (per Standard Methods, 18th Edition, 1992, p.9-33) that was previously dispensed into 6 wells/dilution of a 4 row by 6 well micro-titer plate. The MPN plates will be incubated at room temperature. After a 48 hour incubation period, 100 µl of a 5 mg/mL solution of *p*-iodonitrotetrazolium violet is added to each well to determine growth. Development of a pink or purple color upon standing for 20 minutes was considered a positive response. The number of positive wells and the related dilutions will be entered in a computerized enumeration method, "MPN Calculator" program (version 2.3). The software was developed by Albert J. Klee, (U.S. EPA, Office of Research and Development, Risk Reduction Engineering Laboratory, Cincinnati, OH) and provides the number of microorganisms per mL of the sample.

4.2 Mesocosm study and biodegradation analysis via GC/MS

4.2.1 Mesocosm Description

The mesocosm consisted of tank spilt into three relatively equal sections where water from a natural source could be constantly pumped through to simulate a "typical" fresh water stream. The tanks were constructed of plywood and supporting lumber lined with a polyvinyl swimming pool liner. The base of the tanks were structurally supported by a poured concrete base and covered by a PVC tarpaulin on 2 m supports to protect against rain and casual debris from entering the system. The three tanks were used for the experimental treatment and the controls. Each tank had the same general dimensions (i.e., 3 m x 1 m x 1.3 m), and was filled to a depth of about three feet. The tanks were separated one from another by a fiberglass wall sealed by silicone caulking. The design permitted sampling of the slick, water column at a depth of approximately 0.3 m below the slick, and incoming and outgoing water from each tank.

4.2.2 Water Source

The source of water for the system was provided on a continual basis by one of two near-by streams. Discharge from the system was sent to a large (95,000 L) holding tank to assure that no oil would be inadvertently discharged to the receiving stream. Water from the holding tank was intermittently discharged to a stream via an overland discharge of about 90 m subsequent to physical observation that no oil sheen was present in the holding tank's water.

Water was pumped from the stream at a rate of approximately 49,000 L per day into a an intermediate reservoir. Three identical submersible pumps into the influent section of each test tank pumped the water from the reservoir at the rate of about 11 L per minute per tank. Total flow in the system was about 2,000 L per hour. Turnover in each tank occurred approximately once every 3.2 hours.

To reduce the likelihood of short-circuiting in the tanks, a weir was used to direct water to flow downward beneath the slick, through the tank and then upward past a second weir prior to discharge to the large holding tank. Water was pumped for several days prior to the initiation of the test to allow for stabilization and acclimatization of the system.

4.2.3 Test Conditions
As previously described, the test was conducted in tanks using natural stream water. Weather and water conditions were recorded on a daily basis. These data were collected to provide a daily record for the physical conditions experienced during the experiment. Each of the three test tanks was fitted with a containment boom in a circular fashion to restrict the movement of the oil about the tank and to focus on the effects of the treatment. Each tank was dosed with 3.8 L of fresh (non-weathered) diesel fuel, from a local distributor.

Tank #1 contained the absorbent control, consisting of two one-pound sleeves of polypropylene absorbent within its boom. Tank #2 contained the "no-action" control where the oil was allowed to sit within the boom with no treatment. Tank #3 used the BioBoom for the oil absorption/containment as well as providing the area where the PRP could be applied as the primary means of treatment. In addition to the use of the B system, the oil in Tank #3 was directly treated with 90 g of PRP about 10 minutes after the introduction of the oil.

4.2.4 Chemical analysis
One mL of the n-hexane diluted sample or extract was placed into a 1.5 mL vial for use on the autosampler of the GC/MS instrument (HP 5890 with MSD). To this solution, 20 mL of a 500 ng/mL solution of the internal standards was added. The final concentrations of the internal standards in each sample were 10 ng/mL. This solution contained four deuterated compounds: d_8-naphthalene, d_{10}-anthracene, d_{12}-chrysene, and d_{12}-perylene, in methylene chloride.

4.2.5 Instrument configuration and calibration
A 1 µL aliquot of the hexane extract prepared by the above procedure was injected into a Hewlett-Packard 5890/5971 GC/MS instrument. This instrument was equipped with a DB-5 capillary column (30 m, 0.25 mm I.D., and 0.25 mm film thickness) and a split/splitless injection port operating in the splitless mode. Prior to the sample analysis, a five-point calibration was conducted on a standard mix of compounds to determine relative response factors (RRF) for the analytes. Data from the GC/MS runs are presented as relative amount versus the amount of hopane in the sample: the following relation can estimate the percent depletion of the selected analytes in the oil:

Percent Analyte Depletion = $[1-(C_1/C_0) \times (H_0/H_1)] \times 100$

Where C_1 is the analyte amount in the degraded oil, C_0 is the analyte amount in the time-zero oil, H_1 is the hopane amount in the degraded oil and H_0 is the hopane concentration in the time-zero oil.

Individual peaks were normalized to hopane because it is a non-biodegradable compound over the course of the test. The total alkanes (aliphatics) and the total aromatics were summed and an analysis of variance (ANOVA) was conducted. Quality assurance and quality control techniques used were based on the methods described by the National Environmental Technology Applications Corporation [20].

5 Results

5.1 Comparison of Beeswax with and without added bacteria
A series of tests were run to evaluate the performance the natural population (Natural BioD), the Beeswax formulation with added microorganisms (Beeswax w/ microbes) and Beeswax with out added microorganisms (Beeswax w/o microbes).

Table 1 shows the results of the chemical analysis for diesel range organics (DRO) for the BMR studies. Samples were taken over a 4 week period and DRO results are presented as μg diesel/BMR. Each treatment was performed in triplicate at each time point. As can be seen all treatments resulted in the DRO reduction. The experimental average reduction for all treatments grouped together was 77%. The Beeswax w/o microbes treatment performed slightly better having a reduction of 84% compared to 71% and 77% for the Natural BioD and Beeswax w/ microbes, respectively. Statistical analysis using a 2 way analysis of variance (ANOVA) indicated that the decreases in DRO over time was significant for $P = 0.1$.

Table 1. DRO results for product formulation evaluation			
Time 0	1	2	3	Avg
Natural BioD	142	151	145	146
Beeswax w/o microbes	145	127	166	146
Beeswax w/ microbes	113	112	106	110
Time 2 weeks	1	2	3	Avg
Natural BioD	76	84	67	76
Beeswax w/o microbes	64	76	115	85
Beeswax w/ microbes	60	50	74	61
Time 4 week	1	2	3	Avg
Natural BioD	51	40	35	42
Beeswax w/o microbes	29	15	28	24
Beeswax w/ microbes	31	25	21	26

The differences between treatments were not shown to be significant. However, the 2–way ANOVA groups all data sets to evaluate overall variability. To more accurately evaluate difference between individual treatments a student's T-test was run to compare the Natural BioD vs. Beeswax w/o microbes, Natural BioD vs. Beeswax w/ microbes and Beeswax w/ microbes vs. Beeswax w/o microbes. The analysis indicates the amount of reduction in the Beeswax w/ microbes and Beeswax w/o microbes were significantly different form the

Natural BioD at the 90% confidence interval.   There were no significant differences between the Beeswax w/ microbes and Beeswax w/o microbes.

Table 2. Marker Analysis for BMR studies.

Time 0	1	2	3	Avg
Beeswax w/ Microbes				
C_{17}/Pristane	1.27	1.29	1.32	1.29
C_{18}/Phytane	2.34	2.34	2.26	2.31
Natural BioD				
C_{17}/Pristane	1.24	1.29	1.27	1.27
C_{18}/Phytane	2.25	2.31	2.28	2.28
Beeswax w/o Microbes				
C_{17}/Pristane	1.21	1.30	1.34	1.28
C_{18}/Phytane	2.40	2.38	2.48	2.42
Time 2	1	2	3	Avg
Beeswax w/ Microbes				
C_{17}/Pristane	1.24	1.16	1.25	1.22
C_{18}/Phytane	2.33	1.94	2.14	2.14
Natural BioD				
C_{17}/Pristane	1.09	1.04	1.69	1.27
C_{18}/Phytane	1.77	2.00	1.98	1.92
Beeswax w/o Microbes				
C_{17}/Pristane	1.23	1.16	1.33	1.24
C_{18}/Phytane	2.12	2.26	2.28	2.22
Time 3	1	2	3	Avg
Beeswax w/ Microbes				
C_{17}/Pristane	0.83	0.76	0.54	0.71
C_{18}/Phytane	1.65	1.78	1.67	1.70
Natural BioD				
C_{17}/Pristane	0.63	0.44	0.10	0.39
C_{18}/Phytane	1.84	1.75	0.99	1.53
Beeswax w/o Bugs				
C_{17}/Pristane	0.66	0.08	1.06	0.60
C_{18}/Phytane	1.61	0.87	1.63	1.37

The overall decline in DRO could be the result of physical/chemical loss. The use of ratios of biodegradable to non-biodegradable makers is commonly used to demonstrate the loss is due to biodegradation.   The most common method is the ratio of the alkane C_{17} to the isoprenoid pristane and C_{18} to phytane. These data are present Table 2. As can be seen in all cases the highly degradable alkanes decreased in relationship to the highly branched and recalcitrant isoprenoids. These data are indicative of biodegradation where more readily degradable components are metabolized in preference to less degradable materials. If the loss were physical no change in these ratios would be expected.

Bacterial numbers were followed during the course of the tests.   The bacterial numbers (both heterotrophic and hydrocarbon degraders) increased over time.   The high levels of microorganisms at time 0 indicated that there were a significant number of microorganisms present in the river water at the time of sampling.   The level hydrocarbon degraders increased as a percentage of the population over the course of the experiments.   At the end of the tests, however, treatments containing Beeswax showed higher numbers of organisms (both heterotrophic and hydrocarbon degraders).   Considering that the DRO numbers suggest that the majority of the diesel has been degraded and the bacterial numbers in the Natural BioD had fallen off to level found in the original water, the presence of the Beeswax may be providing a nutrient source to sustain the population. This fact has a couple of positive implications: (1) the Beeswax is being degraded, an integral part of the Beeswax's application and (2) it is maintaining a very high hydrocarbon degrading population to respond to the next release of oil into the bilge.

The overall conclusion from these data is that Beeswax does enhance the natural degradation of the diesel in the BMR system. In addition, the added bacteria placed in the PRP appear to have no impact on the natural biodegradation rate. Finally, the Beeswax can maintain a high population of hydrocarbon degraders for a long period of time even after all oil has been degraded.

5.2 Mesocosm study and analysis via GC/MS

The following section describes the results of the experiment by segment and provides an analysis of the data as demonstrated by the accompanying data charts.

5.2.1 Control Slick

The control slick remained visually unchanged during the course of the experimentation. The hydrocarbon aroma, however, disappeared within the first week. The C_3–phenanthrene normalized GC/MS analysis indicated a change in the alkane envelope (on average a 47 percent decrease in total alkanes) during the three week period. The loss was due mainly to volatilization. This is indicated by the lack of change in the C_{17}/pristane ratio. Pristane is assumed to be non-biodegradable. Thus, a biodegradable analyte will decrease with time in relationship to the pristine. If loss is due to volatilization, the ratio will remain constant. The C_{17}/pristine ratio for the control slick was 1.1, 1.2, 1.2, and 0.99 for the four sampling events (over time). The data suggest volatilization is the main mechanism of loss during the first three weeks of the test. Biodegradation appears to have begun during the fourth week.

5.2.2 Absorbent Slick

The absorbent slick was affected immediately by the presence of the absorbent boom. The slick began to diminish and at 7 days virtually all the oil (visually estimated greater than 95 percent) had been lost from the system, presumably to the boom. Little change in the composition of the oil was detected during the first week and the overall loss was attributed to volatilization. Biodegradation was detected during the 14 and 21 day samplings via a change in the C_{17}/pristine phytane ratios (1.07, 1.03, 0.61, and 0.90 for Days 0, 7, 14 and 21, respectively.) There was an 80 percent decrease in the total aromatics. The "enhanced" biodegradation, compared to the control, detected in the absorbent slick can be attributed to less total oil being present in the tank. When following biodegradation using an analysis based on relative change, the sensitivity of detected changes is enhanced with smaller amounts of oil. As an example, if bacteria degrade 10 mg of oil a day and the initial oil was 1000 mg, 0.1 percent of the oil was degraded over the one day period. However, if only 100 mg of oil is used in 10 percent change will be seen even though the rate of biodegradation remains constant.   Overall, the amount of biodegradation occurring in the absorbent slick for both the alkanes and the aromatics was greater than the control but less than the beeswax product slick.

5.2.3 Beeswax Product Slick

The GC/MS data for the product slick showed extensive loss of both the alkanes and aromatics, 96 and 76 percent, respectively. The majority of the loss occurred within the firs week (Figure 4). The loss was due to biodegradation (C_{17}/pristine ratio of 1.16, 0.97, 0.96, 1.23 for time 0 and 1 through 3 weeks, respectively). The decrease and then increase of the ratio's is typical of an oil that is extensively degraded resulting in a reduction in pristine to very low levels. The higher alkanes ($C_{24} - C_{25}$) appear to be slightly more resistant to biodegradation but it is anticipated that these would be removed with time. The high amount of alkanes as compared to the control (Figure 2) and absorbent slick (Figure 3) is possibly the result of a loss of aromatics to the PRP.   Because the data is normalized to C_3-phenanthrene, the loss of the PAH fraction would mathematically increase the relative amount of all other constituents.   An alternative explanation is that the results are an analytical anomaly, however, the actual relative abundances for n-alkanes are similar for other samples.   This strengthens the explanation of selective absorption of aromatics by the encapsulating material. The encapsulating material having a slightly polar nature would have a tendency to interact with the more polar PAH's rather than the n-alkanes.   At this point, more work would be needed to provide a definitive answer. Overall, the amount of biodegradation occurring in the product slick for both the alkanes and the aromatics was greater than the control and the absorbent slick.

5.2.4 Absorbent Boom

Little change in oil composition was detected in the absorbent boom during the course of the test. A 30 percent loss in alkanes and a 21 percent increase in aromatics were observed during the course of the test. The increase in aromatics is related to low aromatic values at the time zero. This could be attributed to an analytical anomaly or to selective absorption of alkanes by the polypropylene matrix. At this point, not enough data are available to distinguish between the two alternatives. No biodegradation was detected within the boom (C_{17}/pristine ratio of 1.02, 1.06, 1.06, 1.03 for time 0 and 1 through 3 weeks, respectively).

5.2.5 Beeswax Product Boom

The GC/MS data for the product boom showed loss of both the alkanes and aromatics, 83 and 51 percent, respectively. The majority of the loss occurred within the first week. The loss was due to biodegradation (C_{17} /pristine ratio of 0.92, 1.14, 0.82, 1.03 for time 0 and 1 through 3 weeks, respectively). The pristine ratio is unusual in the time zero data and may be affected by the absorption processes occurring in the slick exterior to the BioBoom. The higher alkanes ($C_{24} - C_{25}$) appear to be slightly more resistant to biodegradation but it is anticipated that these would be removed with time. The relative amount of alkanes decreased as compared to the product slick data and is lower than the time zero control slick. This again cold be the results of selective absorption of the PAH's which would be more likely retained in the sample and analyzed during laboratory procedures. Overall, the amount of biodegradation occurring in the product boom for both the alkanes and the aromatics was greater than the absorbent boom.

6 Conclusions

The overall conclusions of the study are:
1. Beeswax (the active ingredient in Petrol Rem Inc.'s products), in the form of PRP, selectively absorbs significantly enhances the natural degradation of the diesel fuel.
2. The degradation rate of diesel is significantly higher when using a BioBoom compared to the use of an absorbent boom in mesocosm studies.
3. The added bacteria placed in past Petrol Rem, Inc. products had no impact on the natural biodegradation rates and could be safely removed from the product without diminishing the products' effectiveness.
4. This beeswax based line of products could prove to be effective in handling isolated oil spills unavailable to conventional techniques or stationary treatment of small amount of petroleum pollution in marine and freshwater applications.

References

[1]   Atlas, R.M. Stimulated petroleum biodegradation. *Crit. Rev. Microbiol.* 5:371-386, 1977.
[2]   Leahy, J.G., R.R. Colwell, Microbial degradation of hydrocarbon in the environment. *Microbiol. Rev.* 54:305-315, 1990.
[3]   Dietz, A.S., "Prospective for integrated bioremediation of oil spills." *A Comprehensive Approach to Problems with Oil Spills in Marine Environments: The Alasks Story.* Ed. V. Molak, W. Davis-Hoover, S. Khan, M. Mehlman. 1st ed. Princeton Scientific Pub., New Jersey. 129-133, 1992.
[4]   Swannell, P.J., K. Lee, M. McDonagh, Field evaluations of marine oil spill bioremediation. *Microbiol. Rev.* 60:342-365, 1996.
[5]   Cooney, J.J., "Microbial ecology and hydrocarbon degradation." *A Comprehensive Approach to Problems with Oil Spills in Marine Environments: The Alaska Story.* Ed. V. Molak, W. Davis-Hoover, S. Khan, M. Mehlman. 1st ed. Princeton Scientific Pub., New Jersey. 121-128, 1992.
[6]   Cookson, J.T., *Bioremediation engineering; design and application.* McGraw Hill, Inc., New York, 1995.
[7]   Macnaughton, S.J., J.R. Stephen, A.D. Venosa, G.A. Davis, Y. Chang, and D.C. White, Oil-spill-induced microbial population changes. *Appl. Environ. Microbiol.* 65:3566-3574, 1999.

[8]   Kirchman, D., H. Ducklow, R. Mitchell, Estimates of bacterial growth from changes in uptake rates and biomass. *Appl. Environ. Mircobiol.* 44:1296-1307, 1982.

[9]   Sekelsky, A.M., G.S. Shreve, Kinetic model of biosurfactant-enhanced hexadecane biodegradation by *Pseudomonas aeruginosa*. *Biotechnol. Bioeng.* 63:401-409, 1999.

[10]   Wright, A.L., R.W. Weaver, J.W. Webb, Oil bioremediation in salt marsh mesocosms as influenced by N and P fertilization, flooding, and season. *Water, Air, and Soil Pollution.* 95:179-191, 1997.

[11]   Atlas, R.M., Microbial hydrocarbon degradation--bioremediation of oil spills. *J. Chem. Tech. Biotechnol.* 54:149-156, 1991.

[12]   Nelson, E.C., M.V. Walter, I.D. Bossert, D.G. Martin, Enhancing biodegradation of petroleum hydrocarbons with guanadinium fatty acids. *Environ. Sci. Technol.* 30:2406-2411, 1996.

[13]   Basson, I., E.C. Reynhardt, An investigation of the structures and molecular dynamics of natural waxes: i. Beeswax. *J. Phys. D: Appl. Phys.* 21:1421-1428, 1988.

[14]   Johnson, K.S., F.A. Eischen, D.E. Giannasi, Chemical composition of north american bee propolis and biological activity towards larvae of greater wax moth (*Lepidoptera: Pyralidae*). *J. Chem. Ecol.* 20:1783-1791, 1994.

[15]   Tulloch, A.P., Beeswax-composition and analysis. *Bee World.* 61(2):47-62, 1980.

[16]   Hanstveit, A.O., *Inherent biodegradability of waxes.* TNO-report. R90/198b, 1991.

[17]   Hanstveit, A.O., Biodegradability of petroleum waxes and beeswax in an adapted CO_2 evolution test. *Chemosphere.* 25:605-620, 1992.

[18]   Lee, K., Merlin, M.F. Bioremediation of oil on shoreline environments: development of techniques and guidelines. Pure Appl. Chem. 71(1):161-171, 1999.

[19]   NETAC, "Evaluation methods manual: oil spill response bioremediation agents," 1993.

[20]   NETAC, "Mesocosm field study: PRP formulation #1", 1993.

Study of fishery networks in Japan

N. Takahashi, Y. Yamada, Y. Maeno & M. Takezawa
Department of Civil Engineering, College of Science and Technology, Nihon University, Japan.

Abstract

There are about 3000 designated fishing ports and about 6000 fishing villages in Japan, with about one fishing village per 10 km scattered along the coastline. The fisheries of Japan appear to have been in slight decline recently. Many fishing ports and fishing villages are located in rural areas, with the result that public facilities connected with rural life are not well maintained. Many young men have consequently migrated to the cities and the populations of numerous fishing villages are now discussing how to cope with depopulation and aging. A statistical analysis of the population census results, and also of the structure of fishery production and fishery management in Japan, is being carried out by the Management & Coordination Agency and the Fisheries Agency of the Japanese Government. In addition, a network model is proposed by unifying networks of land and sea. The results and conclusions are as follows: (1) the production of the coastal fishery is not changing, but total fishery production is decreasing every year, (2) the marine aquaculture production is increasing slowly but steadily, (3) imports of fishery products are rapidly increasing every year, but exports of fishery products are decreasing, such that the self-supply rate of fishery products in Japan is falling, (4) the number of persons working in fisheries is decreasing, and the number of workers over 65 years of age is increasing, (5) the income for fishery households is lower than for worker households and farmer households, (6) the number of fishery cooperative is gradually decreasing due to amalgamation with neighborhood cooperatives, (7) the revitalization of many fishing villages can be expected by applying a unified land and sea network connected with the topography and the fishery sphere of influence, (8) the networks for Japan are classified into 4 classes, and the topography for networks is divided into 8 types.

1 Introduction

People have fished for food, profit, and recreation from early times. The commercial catch from marine and fresh waters worldwide was about 92 million metric tons in 1999. Today, many of the preferred fish stocks are fully or over-exploited, and the supply available may not be sufficient to satisfy human demands by the year 2002. By then, the world's population will have surpassed six billion, with 80% living in low-income developing countries, many of which rely on the fisheries for food and economic growth [1]. The system of a 200 nautical miles zone established by the UN Convention on the Law of the Sea, and the Agreement on Fisheries between Japan, Korea and China is changing the nature of fisheries in Japan. In addition, the reduction of fishery production, the decrease in successors, and aging fishermen among other factors represent a social problem of considerable proportions. The fishery is a basis industry of Japanese life, and the advancement of coastal fisheries was promoted through laws enacted in Japan in 1963. One law was at advancing development of the coastal and small fisheries, and another law was aimed at fishermen who also worked in other industries. Some policies have been altered in order to realize their targets. The base of policy aim was the preservation and expansion of fishery resources, the improvement of fishery productivity, the modernization of management, a rationalization of distribution for aquatic products and the promotion of welfare for fishermen. However, unexpected new problems have occurred recently, such as a rapid increase in imports due to the strong yen, transition to a system with a 200 nautical mile zone, and changes in management, demand for seafood and fishing resources. The recent trend of fisheries in Japan is that problems are experienced regarding supply and demand of fisheries, the durable use of fisheries resources, fisheries-related international relations, the structure of fishery production and fishery management, the preservation of the ocean environment, and active political involvement in fisheries. In this paper, fishery and aquaculture production, fishery economy, the number of fishery households and people engaged in fishery [2][3], and a network system of fisheries are discussed.

2 Fishery and aquaculture production

Fishery production has decreased for 10 successive years although marine aquaculture production has been increasing slowly and steadily as shown in figure 1. Coastal fishery production has been changed little in the last, despite the fact that foreshore reclamation and water pollution have increased. Before 1972, deep-sea fishery production had been increasing rapidly, but thereafter production decreased due to problems related to

international fisheries. The changes in off-shore fishery production are very
irregular because they are influenced by natural phenomena.

Figure 2 shows the changes in marine aquaculture production since 1960.
Marine aquaculture production had been increasing by degrees, but reached
a ceiling recently due to the water pollution generated by the disposal of
food in the water. Common scallop production has been increasing although
production in other sectors has remained at the same level.

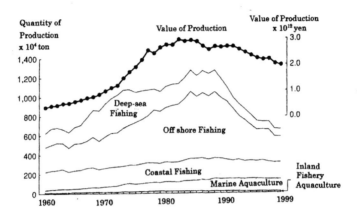

Figure 1: Changes in fishery and aquaculture production.

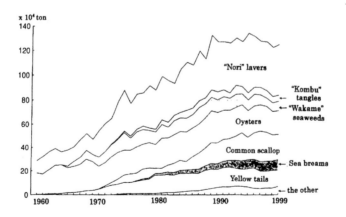

Figure 2: Changes in marine aquaculture production.

Imports of fishery products are increasing every year, as shown in figure 3.
The major imports are shrimp, tuna, salmon, crabs and eels.

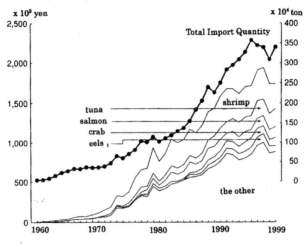

Figure 3: Changes in fishery product imports.

Exports of fishery products have decreased for 10 years now, as shown in figure 4. The major exports are fresh, chilled, and frozen products, and pearls.

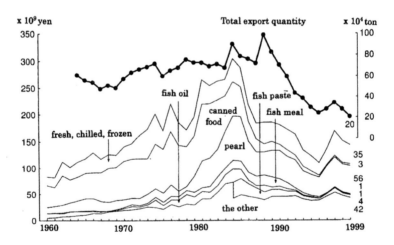

Figure 4: Changes in fishery product exports.

The quantity of production of canned and frozen processed marine food products, fish fats and oils, feeds, salted and dried fish, food made from fish paste, etc. is leveling off or has been decreasing recently, as shown in figure 5.

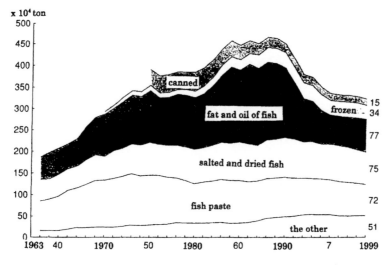

Figure 5: Changes in processed marine products.

The catch quantity of fisheries has decreased in recent years, along with the decrease in national production. Although the quantity of sardines and cuttlefish is increasing, the quantity of horse mackerel and mackerel is decreasing. Many markets of central production districts are managed by fishermen's cooperative associations, and the sum of money for annual management is less than \ 1,000,000,000 per market. In addition, wholesale qualities have recently been decreasing in the markets of consumer districts. The introduction of electronic dealing has led to inefficient distribution of fresh fishery products, such that a project to develop a fast and efficient seafood distribution system has been started by the Fisheries Agency. The cost of seafood is stable in comparison with fresh fruit and vegetables.

3 Structure of fishery production and fishery management

The number of fishery establishment is continually decreasing due to aged proprietors and lack of successors, and since 1953, the number of people working in fisheries has also decreased, as shown in figure 6. Thirty percent of males engaged in fishery work were aged 65 years or older in 2000. One potential loss of the aging male population is technical leadership and another is the classic fishery culture. Seventeen percent of the total workforce engaged in fisheries work are female, and females are engaged mainly in coastal fisheries, and actively promoting such aspects as the cooking/preparation of fish, coastal cleaning, and health care.

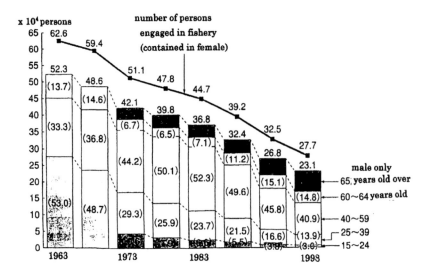

Figure 6: Number of people working in fisheries.

The average coastal fisheries income in 2000 was about \ 5,000,000 with expenses of about \ 2,850,000. Thus the average profit was about \ 2,150,000. The average marine aquaculture income was \6,380,000 in 2000. An example of the average income of a fishery household was determined to be \ 23,430,000 for yellowtails, \ 8,730,000 for sea breams, \ 7,180,000 for oyster, \ 8,160,000 for common scallops, \ 2,930,000 for shell mother of pearl, \ 3,620,000 for pearl, \ 5,750,000 for "nori" (laver) and \ 3,920,000 for "wakame" (seaweed). The average income of \ 6,556,000 per fishery household was lower than the average income of \8,465,000 per farm household and \ 6,869,000 per national worker household in 2000. In addition, the rate of dependence upon the fishery was 45% in comparison with a rate 13.5% of dependence upon farms. Figure 7 shows a comparison of incomes per household for fisheries, farmers and workers.

Figure 7: Comparison of incomes per household.

The number of fishery cooperatives was 2918, of which 1836 were in coastal district, 888 were in inland water districts and 194 were in business type. Figure 8 shows the number of fishery cooperatives in coastal districts and the number of unions between cooperatives. It is necessary that fishery cooperatives perform their role as the core of the fishery by adjusting and strengthening systematic organization by merging.

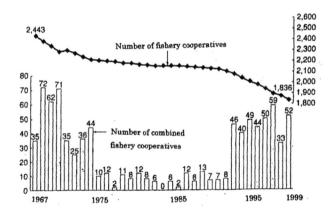

Figure 8: Number of fishery cooperatives.

4 Topographical classifications and networks of fishery

Coastal topography plays an important role in the present construction of fishery networks. The basic elements are the type of networks and the coastal topography. Networks may be classified as shown in table 1.

Table 1: The class of networks.

Class	Definition
First class	Closed bay with 2 or more harbors in the bay.
Second class	Connected with 2 or more first-class networks.
Third class	A large scale second-class network covering a prefecture.
Fourth class	A wide area network including all classes.

Table 2 shows the classification of coastal topography in relation to networks [4].

Table 2: Types of coastal topography.

Classification	Definition
Closed bay type	The opening of the bay is narrow, and the length of the bay is long.
Open bay type	The opening of the bay is wide, and the length of the bay is short.
Ocean type	The opening is wider than the open bay type, and has directly incident waves.
Island type	The distance from islands to the mainland is short, and islands are united with the mainland.
Cape type	United over a whole peninsula.
Channel type	Putting a channel between land areas.
Isolated type	Constructed of networks covering a whole island separated from a mainland.
Lake type	Constructed of networks entirely covering lakes and marshes.

Figure 9 shows the coastal topography in Japan, where a circle is the minimum inscribed in topography and a rectangular is the maximum inscribed in topography. Table 3 shows the number of networks (N), the average of fishing ports (G), the average density of fishing ports (E/G), the average incline ratio (L/W), the average winding ratio (E/D), and the average area (TS) in Japan. The total number of networks of the closed bay type, the open bay type and the ocean type was 342 (70%). In addition, the most common type of topography is the island type (85%) for first class, cape type (26%) for second class, and third class (100%), and channel type (43%) for fourth class. The average distance between fishing ports is 6.8 km in Japan

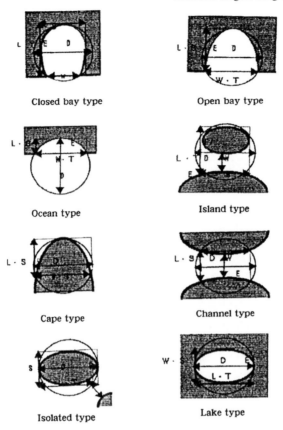

Figure 9: Relationship between networks and coastal topography.

Table 3: Fishery networks in Japan.

	N	G	E/G	L/W	E/D	TS
Closed	98	12.0	6.9	3.1	2.7	666
Opened	76	10.3	6.5	0.6	2.2	694
Ocean	168	8.8	6.8	0.2	1.3	856
Island	39	10.0	8.0	7.4	3.0	608
Cape	91	14.1	5.5	1.7	2.4	914
Channel	7	17.7	5.5	7.7	3.6	533
Isolate	30	14.3	8.7	2.7	3.4	578
Lake	2	2.3	10,7	2.8	3.2	1000
Total	511	10.1	6.8	-	-	769

5 Conclusion

The world population is about 6 billion in 2002, and it is expected to increase to about 8 billion in 2025. However, it is estimated that Japanese population will decrease from about 126 million in 2002 to 121 million in 2025, as the number of young laborers continues to decrease while the number of old people aged over 60 years increases. The number of persons working in marine fisheries is also decreasing, but the number of aged persons (60 years plus) engaged in marine fishery work is increasing every year. The catches from marine fisheries in 2000 were about half the quantity of that in 1980. The quantity of imported marine products has recently been increasing alongside a decreasing quantity of exported marine products. The fisheries in Japan are facing numerous problems including of successors, aging, workers, fisheries resources, international relations, and fishery management. Marine habitat rehabilitation projects, fishery management, a high-grade distribution system and the revitalization of fisheries are necessary to counteract the decrease of fishery resources, the experimental deterioration of fishing ground, the decrease in number and the aging of people working in fisheries, and the diversity of consumers. In addition, the spread of oceanic recreation involving pleasure boats and scuba diving means that ordinary people are creating problems for fisheries due to violation of fishing rights and accidents with fishing boats. These problems interfere with the use and the management of fisheries, and fisheries may supply less fish, and the coastline may be environmentally degraded. Therefore, fishing ports must be connected by networks according to topography in order that problems of economic and effective management of fisheries, conflicts between fishermen and townspeople, and fishery revitalization among other issues will be resolved.

References

[1] ICOD, *World Fisheries*, Canada, 2001.
[2] Statistics Bureau, Management and Coordination Agency, *Japan Statistical yearbook 2000*, Government of Japan, pp.248-264, 2000.
[3] Statistics Society of Agriculture and Forestry, *Fishery White Paper*, pp. 40-108, 2001.
[4] Nagano, A. & Inada, T. , *Development of Fishery by Topography*, Journal of JACZS, No.5, pp.25-39, 1993.

Section 3
Hydrodynamic aspects

A DBIEM analysis of free surface oscillations in arbitrary shaped harbours

M. Calzà, F. D'Este & G. Contento
Dept. of Naval Architecture, Ocean and Environmental Engineering, University of Trieste, Italy.

Abstract

The design of a harbour or a marina is primarily aimed to a safe and comfortable anchorage and to easy and efficient cargo-passengers operations [1-2]. Prevailing weather conditions and their extremes at the site determine thoroughly the design of the plan view and the height of the breakwaters. Nevertheless, even in not extreme conditions, the geometry of the harbour can affect directly the onset and grow of standing or partially standing waves inside it, inducing large rolling, surge and yaw of the moored vessels with exceeding stresses on the mooring lines and causing the interruption of up-downloading operations.

In this paper we investigate the free surface oscillations in an arbitrary shaped harbour by means of a Time Domain Simulation tool developed at DINMA [3-4] in the frame of the so-called Numerical Wave Tank approach. The method proposed here is able to handle the bottom bathymetry, so that the important refraction effects can be taken into account.

The capability of the method is first checked in the case of 2 harbours with simple rectangular plan shape. Afterwards the method is applied to the harbour of Trieste (Italy-North Adriatic Sea) with regular waves coming from Southwest in open sea and from West at the harbour opening. In particular the study is focussed on the magnification of the wave amplitude due to the change of the main dimension of a large pier planned to berth cruise ships.

Introduction

It is well known that the motion of the free surface in a closed or almost closed basin is characterised by extremely large amplitudes at prescribed frequencies and related wavelengths (natural modes). These frequencies can lay within the energetic part of the forcing cause with obvious consequences (resonance), in the specific case of a harbour this being related to the open sea conditions. Thus the prediction of the natural frequencies of the harbour at the design stage becomes extremely important. On the other hand, the prediction of the wave amplitude in a supposed shelter area is of fundamental importance for small vessels or pleasure boats also in non-resonant conditions, since small crafts are more sensitive to high frequency waves. Practical guidelines to achieve or improve the harbour tranquillity are shown by Goda [2]. Closed form mathematical solutions of the harbour oscillations problem are available only for very simple plan shapes and for constant depth, so that in most cases the analysis is conducted by means of experiments. McNown [5] has studied the response of a circular harbour with narrow opening assuming that at resonance the anti-node of the inner standing wave is positioned at the entrance. The same assumptions have been used by Kravtchenko [6] for a rectangular basin. Miles & Munk [7] have analysed the rectangular harbour with a real opening including the incoming and outgoing waves at the entrance, thus obtaining bounded amplitudes of waves even at resonance. Ippen & Goda [8] used a Fourier Transform Method to include the effect of outgoing waves. Wilson et al. [9] studied the harbour oscillations for long waves in variable depth by a finite difference scheme. Lee [10] developed the 'arbitrary-shape harbour' theory with constant depth.

In this work we attack the problem of an arbitrarily shaped plan view of a harbour with variable water depth by a Time-Domain Mixed Eulerian-Lagrangian approach. The inviscid fluid assumption is enforced but no specific limitations are given to the geometry of the harbour, to the bottom shape and to the incoming/outgoing wave characteristics. This allows for reflections, diffraction and refraction effects due to reflecting walls or piers that modify the wave path in sheltered areas and bottom bathymetry respectively. The method adopted takes origins from the pioneering work of Longuet–Higgins and Cokelet [11] and is widely used in the Naval Architecture and Offshore Engineering Community to determine wave-loads and motions on fixed, moored or freely floating marine structures in a given fluid domain, typically a wave tank. The linearized free surface conditions are applied and the related BVP for Laplace equation in the unknown velocity potential is solved by a Desingularized Boundary Integral Equation Method [12] that allows for an efficient and accurate solution of the BVP.

Even if the main interest of this work is the application of the method to real harbour shapes, some preliminary tests have been conducted on simple geometries. The test case of a rectangular harbour has been considered with two length/width ratios and the results have been compared to analytical/experimental data available in the literature [13]. Finally, the scheme developed has been applied to the harbour of Trieste in the Northern Adriatic

Sea (Fig. 1). The selected area of the harbour is opened to Western winds and waves, such events being unusual but strong at the same time due to the relatively wide fetch. The results presented refer to regular waves only in the frame of the superposition effect assumptions (linear waves). In particular, the analysis is conducted for three different harbour shapes, derived from the present shape changing the main dimension of a large pier planned to berth new generation cruise ships (side $\overline{DE}$ in Fig.1). The tool developed captures the main features of the new wave field inside the modified harbour, showing large magnifications of the local wave amplitude in supposed sheltered areas.

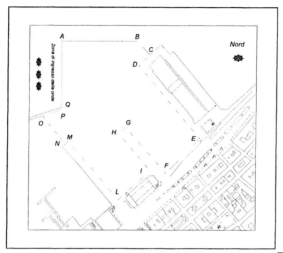

Fig. 1 Harbour of Trieste and computational domain (poliline $\overline{AB...PQ}$).

Mathematical model, numerical procedure and data analysis

Since the propagation and transformation of waves inside a harbour are mainly dominated by inertia, diffraction and refraction effects, viscous effects being restricted to bottom/wall friction and to confined vortex sheddings by the corners of piers, the fluid can be assumed inviscid and the flow irrotational. Under these assumptions, the velocity potential $\phi(x,y,z,t)$ yields in the fluid domain D and the velocity field is written as $\overset{\rho}{V} = \nabla\phi$. For computational purposes, the free surface F is formally subdivided in two distinct parts, $\widetilde{F}$ and $\hat{F}$, the latter corresponding to an artificial absorber that prevents the outgoing waves to be reflected by the closure of the fluid domain (open boundary condition). The free surface profile is assumed to be single valued so that it can be written as $z = \eta(x,y,t)$, where η is taken positive upwardly from the still water level and the x-y axis lay on the horizontal plane. Laplace equation in the unknown velocity potential $\phi(x,y,z,t)$ is solved by a Desingularised Boundary Integral Equation Method [12], that provides accurate results and fast computation of the influence matrix if compared to traditional low order BEM. According to Cao et al. [12], here the distance between collocation points and sources (indirect method) is chosen according to $L_d = l_d (D_m)^\alpha$ where D_m is the local mesh size (area of the related facet), $\alpha = 0.5$ and $0.75 \le l_d \le 2.0$. Linear kinematic and dynamic boundary conditions are applied on the free surface, as follows:

$$\begin{cases} \dfrac{\partial \phi}{\partial t} = -g\eta(x,y,t) - v(x,y) \cdot \phi(x,y,z,t) \\[3mm] \dfrac{\partial \eta}{\partial t} = \dfrac{\partial \phi}{\partial z}(x,y) - v(x,y) \cdot \eta(x,y,t) \qquad \text{on } z = 0 \end{cases} \qquad (1)$$

where the rightmost terms in both equations represent the artificial absorption in $\hat{F}$. The damping term $v(x,y)$ is derived according to

$$v(x,y) = \begin{cases} 0 & , \quad (x,y) \in \tilde{F} \\[3mm] \mu\omega \left(\dfrac{\overline{s - s_0}}{\lambda} \right)^2 & , \quad (x,y) \in \hat{F} \end{cases} \qquad (2)$$

$\overline{s - s_0}$ is the normal horizontal oriented distance from the point (x,y), where the absorption is applied, to the boundary of the domain.

Waves entering the harbour are generated at the virtual interface between the computational domain and the outer sea. This numerical interface is generally given by one or more flat vertical walls where a wavemaker boundary condition [13] is applied accounting for the wave length and height in the given depth.

Eqs. (1) at each node of the free surface are time stepped by a 4th order Runge-Kutta scheme and the start-up conditions are those of the still water. Thus the data obtained from the simulations are N_{frs} time traces of the free surface elevation at each node of the computational grid, where N_{frs} is of order $O(10^4)$. They include the transient stages of wave generation and propagation in the harbour. The data presented here refer to the steady state regime that corresponds to the energy balance between incoming and outgoing waves at the harbour entrance. The time window selected as steady state part of the records is obtained by means of the sliding window Fourier technique. Finally, in the frame of the linear analysis employed, the results related to the free surface oscillation at the N_{frs} nodes are presented as amplification factors R, i.e. as the ratio between the local wave height and the incident wave height (outer undisturbed sea state).

Results and discussion

The performances of the numerical scheme have been first checked by comparing the results with theoretical and experimental data. As mentioned previously, most theoretical and experimental studies available in the literature refer to simple harbour shapes, basically rectangles with different aspect ratios and circles with different opening angles [10,14]. Here we show only a selection of the results obtained for two rectangular harbours with a whole side opened to the outer sea. The incident wave direction is perpendicular to the opening. Fig. 2 shows the details of the geometric configuration of the harbours (l and b are the dimensions of the rectangle, d is the water depth considered constant everywhere;. Test Case A $l/b=1$; Test Case B $l/b=5.147$).

In Fig. 3 the main dimensions of the outer domain l_1 and l_2 are reported. They have been varied systematically in the following range $4 \leq l_1/\lambda \leq 8$ and $2 \leq l_2/\lambda \leq 6.6$ to check their influence on the results in the harbour.

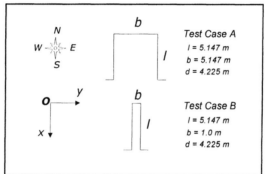

Fig. 2   Definitions/details of the rectangular harbours (Test Cases A & B).

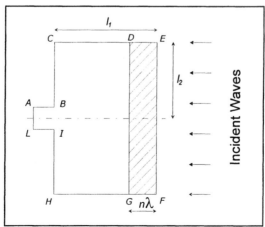

Fig. 3   Definitions/details of the outer domain (Test Cases A & B).

Fig. 4 shows the contour plot of R for Test Case A and $kl = 7.4$, restricted to the scattered waves at the steady state. The plots refer to five different outer domains. From the tests, it results that no appreciable differences appear in the harbour for $l_1/\lambda \geq 5$ and $l_2/\lambda \geq 4.5$.

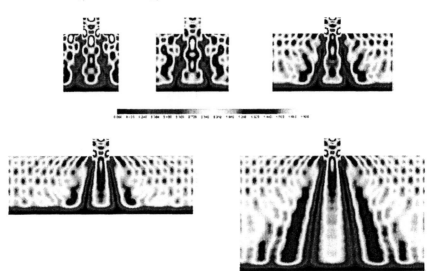

Fig. 4   Contour plot of the amplification factor R for Test Case A with different outer domains (kl=7.4).

In Fig. 5 the results (R Vs. kl) related to the middle point of the side $\overline{AL}$ (Fig. 3) are presented. They are compared with analytical results from Gorman [14] in the range $kl \geq 4$. It can be seen that the overall behaviour is captured with a small underestimate of the peak at kl=7.4.

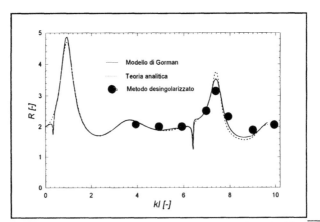

Fig. 5   Amplification factor R Vs kl at the middle point of side $\overline{AL}$ in Test Case A.

Fig. 6 shows the comparison between the present results and the experimental data from Lee [10] and Ippen & Goda[8] and the theoretical results from Gorman [14] for Test Case B. The agreement is rather good in the whole frequency range considered. Again there is a small underestimate of the theoretical peak whereas the experimental results are satisfactorily reproduced.

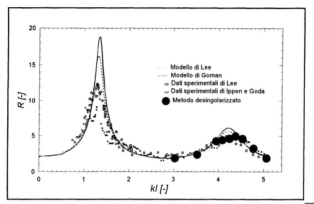

Fig. 6   Amplification factor R Vs kl at the middle point of side $\overline{AL}$ in Test Case B.

Finally the numerical procedure has been applied to the harbour of Trieste (Northern Adriatic Sea) for waves coming from West. The computational domain is shown in Fig. 1. The side $\overline{QA}$ corresponds to the wavemaking boundary. In the proximity of the wavemaker side an absorbing condition has been introduced to damp the outgoing waves, which otherwise would be newly reflected in the domain by the paddle generating the waves. The sides $\overline{AB}$, $\overline{BC}$ and $\overline{ON}$ are the artificial absorbing boundaries where outgoing waves are progressively damped (Eqn. 1). This allows the simulation to reach a realistic steady state of the wave pattern inside the harbour (balance between incoming and outgoing wave energy). The study has been conducted with two wavelengths, 20 and 30 m respectively, 25 m being the wavelength at the peak of the power spectrum measured few nautical miles West from the harbour. In the frame of a preliminary investigation, the water depth has been averaged on the whole domain to 10 m.

Moreover we have considered three different lengths of the side $\overline{DE}$ of the pier planned to berth last generation cruise ships, the shortest length corresponding to the present situation, the others 50 and 100 m longer respectively. Fig. 7a,b and Fig. 8a,b show the contour plot of the magnification factor R for the shortest and longest piers with 30 and 20 m wavelengths respectively. It can be seen that the effect of the longer pier is to induce larger oscillations in a previously sheltered area ($\overline{HILM}$ of Fig. 1). Fig. 9 shows the development of the wave pattern (λ=30 m) with snapshots taken at the specified wave periods. The diffraction and reflection effects by the piers are clearly evidenced.

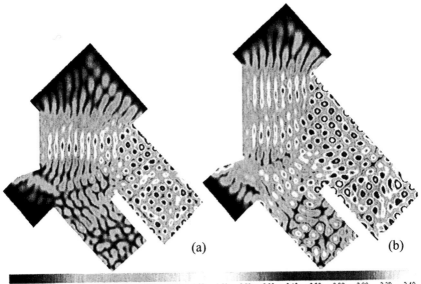

0.00   0.20   0.40   0.60   0.80   1.00   1.20   1.40   1.60   1.80   2.00   2.20   2.40   2.60   2.80   3.00   3.20   3.40

Fig. 7a,b   Contour plot of the amplification factor R for the shortest and longest piers with a wave 30 m long.

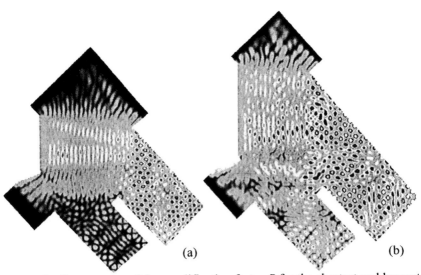

Fig. 8a,b   Contour plot of the amplification factor R for the shortest and longest piers with a wave 20 m long.

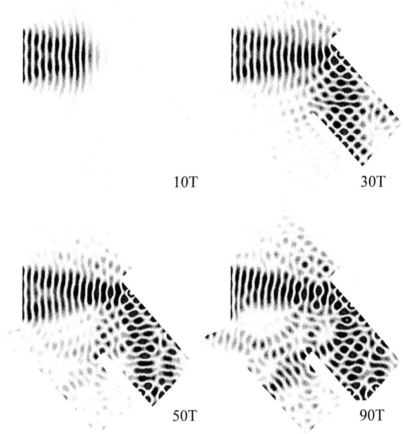

Fig. 9   Development of the wave pattern (λ =30 m) with snapshots at the specified wave periods.

Conclusions

This paper has presented a numerical study on the prediction of the amplitude of waves propagating inside a harbour of arbitrary plan shape with variable water depth, induced by a given outer sea state. The solution is achieved by a Time-Domain Mixed Eulerian-Lagrangian approach with linearised free surface boundary conditions. The BVP is solved by a Desingularised Boundary Integral Method. The results obtained on simplified harbour shapes (rectangles) confirm the capability of the method to capture the main features of the physical phenomenon (waves entering and propagating in a harbour). The application to a practical case has given the chance to discuss the consequences of a change of the main dimension of a pier.

Acknowledgements

This research has been supported by MURST 60%, 2001, Project: "Studio nel dominio del tempo dell'interazione onde-strutture marine in presenza di frontiera libera non lineare" and by CETENA SpA – Research plan 2000-2002. CINECA (Bo) and CSIA (Ts) are also acknowledged for the computing resources.

References

[1] Wiegel, R.L., 1964, *Oceanographical Engineering*, Prentice-Hall.
[2] Goda, Y. 1985, *Random Seas and Design of Maritime Structures*, University of Tokyo Press.
[3] Contento, G., Codiglia, R., D'Este, F., 2001, Nonlinear effects in transient non-breaking waves in a closed basin, *Int. Jou. Applied Ocean Research*, Vol. 23/1, pp. 3-13.
[4] D'Este, F., Codiglia, R., Contento, G., 2001, Fully Nonlinear Numerical Wave Tank Computations of Wave Loads on an Array of Bottom Mounted Circular Cylinders, *1st Int. Conf. on Fluid Structure Interaction*, Halkidiki, Greece, September 26 – 28, pp. 291-303.
[5] McNown, J.S., 1952, Wave and seiche in idealized ports. *Gravity Waves Symposium National Bureau of Standards*, Vol. 521, pp. 153-164.
[6] Kravtchenko, J., 1955, Seiche in rectangular ports. *Quart. Appl. Math.*, Vol. 13, pp. 19-26.
[7] Miles, J., Munk, W., 1961, Harbour paradox, *J. Waterways Harbour Div.*, Vol. 87, pp. 111-130.
[8] Ippen, A.T., Goda, Y., 1963, Wave-induced oscillations in harbours: the solution for a rectangular harbour connected to the open-sea, *Hydrodynamics Lab.*, Vol. 59.
[9] Wilson, B.W., Hendrickson, J.A., Kilmer, R.C., 1965, Feasibility study for surge motion model of Monterey harbour, *Science engineering Associates*, pp. 2-136.
[10] Lee, J.J., 1971, Wave-induced oscillations in harbours of arbitrary geometry, *Journal of Fluid Mechanics*, Vol.45, part.2, pp. 375-394
[11] Longuet-Higgins M.S., Cokelet E.D., 1976, The Deformation of Steep Surface Waves on Water. 1. A Numerical Method of Computation, *Proc. Royal Society of London*, A, Vol. 350, pp. 1-26.
[12] Cao Y., Beck R.F., Schultz W.W., 1991, Three-Dimensional Desingularized Boundary Integral Methods for Potential Problems, *Int. Journal for Numerical Methods in Fluids*, Vol.12, pp. 785-803.
[13] Dean, R.G., Dalrymple, R.A., 1984, Water waves mechanics for scientists and engineers, *Prentice Hall, Englewood Cliffs*, New Jersey.
[14] Gorman, R.M., 1992, Wave diffraction in step-walled harbours, *Coastal Engineering*, Vol.18, pp.39-61.

Finite element modelling of floating pier units in personal computers

R. C. Barros
Department of Civil Engineering, Faculdade de Engenharia
FEUP, Porto, Portugal

Abstract

Floating pier assemblages constituting a floating marina infrastructure are studied for a potential site, on the banks of Douro River at the city of Porto, Portugal. Buoyancy characteristics of a singular floating pontoon, as referred in the literature, are extended to redundant systems of floating units. Finite element modelling of such floating pier structure permits to access its static performance in terms of safe advisable pontoons displacements and rotations. Floating pier dynamic stability is addressed preliminarily, using simple formulas for determining rolling and pitching periods and insuring adequately long periods and acceptable motions with respect to human perception.

1 Introduction

During last decade the riverfront at the city of Porto as been witnessing a series of investments, contributing not only to an increased quality of life of its natural population but mainly constituting an incentive and a needed added value for the local and regional tourism. As a gateway for river Douro local cruises (at this city that during 2001 was one of the two European cultural capitals) or for inland regional cruises (to the Douro-Port wine region), some floating pontoons units were developed constituting small floating piers with associated articulated approach bridges (Figure 1).

However, in view of the large number of sailing vessels and yachts that pass along the Portuguese coast (without a northern nearby safe haven from harsh sea-weather) and as an additional means to attract tourists to the city, some riverfront sites for implementation of a complete floating marina infrastructure have been accessed. The present work addresses the study of such a possible floating marina, modelling its overall static performance by the finite element method.

Figure 1: Some views of riverfront developments at Porto

2   Analysis of redundant pier floating structures

In zones where tides alter significantly the path of water and of ferry traffic, a floating multi-span bridge constitutes a unique low cost method for providing a link span between fluvial communication points, at the edge of rivers or lakes. This is particularly significant specially where piling, for hypothetical fix standard piers, is not practicable or is too expensive.

Also the increase in freight carried by trailers driving on and off the ferries, require roll-on roll-off terminals with sufficient float stability. These Ro-Ro floating piers, link the span from the ferry to shore, rising and falling with the tide. The Ro-Ro terminals are designed to meet the requirements of each individual customer or project application, for a variety of ships and loading situations.

A floating pier is the basic unit for more elaborate assemblages constituting floating bridges or floating marinas. Buoyancy and stability characteristics of a singular floating pontoon are here referred from Tsinker [1, 2] and other available literature, and extended to redundant systems of floating units. Consider the assemblage of generic individual hinged pontoons and their mechanical analogues, represented in Figure 2.

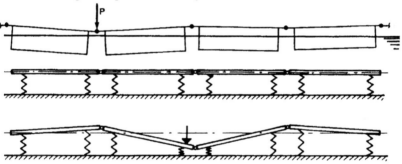

Figure 2: Assemblage of hinged individual pontoons and mechanical analogues

Each individual pontoon of length l can be equivalently modeled as an idealized rigid member supported by linear and rotational springs (Tsinker [1,2]), as represented in Figure 3. Describing the deformation of the pontoon by the 2 vertical displacements $\{y_1, y_2\}$ at the connecting nodes, and designating $s = \gamma A$ and $r = \gamma I$ (where γ is the water specific weight; and A, I are the pontoon cross-section area and second moment of inertia) the nodal loads $\{V_1, V_2\}$ are related with the nodal displacements by the matrix equation:

$$\begin{Bmatrix} V_1 \\ V_2 \end{Bmatrix} = \begin{bmatrix} \dfrac{s}{4} + \dfrac{r}{l^2} & \dfrac{s}{4} - \dfrac{r}{l^2} \\ \dfrac{s}{4} - \dfrac{r}{l^2} & \dfrac{s}{4} + \dfrac{r}{l^2} \end{bmatrix} \begin{Bmatrix} y_1 \\ y_2 \end{Bmatrix} = \begin{bmatrix} k_1 & k_2 \\ k_2 & k_1 \end{bmatrix} \begin{Bmatrix} y_1 \\ y_2 \end{Bmatrix} \qquad (1)$$

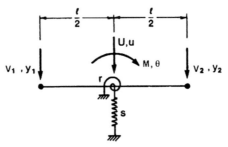

Figure 3: Pontoon structural-mechanics analogue

When the assemblage of such pontoon units constitute hinged pontoon systems, like the ones represented in Figures 2 and 4, the vertical equilibrium of the nth connecting node is expressed by:

$$k_2 \, y_{n-1} + 2k_1 y_n + k_2 \, y_{n+1} = p_n = V_{2n} + V_{1n} \tag{2}$$

After assemblage for all nodes the equilibrium matrix equation would be $[K]\{y\}=\{p\}$, where $[K]$ is the overall stiffness matrix of the hinged floating structure and $\{y\}$, $\{p\}$ are the nodal displacements and nodal loads vectors.

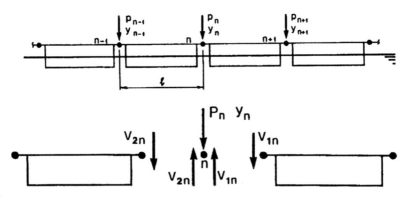

Figure 4: Free-body diagram of a connecting node of a hinged pontoon system

When the floating pier units constitute a continuous beam of infinite length over pontoons, like the ones represented in Figure 5, from the moment equilibrium and the vertical equilibrium a fifth order equation in displacements $\{y\}$ can be derived (Hetinyi [3], Tsinker [1, 2]) and is expressed by:

$$y_{n-2} - (4-\alpha)y_{n-1} + (6+4\alpha)y_n - (4-\alpha)y_{n+1} + y_{n+2} = 0 \tag{3}$$

in which $\alpha = s l^3 / (6EI) = \gamma A l^3 / (6EI)$.

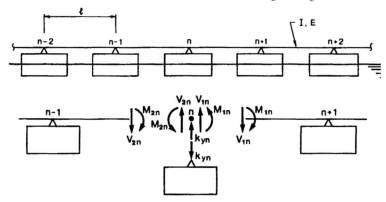

Figure 5: Free-body diagram of the support node of an infinite length continuous beam over pontoons

Notice however that from the general solution of this fifth order equation the slope, shears and moments of the infinite length continuous beam can be derived. Moreover, the forces and displacements in floating beams of finite length over pontoons can be derived from appropriate combination of solutions determined for beam of infinite length (Hetinyi [3]).

Numerical examples carried out analytically in detail by Tsinker [1, 2] were also modeled by Barros et al. [4] in a standard program of structural analysis, and also using Femix (Azevedo et al. [5]), in order to ascertain its adequacy and accuracy in light of required simplifications or modeling characteristics. Such accurate computer analysis of the numerical examples of linked pontoons and of continuous finite length floating beams, constituted a needed and efficient computer program calibration.

3   Finite element modelling of a floating marina pier over pontoons

One of the possible riverfront sites for implantation of a complete floating marina infrastructure is situated at the left bank of the river Douro at Porto, clearly visible in the top two pictures of Figure 1. Such solution has been accessed in view of the large implantation area available as well as on the width of the river at this potential site. For the structural analysis of a marina by the finite element method, a preliminary solution already conceived by Gomes and Barros [6] for a marina at the harbour of Leixoes near Porto is used herein. Such report contains details of the engineering design principles used as well as of the berthing arrangements, like the fingers and pontoons spacing according to the class of berthed vessels defined by P.I.A.N.C. (Adie [7]), and therefore will be omitted herein. Additionally, the shelter conditions are also defined by criteria of maximum allowed wave oscillations within the sheltered area. More technical details on the statutory services provided [6] can also be found in Adie [7].

Initially the finite element computer program used was the already mentioned Femix 2.1 [5]. Among its possible modelling options, it was chosen to use thick shell Ahmad et al. [8] elements, since it permits to define a variable thickness laminar structure (shell) with any mean surface and with sharp edges where two or more surfaces may intersect. The isoparametric Serendipity 8 nodes element is used throughout.

The mesh used for the discretization of the preliminary solution is composed of 856 thick shell elements with Ahmad et al. [8] formulation (Figure 6).

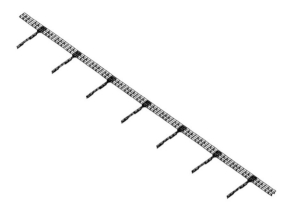

Figure 6: Mesh used for the floating marina pier study

Figure 7 shows the typical mesh of a pontoon on floaters, constituting a catamaran-type of floating structure, as well as the details of the reinforced angle connection between finger and adjacent pontoon.

The pontoons, behaving like elastic spring supports, were also simulated with shell elements with cross section equal to their real or prototype counterpart. However their thickness was chosen in such a way that, together with the modulus of elasticity and their length, their axial stiffness would be comparable with the stiffness of elastic supports. An average pontoon stiffness of 55 kN/m was used, similar to the one used at the akin marina of Leixoes [6], so that the computer model thickness for pontoon shell elements is obtained from:

$$k_{pontoon} = \frac{EA}{l} = \frac{30000\,x\,(1.1\,x\,t)}{0.6} = 55kN\,/\,m \quad \Rightarrow \quad t = 0.001m = 1mm$$

For the simulation of the connecting hinges were used elements with the same cross section of the pontoons but now with a thickness of 2 mm. A modulus of elasticity of 200 MPa was chosen, which together with the minor dimensions make such finite elements practically non-deformable, therefore achieving the desired hinge effect.

The loading combinations can be obtained from the three load cases used: dead load of the weights, symmetric alternate live loads and one-sided live loads. The uniform live load used for the last two load cases was 4 kN/m^2.

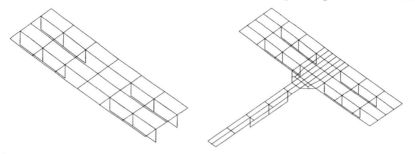

Figure 7: Catamaran behavior of individual pontoon and its connection to finger

The associated articulated approach bridge, at the middle of the floating marina pier, was simulated by 2 concentrated loads of 2.45 kN each, 0.5 m apart. For the first load case a maximum vertical displacement of 3.2 cm was obtained at node (3021) corresponding to the middle section where the articulated approach bridge is supported on the pier (Figure 8).

Figure 8: Floating marina pier displacements for 1st load case (dead weights)

Other results associated with the 1st load case are given in Figure 9, namely the plan views of both the displacement field and the distribution of Von Mises reference stresses along the floating marina pier.

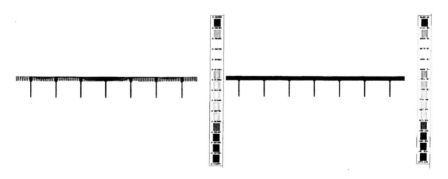

Figure 9: Displacements field and Von Mises reference stresses for 1st load case (dead weights)

In Figure 10 the 2nd and 3rd load cases are diagramatically represented. In Figure 11 the floating pier spatial displacements for the 2nd and 3rd load cases are compared: it is quite perceptible the global pier distortion associated with 2nd load case. Figures 12 and 13 compare the displacement fields and the distribution of the Von Mises reference stresses, associated with 2nd and 3rd load cases. In Figure 14 the importance of detailing the connection finger-pier can be accessed, by comparing with stress mappings without transition angle elements.

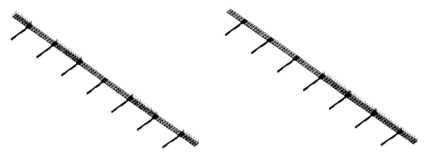

Figure 10: Second and third load cases (sym.-alternate and one-sided live loads)

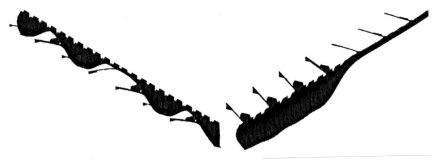

Figure 11: Pier displacements for 2nd (sym.) and 3rd (one sided) load cases

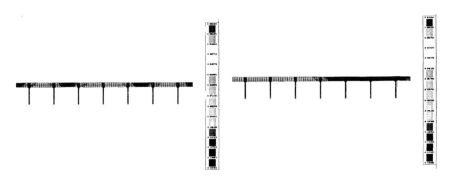

Figure 12: Displacements field for 2nd (sym.) and 3rd (one sided) live load cases

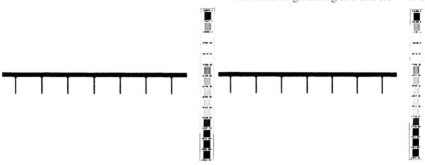

Figure 13: Von Mises reference stresses for 2nd (sym.) and 3rd (one sided) live load cases

Figure 14: Detail of Von Mises reference stresses at the connection pontoon-finger walkway, for 2nd (sym.) and 3rd (one sided) live load cases

Finally it should be mentioned that these results were equally well obtained, when the floating marina pier was modelled by the more reliable, user-friendly, versatile, interactive and well-documented software COSMOS/M 2.5 [9].

4 Considerations on floating pier dynamic stability

Of the six possible degrees of freedom of the pier as a floating body, the three predominant motions are heave, pitch and roll (Hooft [10]). The heave motion under quasi-static or very small frequency regime is preliminarily characterized either by the solution of equations (2) and (3), or by the finite element modelling previously detailed. Although the finite element analysis allows the perception of some distortion for some load combinations, the magnitude of the corresponding displacements is considerably low. Besides, in a real marina site situation, the pitching motion is usually not important because of the long length of the floating pier as compared to the incident wave-length; in some very special cases it may be important, namely when the pier is a continuous beam.

The following recommended limiting values for the pitch and roll motions are motivated by human perception and comfort in response to motion: maximum roll motion of 6°; maximum linear accelerations of 0.4 m/s²; maximum angular accelerations of 2°/s². By the results of the finite element analysis of the complete floating structure, the maximum static angle of roll was satisfied for the floating marina pier previously addressed.

In what concerns the resonant conditions in heave and pitch, preliminary analysis on a single individual pontoon revealed that the heaving and pitching periods (T_H and T_P) are expressed by:

$$T_H = 2\pi \sqrt{\frac{M_v}{\rho g A_f}} \qquad (4)$$

$$T_P = 2\pi r_l \sqrt{\frac{1 + \dfrac{w_2}{w_1}}{g(R_l + \dfrac{d}{2})}} \qquad (5)$$

where M_v is the virtual mass in heave (mass of pier pontoon plus added mass of entrained water), ρ is the specific mass of salted sea water, A_f is the section area in the floatation plane of the single individual pontoon, r_l is the pontoon longitudinal radii of gyration, R_l is the pontoon longitudinal metacentric radius above the pontoon center of buoyancy, w_2 / w_1 is the ratio between the added weight and the weight of the pontoon, and d is the pontoon draft. Similar considerations can be made for the rolling period T_R with an equation akin to (5), however with neglected added or hydrodynamic mass of the pier in roll because it is usually relatively small.

With the marina data detailed in [6] the above mentioned periods of a single individual pontoon where found to be $T_H =1.917$ sec, $T_P =1.193$ sec and $T_R =4.5$ sec, to which correspond natural frequencies of $f_H =0.5216$ Hz, $f_P =0.838$ Hz and $f_R =0.222$ Hz. Notice that the heaving period calculated for the heavy floatation (dead load plus live load) by the approximate formula $T_H \approx 2.83\sqrt{d}$ also gives $T_H \approx 2.08$ sec, similar to the previously obtained.

However the connected pontoons, constituting the complete pier, not only induce an increase of the resonant periods of the complete floating structure but also will decrease or attenuate the resonant amplifications associated with the individual single pontoon.

Conclusions

A floating marina pier infrastructure was studied for a potential site, on the banks of Douro River at the city of Porto, Portugal. Buoyancy characteristics of a singular floating pontoon are extended to redundant systems of floating units. Finite element modelling of such floating pier accessed its static performance in terms of safe advisable pontoons displacements, rotations and stress resultants. Individual pontoon dynamic stability was preliminarily addressed using simple formulas for heave, pitch and roll periods.

Acknowledgements

This work might be sponsored by a research and development project under Program SAPIENS, whose proposal will be filled-in shortly. In the event of its approval, the author acknowledges the funds that might be receiving from "Fundação para a Ciência e a Tecnologia (FCT)" of the "Ministério da Ciência e Tecnologia (MCT)", Lisbon - Portugal, during the duration of the project.

References

[1] Tsinker, G.P., *Floating Ports: Design and Construction Practices*, Gulf Publishing Company, Houston, Texas, 1986.

[2] Tsinker, G.P., *Marine Structures Engineering: Specialized Applications*, Chapman & Hall, ITP, New York, 1995.

[3] Hetinyi, M., *Beams on Elastic Foundation*, University of Michigan Press, 1946.

[4] Barros, R.C., Gonçalves, L.P., Bagorra, M.G., and Azevedo, N.G., *Análise Estrutural de uma Marina de Recreio pelo Método dos Elementos Finitos*, Relatório Técnico Interno, Dept° Eng^a Civil, FEUP, Porto, Julho 1999.

[5] Azevedo, A.F.M., and Barros, J.A.O., *Manual de Utilização do Programa Femix*, Version 2.1, Porto, Fevereiro 1992.

[6] Gomes, F.V., and Barros, R.C., *Empreitada de Construção de Instalações de Apoio à Marina de Recreio a Implantar da Doca de Serviços e Recreio do Porto de Leixões*, Projecto de Execução: Vol. 1, VERTICE – Centro de Projectos de Construção (Grupo Soares da Costa), Porto, Outubro 1985.

[7] Adie, D.W., *Marinas: a working guide to their development and design*, The Architectural Press Ltd, London, England, 1975.

[8] Ahmad, S., Irons, B.M., & Zienkiewicz, O. C., Analysis of thick and thin shell structures by curved finite elements, *International Journal for Numerical Methods in Engineering*, vol. 2, pp. 419-451, 1970.

[9] COSMOS/M, *A Complete Finite Element Analysis System*, Version 2.5, Structural Research and Analysis Corporation, Los Angeles, California, 1999.

[10] Hooft, J.P., *Advanced Dynamics of Marine Structures*, John Wiley & Sons, New York, USA, 1982.

Some considerations about the bound long waves evaluation

R. Gentile, L Rebaudengo Landò & G. Scarsi
Department of Environmental Engineering, Genoa University, Italy.

Abstract

Two non linear propagation models (indicated by the notations $[R]$ and $[A]$) are adopted to evaluate the height and period of the significant bound long waves which contribute to the low frequency range of the non linear spectra. The comparison made with some results obtained by using a numerical simulation indicates that the saturation process, which is considered in the $[A]$ model, gives rise to more realistic values, in agreement with experimental results of other authors.

1 Introduction

The non linear wave propagation spectral models usually adopted to describe the evolution of sea states in decreasing depths give rise to local wave spectra which exhibit, in the low frequency range, a part related to the bound long waves and, in the high frequency range around twice the main peak frequency, a part related to the bound short waves. The first part is of considerable interest as regards the behaviour of the port water areas, as long waves excite oscillations of the free surface which may become particularly troublesome with respect to the suitability for use of quays, when the amplitudes of the previously-mentioned waves exceed an operating threshold.

The present paper shows how the choice of propagation model may greatly influence the results obtained with reference to the characteristics of the bound long waves, analysed here in terms of significant waves.

The paper illustrates the following steps.

A non linear wave propagation spectral model which takes into account the refraction process, which automatically involves the shoaling process, is introduced, that model being formalised by adjusting a procedure suggested by Hasselmann et al. [1] and Laing [2] which requires the knowledge of the corresponding linear model specified here by means of the well-known Le Méhauté and Wang [3] model. The non linear model gives both the directional spectra and the frequency spectra in decreasing depths. The part of the frequency spectra related to the bound long waves is examined, the relevant sea states in the time domain are obtained through numerical simulations, thus the heights and periods of the significant waves are evaluated.

A non linear wave propagation model which takes into account, in addition to the refraction process, also the saturation one is considered, by following a model proposed by Rebaudengo Landò et al. [5]. The part of the frequency spectra related to the bound long waves is analysed in the same way as that described with reference to the previous model.

Some typical situations are examined and the results obtained by using the two non linear models are compared, thus the importance of the saturation process on the bound long waves is highlighted, noting that this process plays a significant role even if it is often disregarded as still not well-known.

Finally, the agreement between the results obtained by adopting the model which takes into account the saturation process and field data given by Bowers [13] is shown.

2 Spectral wave propagation model without the saturation process

The spectral wave propagation model which takes into account the refraction process is related to parallel contours with slowly varying bathimetry but its extension to a three-dimensional bottom usually does not involve special difficulties. It is considered to the first and second order of approximation, the primary peak frequency being assumed unchanged during wave propagation.

The first order model suggested by Le Méhauté and Wang, identified here by the notation $[R]_1$, provides the linear directional spectrum $[S_R(f, \phi, \phi_m, h)]_1$ on finite depth in the form

$$[S_R(f, \phi, \phi_m, h)]_1 = [S_o(f, \phi_o, \phi_{mo})]_1 \; K_{SH}^2(f, h) K_{RE}^2(f, \phi_o, h) \partial \phi_o / \partial \phi \quad (1)$$

where: the index o indicates deep water conditions; f is the frequency; h is the water depth; ϕ, ϕ_o and ϕ_m, ϕ_{mo} are the angles which define the wave component direction and the overall mean wave direction with respect to the normal to the bottom contours, as Figure 1 shows; K_{SH} and K_{RE} are the shoaling and refraction coefficients. The angles ϕ, ϕ_o and ϕ_m, ϕ_{mo} are related to each other by Snell's law (see Appendix), noting that the angles ϕ_o lie in the ranges

$$-\pi/2 < \phi_o < \pi/2 + \phi_{mo}; \; \phi_{mo} < 0 \quad (2)$$

$$-\pi/2 + \phi_{mo} < \phi_o < \pi/2; \; \phi_{mo} > 0 \quad (3)$$

which, as the figure clearly shows, ensure that only the wave components able to participate in the move towards decreasing depths are correctly retained. Consequently, eqns (2) and (3) supply the actual domain $\{\phi_o\}$ of ϕ_o from which the corresponding domain $\{\phi\}$ of ϕ is deduced, in decreasing depths.

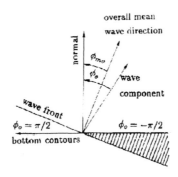

Figure 1: Sketch in deep water.

The shoaling and refraction coefficients are obtained by using the relationships relevant to linear Stokian waves (see Appendix) and the derivative $\partial\phi_o/\partial\phi$ is expressed by

$$\partial\phi_o/\partial\phi = \cos[\sin^{-1}(\sin\phi_o\tanh kh)],$$
$$/ \{\tanh^2 kh - \sin^2[\sin^{-1}(\sin\phi_o\tanh kh)]\}^{0.5} \tag{4}$$

which is associated with the condition

$$\sin^2[\sin^{-1}(\sin\phi_o\tanh kh)]/\tanh^2 kh < 1 \tag{5}$$

that is automatically verified for the angles ϕ_o lying in the ranges given by eqns (2) and (3). In the previous equation k is the wave number modulus obtained from the isotropic dispersion relationship

$$(2\pi f)^2 = gk\tanh kh \tag{6}$$

where g is the acceleration of gravity.
The linear frequency spectrum $[S_R(f,h)]_1$ which corresponds to the linear directional spectrum $[S_R(f,\phi,\phi_m,h)]_1$ is given by

$$[S_R(f,h)]_1 = \int_{\{\phi\}} [S_R(f,\phi,\phi_m,h)]_1 d\phi \tag{7}$$

which leads to

$$[S_R(f,h)]_1 = \int_{\{\phi_o\}} [S_o(f,\phi_o,\phi_{mo})]_1 K_{SH}^2(f,h)K_{RE}^2(f,\phi_o,h)d\phi_o. \tag{8}$$

Of course, the linear directional spreading function $[D(f, \phi, \phi_m, h)]_1$ on finite depth is expressed by

$$[D(f, \phi, \phi_m, h)]_1 = [S_R(f, \phi, \phi_m, h)]_1 / [S_R(f, h)]_1. \tag{9}$$

The second order model suggested by Rebaudengo Landò et al. [4], identified here by the notation $[R]_2$, provides the non linear finite depth directional spectrum $[S_R(f, \phi, \phi_m, h)]_2$ starting from the relevant linear directional spectrum $[S_R(f, \phi, \phi_m, h)]_1$ by adopting and adjusting the procedure proposed by Laing. That spectrum is formally expressed by the sum of the first and second order spectral components

$$[S_R(f, \phi, \phi_m, h)]_2 = [S_R(f, \phi, \phi_m, h)]^{(1)} + [S_R(f, \phi, \phi_m, h)]^{(2)} \tag{10}$$

where the term to first order is provided by eqn (1) and the term to second order is supplied by

$$
\begin{aligned}
[S_R(f, \phi, \phi_m, h)]^{(2)} = &\frac{1}{4} \int_{\{\phi\}} \int_o^f (B_s)^2 [S_R(f', \phi', \phi_m, h)]_1, \\
&\cdot [S_R(f - f', \phi_s'', \phi_m, h)]_1 df' d\phi', \\
&+ \frac{1}{2} \int_{\{\phi\}} \int_{\{f\}} (B_d)^2 [S_R(f', \phi', \phi_m, h)]_1, \\
&\cdot [S_R(f + f', \phi_d'', \phi_m, h)]_1 df' d\phi', \tag{11}
\end{aligned}
$$

the quantities B_s and B_d being given in the Appendix. The angles ϕ', ϕ_s'', ϕ_d'' identify the directions of the vectors $\boldsymbol{k}$, $\boldsymbol{k} - \boldsymbol{k}'$, $\boldsymbol{k} + \boldsymbol{k}'$, noting that the wave number vectors $\boldsymbol{k}'$, which are associated with each wave number vector $\boldsymbol{k}$, range in the $\{\boldsymbol{k}\}$ domain with the constraint that the angles ϕ_s'' and ϕ_d'' fall in the $\{\phi\}$ domain. The first order wave components verify eqn (6), that is

$$(2\pi f')^2 = g|\boldsymbol{k}'|\tanh|\boldsymbol{k}'|h \tag{12}$$

$$(2\pi f - 2\pi f')^2 = g|\boldsymbol{k} - \boldsymbol{k}'|\tanh|\boldsymbol{k} - \boldsymbol{k}'|h \tag{13}$$

$$(2\pi f + 2\pi f')^2 = g|\boldsymbol{k} + \boldsymbol{k}'|\tanh|\boldsymbol{k} + \boldsymbol{k}'|h. \tag{14}$$

The non linear frequency spectrum $[S_R(f, h)]_2$ which corresponds to the non linear directional spectrum $[S_R(f, \phi, \phi_m, h)]_2$ is given by

$$[S_R(f, h)]_2 = \int_{\{\phi\}} [S_R(f, \phi, \phi_m, h)]_2 d\phi. \tag{15}$$

The following two observations suggested by Rebaudengo Landò et al. [5] are recalled. As the second order model originates from a perturbation method, a limit must be introduced for the lowest water depths, as happens for the non linear

Stokian waves. That limit may be specified starting from eqn (10) and referring to the zero-th moments of the spectra, that is

$$[m_o]_2 = [m_o]^{(1)} + [m_o]^{(2)} = \delta[m_o]'_1 + \delta^2[m_o]'_2 \tag{16}$$

δ being a proper perturbation parameter. The constraint is that the terms $[m_o]'_1$ and $[m_o]'_2$ have to keep the same order of magnitude.

Moreover, a check is needed to ensure that the sea states in finite depths associated with the non linear spectra have stable random waves. A comparison is made between the height H of each wave, with period T, and the breaking wave height H_{br} provided by Goda's relationship [6], referred here to a gentle slope and given by

$$H_{br} = AgT^2\{1 - \exp[-0.75(2\pi/T)^2(h/g)]\} \tag{17}$$

where the mean value of the coefficient $A = 0.15/2\pi$ is adopted for random waves, according to Li and Dong [7].

The deep water directional spectrum $[S_o(f, \phi_o, \phi_{mo})]_1$ in deep water is assumed in the usual form

$$[S_o(f, \phi_o, \phi_{mo})]_1 = [S_o(f)]_1[D_o(\phi_o, \phi_{mo})]_1 \tag{18}$$

which involves the linear frequency spectrum $[S_o(f)]_1$ and the directional spreading function $[D_o(f, \phi_o, \phi_{mo})]_1$.

The mean JONSWAP J and the Battjes B frequency spectra are assumed (Hasselmann et al. [8]; Battjes et al. [9]), which involve a -5 and a -4 power law, respectively, as principal frequency dependence.

These spectra are expressed by

$$[S_o(f)]_1 = \alpha_o g^2 (2\pi)^{-4} \psi'_{ao} \psi_{bo} \; ; \; (J) \tag{19}$$

$$[S_o(f)]_1 = \beta_o g(2\pi)^{-3} U_* f^{-4} \psi''_{ao} \psi_{bo} \; ; \; (B) \tag{20}$$

$$\psi'_{ao} = \exp\{-1.25(f/f_p)^{-4})\} \tag{21}$$

$$\psi''_{ao} = \exp\{-(f/f_p)^{-4})\} \tag{22}$$

$$\psi_{bo} = \exp\{\ln\gamma_o \exp[-0.5(f/f_{po} - 1)^2/\sigma_o^2]\} \tag{23}$$

where the dimensionless parameters α_o, β_o (equilibrium parameters), γ_o (enhancement parameter), σ_o (peak width parameter) and the wind shear velocity U_* are given by the relationships shown in the Appendix, after assuming the index p to indicate a quantity referred to the peak frequency.

It is to be noted that hereafter the notations $[R_J]_1$, $[R_J]_2$ and $[R_B]_1$, $[R_B]_2$ are used to indicate the JONSWAP or Battjes spectrum, respectively, with reference to the $[R]_1$ and $[R]_2$ models.

The directional spreading function suggested by Hasselmann et al. [1] and revised by Laing [2] is adopted, that function being expressed by

$$[D_o(f, \phi_o, \phi_{mo})]_1 = N[s_o(f)]\cos^{2s_o}[(\phi_o - \phi_{mo})/2] \qquad (24)$$

$$s_o = 15.3(f/f_p)^{-4} \;\; ; \;\; f < f_p \;\; \text{and} \;\; s_o = 15.3(f/f_p)^{-3} \;\; ; \;\; f \geq f_p \qquad (25)$$

where $N[s_o(f)]$ is a normalising factor.

As an example, Figure 2 shows the frequency spectra on the depth $h = 12.5$ m relevant to the linear and non linear models obtained from a deep water mean JONSWAP spectrum characterised by $f_p = 0.988$ Hz and $\alpha_o = 0.010$.

The figure clearly shows that the non linear model gives rise, in the low frequency range, to a part related to the bound long waves and, in the high frequency range around $f = 2f_p$, to a less evident part, related to the bound short waves.

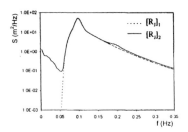

Figure 2: Frequency spectra deduced with the $[R_J]_1$ and $[R_J]_2$ models ($h = 12.5$ m, $f_p = 0.988$ Hz and $\alpha_o = 0.010$).

3 Spectral wave propagation model with the saturation process

The saturation process takes into account the surface energy dissipation due to partial wave breaking of the spilling type and it gives rise to saturated spectral forms that cannot be exceeded, like the mean JONSWAP and Battjes frequency spectra in deep water.

By adopting a scheme suggested by Bouws et al. [10], which is based on an extension of the self-similarity shape hypothesis suggested by Kitaigorodskii et al. [11], the linear saturated wave number modulus spectrum in finite depth can be expressed by the relationship that gives the corresponding wave number modulus spectrum in deep water after replacing k_o by k, which are related to each other through the following relationship

$$k(f, h) = k_o(f)\chi(f, h) \qquad (26)$$

where the function χ can be specified starting from

$$\chi \cdot \tanh(\sigma_h^2 \chi) = 1 \;\; ; \;\; \sigma_h = 2\pi f(h/g)^{0.5} \qquad (27)$$

σ_h being the dimensionless depth.

Thus, from the wave number spectrum, the linear frequency spectrum $[S_{SAT}(f,h)]_1$ can be deduced from

$$[S_{SAT}(f,h)]_1 = [S_o(f)]_1 K^2_{SAT}(f, f_p, h) \qquad (28)$$

taking into account that the relationship which gives the saturation coefficient K_{SAT} depends on the form of the frequency spectrum $[S_o(f)]_1$, as shown in the following.

The actual linear frequency spectrum $[S_A(f,h)]_1$ is thus provided by

$$[S_A(f,h)]_1 = \min\{[S_R(f,h)]_1; [S_{SAT} = (f,h)]_1\} \qquad (29)$$

and the actual linear directional spectrum $[S_A(f, \phi, \phi_m, h)]_1$ is expressed by

$$[S_A(f, \phi, \phi_m, h)]_1 = [S_A(f,h)]_1 [D(f, \phi, \phi_m, h)]_1 \qquad (30)$$

where the directional spreading function $[D(f, \phi, \phi_m, h)]_1$ is given by eqn (9).

Eqns (29) and (30) formalise the linear wave propagation spectral model identified here by the notation $[A]_1$.

The saturation coefficients K_{SAT} relevant to spectral forms which involve the deep water mean JONSWAP J and Battjes B frequency spectra are expressed by

$$K_{SAT} = \{\psi'_a \psi_b \psi_c \chi_p^{0.33} \chi^{-2} / \psi'_{ao} \psi_{bo}\}^{0.5} \quad ; \quad (J) \qquad (31)$$

$$K_{SAT} = \{\psi''_a \psi_b \psi_c \chi_p^{0.005} \chi^{-1.5} / \psi''_{ao} \psi_{bo}\}^{0.5} \quad ; \quad (B) \qquad (32)$$

where the functions ψ'_a, ψ''_a, ψ_b, ψ_c are given by

$$\psi'_a = \exp\{-1.25(f\chi^{0.5} / f_p \chi_p^{0.5})^{-4}\} \qquad (33)$$

$$\psi''_a = \exp\{-(f\chi^{0.5} / f_p \chi_p^{0.5})^{-4}\} \qquad (34)$$

$$\psi_b = \exp\{\ln\gamma_o \exp[-0.5(f\chi^{0.5} / f_p \chi_p^{0.5} - 1)^2 / \sigma_o^2]\} \qquad (35)$$

$$\psi_c = \{1 + 2\sigma_h^2 \chi / \sinh(2\sigma_h^2 \chi)\}^{-1}. \qquad (36)$$

The actual non linear directional $[S_A(f, \phi, \phi_m, h)]_2$ and frequency $[S_A(f,h)]_2$ spectra can be obtained by adopting the procedure previously explained to deduce the $[S_R(f, \phi, \phi_m, h)]_2$ and $[S_R(f,h)]_2$ spectra, giving rise to the non linear wave propagation spectral model identified hereafter by the notation $[A]_2$.

It is to be noted that the notations $[A_J]_1$, $[A_J]_2$ and $[A_B]_1$, $[A_B]_2$ are used to indicate the JONSWAP or Battjes spectrum, respectively, with reference to the $[A]_1$ and $[A]_2$ models.

4 Numerical simulations of the bound long waves in the time domain

The bound long waves in the time domain t are evaluated by considering the low frequency part $\{[S(f,h)]_2\}_L$ of the non linear spectrum $[S(f,h)]_2$, from $f' = 0.03 f_p$ to $f'' = 0.3 f_p$.

The vertical displacement $\{\eta(t)\}_L$ of the bound long waves is obtained by carrying out numerical simulations based on the random phase method, described in detail by Gentile [12] with reference to the whole spectrum, which can be formalised here through

$$\{\eta(t)\}_L = \sum_{n=1}^{N} a_n \cos(2\pi f_n t + \epsilon_n) \tag{37}$$

where a_n is the deterministic amplitude $a_n = \{2[S(f_n,h)]_2 \triangle f\}_L^{0.5}$, N is the number of frequencies f_n considered, with constant interval $\triangle f$ and ϵ_n are the random phases, uniformly distributed from 0 to 2π.

Obviously, $[S(f,h)]_2$ can be alternatively specified by

$$[S(f,h)]_2 = [S_R(f,h)]_2 \tag{38}$$

$$[S(f,h)]_2 = [S_A(f,h)]_2. \tag{39}$$

Knowledge of the vertical displacements allows successions of bound long waves to be identified, from which the significant wave heights $(H_{1/3})_L$ and periods $(T_{H1/3})_L$ can be evaluated by adopting a statistical approach.

5 Comparison between the two analytical models

Different results obtained by using the two above-mentioned models are given in the following, with reference to two littoral areas of the Ligurian Gulf (Italy) characterised by straight and parallel bathimetry and with regard to different wave climates with increasing return period T_r, related to Scirocco storms.

The relevant deep water significant wave and peak period are given in Table 1.

The numerical investigation is carried out by considering three different dimensionless depths $(\sigma_{hp})_a = 0.8$, $(\sigma_{hp})_b = 0.7$ and $(\sigma_{hp})_c = 0.6$ for which the constraint relevant to eqn (16) is verified. The corresponding values of the depths for the different values of T_R are given in Table 2. The mean wave direction relevant to the two selected littoral areas are $\phi_{mo} = 30$ deg and $\phi_{mo} = 0$ deg, which correspond to situations with and without global refraction, respectively.

Tables 3 and 4 give, as an example, the values of the significant wave heights $[H_{1/3}]_2$, $[H_{1/3}]_L$ and periods $[T_{H1/3}]_2$, $[T_{H1/3}]_L$ evaluated from the whole second order spectrum and from the low frequency range, respectively, with reference to the $[A]_2$ and $[R]_2$ models. The values obtained from the $[A]_2$ model are lower than those obtained from the $[R]_2$ model, in analogous situation.

Table 1: Ligurian Gulf; Scirocco storms; deep water: wave climate.

T_r (yrs)	$(H_{1/3})_o$ (m)	T_p (s)
1	2.89	7.25
5	4.02	8.55
10	4.51	9.05
50	5.64	10.12
100	6.13	10.55
200	6.61	10.96

Table 2: Ligurian Gulf; Scirocco storms: finite depths adopted.

T_r (yrs)	h_a (m)	h_b (m)	h_c (m)
1	8.36	6.40	4.70
5	11.62	8.89	6.53
10	13.02	9.97	7.33
50	16.29	12.47	9.16
100	17.69	13.55	9.95
200	19.12	14.64	10.75

Tables 5 and 6 give, for the two mean wave directions and the three dimensionless depths, the ratios $\xi_{[A]L2}^{H1/3}$, $\xi_{[R]L2}^{H1/3}$ between the significant wave heights relevant to the low frequency range and those relevant to the whole spectrum, with reference to the $[A]_2$ and $[R]_2$ models, respectively. The ratios obtained from the $[A]_2$ model are lower than those obtained from the $[R]_2$ model, in analogous situation.

Table 7 gives, for the two mean wave directions and the three dimensionless depths, the ratios $\xi_{AR}^{[H1/3]_L}$ between the significant wave heights relevant to the low frequency range evaluated with the $[A]_2$ model and the corresponding ones evaluated with the $[R]_2$ model.

An examination of Tables 3 to 6 suggests that the bound long waves, present in the second order spectra, show greater heights and periods when the $[R]_2$ model is adopted, taking into account that the deep water conditions in terms of severity and shape of the frequency spectrum do not give rise to appreciable differences. The presence of global refraction gives slightly appreciable effects. In addition, the ratios given in Table 7 show that the differences between the two models in the low frequency range are even more important than those relevant to the whole frequency range, suggesting that the saturation process gives rise to more reasonable results not only with the linear models but also with the non linear ones.

Table 3: Ligurian Gulf; Scirocco storms; $[A_J]_2$, ($[A_B]_2$) models: significant wave heights and periods ($\phi_{mo}=30$ deg, $h = h_b$).

T_r (yrs)	$[H_{1/3}]_2$ (m)	$[T_{H1/3}]_2$ (s)	$[H_{1/3}]_L$ (m)	$[T_{H1/3}]_L$ (s)
1	1.81	6.52	0.12	58.17
	(1.84)	(6.61)	(0.12)	(57.19)
5	2.52	7.68	0.16	68.56
	(2.56)	(7.80)	(0.17)	(68.29)
10	2.82	8.13	0.18	72.59
	(2.87)	(8.25)	(0.19)	(72.31)
50	3.53	9.10	0.23	81.18
	(3.59)	(9.23)	(0.23)	(80.88)
100	3.83	9.48	0.24	84.61
	(3.90)	(9.63)	(0.26)	(84.29)
200	4.14	9.86	0.26	87.95
	(4.21)	(10.01)	(0.28)	(87.62)

Table 4: Ligurian Gulf; Scirocco storms; $[R_J]_2$, ($[R_B]_2$) models: significant wave heights and periods ($\phi_{mo}=30$ deg, $h = h_b$).

T_r (yrs)	$[H_{1/3}]_2$ (m)	$[T_{H1/3}]_2$ (s)	$[H_{1/3}]_L$ (m)	$[T_{H1/3}]_L$ (s)
1	2.40	6.78	0.22	62.95
	(2.40)	(6.89)	(0.22)	(62.73)
5	3.34	7.99	0.30	74.20
	(3.33)	(8.12)	(0.30)	(73.94)
10	3.74	8.46	0.34	78.56
	(3.74)	(8.59)	(0.34)	(78.30)
50	4.68	9.46	0.42	87.87
	(4.67)	(9.61)	(0.42)	(87.57)
100	5.08	9.86	0.46	91.58
	(5.07)	(10.02)	(0.46)	(91.27)
200	5.49	10.25	0.50	95.19
	(5.48)	(10.42)	(0.50)	(94.88)

Table 5: Ligurian Gulf; Scirocco storms; $[A_J]_2$, $([A_B]_2)$ models: ratios $\xi_{[A]L2}^{H1/3}$.

T_r (yrs)	$\xi_{[A]L2}^{H1/3}$ (ϕ_{mo} = 30 deg)			$\xi_{[A]L2}^{H1/3}$ (ϕ_{mo} = 0 deg)		
	h_a	h_b	h_c	h_a	h_b	h_c
1	0.040	0.066	0.110	0.040	0.061	0.099
	(0.040)	(0.065)	(0.108)	(0.040)	(0.060)	(0.096)
5	0.040	0.063	0.107	0.040	0.060	0.102
	(0.040)	(0.066)	(0.113)	(0.040)	(0.063)	(0.103)
10	0.039	0.064	0.106	0.039	0.060	0.103
	(0.042)	(0.066)	(0.112)	(0.038)	(0.063)	(0.104)
50	0.042	0.065	0.107	0.039	0.059	0.101
	(0.041)	(0.064)	(0.111)	(0.039)	(0.061)	(0.105)
100	0.041	0.063	0.107	0.038	0.060	0.102
	(0.040)	(0.067)	(0.113)	(0.040)	(0.062)	(0.105)
200	0.040	0.063	0.107	0.038	0.060	0.102
	(0.042)	(0.066)	(0.113)	(0.039)	(0.062)	(0.113)

Table 6: Ligurian Gulf; Scirocco storms; $[R_J]_2$, $([R_B]_2)$ models: ratios $\xi_{[R]L2}^{H1/3}$.

T_r (yrs)	$\xi_{[R]L2}^{H1/3}$ (ϕ_{mo} = 30 deg)			$\xi_{[R]L2}^{H1/3}$ (ϕ_{mo} = 0 deg)		
	h_a	h_b	h_c	h_a	h_b	h_c
1	0.051	0.092	0.181	0.052	0.091	0.178
	(0.051)	(0.092)	(0.177)	(0.053)	(0.091)	(0.179)
5	0.051	0.090	0.179	0.052	0.091	0.177
	(0.052)	(0.090)	(0.179)	(0.053)	(0.091)	(0.178)
10	0.051	0.091	0.177	0.052	0.091	0.178
	(0.052)	(0.091)	(0.178)	(0.052)	(0.092)	(0.178)
50	0.052	0.090	0.179	0.052	0.091	0.177
	(0.052)	(0.090)	(0.179)	(0.052)	(0.091)	(0.180)
100	0.052	0.091	0.178	0.051	0.089	0.177
	(0.052)	(0.091)	(0.178)	(0.052)	(0.092)	(0.180)
200	0.052	0.091	0.191	0.051	0.089	0.177
	(0.052)	(0.091)	(0.180)	(0.052)	(0.092)	(0.180)

Table 7: Ligurian Gulf; Scirocco storms: ratios $\xi_{AR}^{[H1/3]_L}$ with reference to the JON-SWAP and Battjes (in parenthesis) deep water spectra.

T_r (yrs)	$\xi_{AR}^{[H1/3]_L}$ ($\phi_{mo} = 30$ deg)			$\xi_{AR}^{[H1/3]_L}$ ($\phi_{mo} = 0$ deg)		
	h_a	h_b	h_c	h_a	h_b	h_c
1	0.667	0.545	0.400	0.615	0.478	0.340
	(0.667)	(0.545)	(0.409)	(0.615)	(0.478)	(0.340)
5	0.647	0.533	0.387	0.611	0.469	0.354
	(0.647)	(0.567)	(0.419)	(0.611)	(0.500)	(0.369)
10	0.631	0.529	0.391	0.600	0.472	0.356
	(0.684)	(0.559)	(0.420)	(0.600)	(0.500)	(0.370)
50	0.667	0.548	0.391	0.600	0.467	0.352
	(0.667)	(0.548)	(0.414)	(0.600)	(0.489)	(0.369)
100	0.654	0.522	0.394	0.592	0.479	0.353
	(0.654)	(0.565)	(0.425)	(0.630)	(0.490)	(0.370)
200	0.643	0.520	0.367	0.586	0.481	0.355
	(0.678)	(.560)	(0.421)	(0.621)	(0.490)	(0.398)

6 Comparison with field data

In order to apply the $[A]_2$ model to experimental results, those given by Bowers [13] are adopted. The local value of the significant wave height and peak period are reconstructed taking into account the saturation process. The results given in Table 8 with reference to the low frequency range show good agreement with the original ones. Further comparisons may be carried out, if other field data are available.

Table 8: Comparisons between some results given by Bowers and those obtained with the $[A]_2$ model with reference to the JONSWAP spectra.

Local values			Bowers	$[A]_2$
h (m)	$H_{1/3}$ (m)	T_p (s)	$[H_{1/3}]_L$ (m)	$[H_{1/3}]_L$ (m)
12.4	3.3	7.5	0.14	0.15
12.4	4.0	8.4	0.27	0.28
12.4	4.7	9.2	0.45	0.45
13.1	2.4	7.5	0.10	0.07
13.1	4.0	9.2	0.32	0.30
13.1	4.8	10.0	0.53	0.51

7 Concluding remarks

The following conclusions may be drawn.

1. The bound long waves which arise in finite depth from the non linear models are more and more appreciable, as the depth decreases.
2. The deep water condition being assigned, the value of the significant bound long wave height is influenced by the non linear model adopted for the propagation.
3. The non linear $[A]_2$ model which takes into account also the saturation process gives rise to local sea states with lower significant wave heights and even lower significant bound long wave heights than those obtained with the $[R]_2$ model which considers only the usual shoaling and refraction processes.
4. The results obtained with the $[A]_2$ model are in agreement with field data from Bowers.

8 Appendix

A1) Correlations between ϕ, ϕ_m and ϕ_o, ϕ_{mo}

$$\phi(f,\phi_o,h)=\sin^{-1}(\sin\phi_o\tanh kh)\,;\; \phi_m(f,\phi_{mo},h)=\sin^{-1}(\sin\phi_{mo}\tanh k_p h) \quad (40)$$

A2) Shoaling and refraction coefficients

$$K_{SH}(f,h) = \{2\cosh^2 kh/(2kh+\sinh 2kh)\}^{0.5} \quad (41)$$
$$K_{RE}(f,\phi_o,h) = \{\cos\phi_o/\cos\phi\}^{0.5} \quad (42)$$

A3) Quantities B_s and B_d, with reference to eqn (11)

$$B_s = A_s - k'\cdot(k-k')/(R'R''_s)^{0.5} + (R'+R''_s)+(R'R''_s)^{0.5} \quad (43)$$
$$B_d = A_d - k'\cdot(k+k')/(R'R''_d)^{0.5}+(R'+R''_d)-(R'R''_d)^{0.5} \quad (44)$$

where the quantities A_s, A_d are given by

$$A_s=\{[(|k-k'|^2-R''^2_s)/(R''_s)^{0.5}+(|k'|^2-R'^2)/(R')^{0.5},$$
$$/[(R')^{0.5}+(R''_s)^{0.5}]+2[k'\cdot(k-k')-R'R''_s]/(R'R''_s)^{0.5}\},$$
$$/\{1-|k|\tanh|k|h/[(R')^{0.5}+(R''_s)^{0.5}]^2\} \quad (45)$$

$$A_d=\{[(|k+k'|^2-R''^2_d)/(R''_d)^{0.5}-(|k'|^2-R'^2)/(R')^{0.5}],$$
$$/[(R''_d)^{0.5}-(R')^{0.5}]+2[k'\cdot(k+k')+R'R''_d]/(R'R''_d)^{0.5}\},$$
$$/\{1-|k|\tanh|k|h/[(R''_d)^{0.5}-(R')^{0.5}]^2\} \quad (46)$$

and the quantities R', R''_s, R''_d are deduced from

$$R' = (2\pi f')^2/g \;;\; R''_s = (2\pi f-2\pi f')^2/g \;;\; R''_d = (2\pi f+2\pi f')^2/g. \quad (47)$$

A4) Parameters referred to the J and B spectra

$$\alpha_o = 0.033\tilde{U}_o^{0.667} \;;\; \tilde{U}_o = U_o f_p/g \;;\; \gamma_o = 3.3 \;(J) \quad (48)$$

$$\sigma_o = 0.07 \text{ for } f < f_p \;\; ; \;\; \sigma_o = 0.09 \text{ for } f \geq f_p \;\; (J) \tag{49}$$

$$\beta_o = 0.119 \tilde{U}_o^{0.01} ; \gamma_o = 3.02 \tilde{U}_o^{-0.16} ; U_z = 2.5 U_* \ln\{z/(0.0144 U_*^2/g)\} \;\; (B) \tag{50}$$

$$\sigma_o = 0.07 \tilde{U}_o^{-0.28} \text{ for } f < f_p \;\; ; \;\; \sigma_o = 0.14 \tilde{U}_o^{0.18} \text{ for } f \geq f_p \;\; (B) \tag{51}$$

where U_o is the wind speed U_z at $z = 10$ m above the mean water level and U_* is the friction velocity.

References

[1] Hasselmann, D.E., Dunkel, M. & Ewing, J.A., Directional wave spectra observed during JONSWAP 1973. *J. of Physical Oceanography*, **10**, pp. 1264–1280, 1980.

[2] Laing, A.K., Nonlinear properties of random gravity waves in the water of finite depth. *J. of Physical Oceanography*, **16**, pp. 2013–2030, 1986.

[3] Le Méhauté, B. & Wang, J.D., Wave spectrum changes on sloped beach. *J. of Waterway, Port, Coastal and Ocean Engineering*, **108**, pp. 33–47, 1982.

[4] Rebaudengo Landò, L., Gentile, R. & Scarsi, G., Multidirectional wave transformations on decreasing depths: a nonlinear model. *Proc. of the 15th Int. Conf. on Offshore Mech. and Arctic Engineering*, Firenze, pp. 29–40, 1996.

[5] Rebaudengo Landò, L., Gentile, R. & Scarsi, G., A nonlinear spectral model for directional random waves in decreasing depths. *International Journal of Offshore and Polar Engineering*, **9–2**, pp. 81–89, 1999.

[6] Goda, Y., Irregular wave deformation in the surf zone. *Coastal Engineering in Japan*, **18**, pp. 13–26, 1975.

[7] Li, Y. & Dong, G., Wave breaking phenomena of irregular wave combined with opposing current. *Proc. of the 3rd Int. Offshore and Polar Engineering Conf.*, Singapore, pp. 64–70, 1993.

[8] Hasselmann, K. et al., Measurements of wind-wave growth and swell decay during the Joint North Sea Wave Project (JONSWAP). *Deut. Hydrogr. Z.*, **A8–12**, pp. 9–95, 1973.

[9] Battjes, I.A., Zitman, T.J. & Houlthuijsen, L.H., A re-analysis of the spectra observed in JONSWAP. *J. of Physical Ocean.*, **17**, pp. 1288–1295, 1987.

[10] Bouws, E., Gunter, H., Rosenthal, W. & Vincent, C.L., Similarity of wind wave spectrum in finite depth water. Part I: Spectral form. *J. of Geophysical Research*, **90–C1**, pp. 975–986, 1985.

[11] Kitaigorodskii, S.A., Krasitskii, V.P. & Zarlavskii, M.M., On Phillips theory of equilibrium range in the spectra of wind-generated waves. *J. of Physical Oceanography*, **5**, pp. 410–420, 1975.

[12] Gentile, R., Statistical properties of random waves in deep water directional seas involving f⁻⁴ frequency spectra. *Proc. of the 8th Int. Offshore and Polar Engineering Conf.*, Montreal, pp. 203–211, 1998.

[13] Bowers, E.C., Low frequency waves in intermediate water depths. *Proc. of the 23rd Int. Conf. on Coastal Engineering*, Venice, Italy, **62**, pp. 832–845, 1992.

Long-term wind climate in a large oceanic island harbour

G. Rodríguez
Departamento de Fisica, Universidad de Las Palmas de G.C.,
Las Palmas, Spain.

Abstract

Knowledge of wind climate is of great importance for the adequate design and construction of harbours and for operational considerations. Statistical properties of wind climate at Las Palmas Port, a large harbour located in an small oceanic island, are studied by using an incomplete data set of maximum daily wind speed covering a period of 10 years. Annual and seasonal variabilities, as well as probability of extreme values occurrence are examined. Additionally, a time-frequency representation of this nonstationary time series is developed.

1 Introduction

Wind climate is an essencial input for many engineering practices related to ports and marinas design and functioning. Harbour facilities should be designed to sustain extreme wind forcing during their lifetime. Furthermore, while in general the wind loads on ships constitute a relatively small part of the total environmental load, the accurate knowledge of the magnitude and character of the wind loads plays an important role in connection with harbour and near harbour operations, such as manoeuvring, mooring, stability, and dynamic positioning, among others. The problem of wind loads on berthing structures is more complex because of loads can be exerted directly on the structure and indirectly through the forces on moored ships, which are transmited to the structure along the mooring lines. A detailed description of wind effects on structures can be found in [1], while mathematical models to estimate the wind forces and moments on a vessel have been described in [2].

It is well known that wind is a phenomenon of random nature. Furthermore, wind characteristics in coastal zones are the result of interacting meteorological, oceanographic and topographic factors. Consequently, meteorological flows in coastal zones display a very complex stochastic behaviour and their practical study must rely on probabilistic methodologies. Additionally, it is also well known that, in general, wind

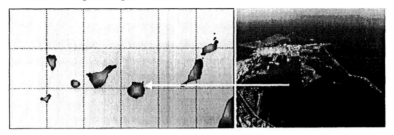

Figure 1: Geographical location of Canary Islands and aerial view of Las Palmas Port

speed is larger at offshore than at onshore areas, and small oceanic islands may be considered as locations offshore the main continental lands. Then, knowledge of wind climate at a large port located in an small oceanic island, such as the Port of Las Palmas, results of great practical interest.

This study deals primarily with long-term wind characteristics based on daily maximum wind speed observations recorded at Las Palmas Port. The rest of the paper first gives a brief description of the study area and the characteristics of the analysed data set in section 2. Directional and non-directional long-term statistical properties of wind velocity, as well as seasonal variabilities, are examined in section 3. Section 4 presents the probability of occurrence of extreme wind speeds. The time-frequency description of wind speed time series using continuous wavelet transform is presented in section 5. Section 6 presents the discussion of results and conclusions.

2 Study area and data

Prevailing winds of the Atlantic subtropical oceans are the Trade Winds, which blow steadily westward and slightly toward the equator at average speeds of around 18 to 21 kilometers per hour. These are found at around 30 degrees north and 30 degrees south latitude, sandwiched between a band of low pressure near the equator and high pressure belts in the middle latitudes.

The Canary Archipelago is located on the Northwest African continental shelf, in the Eastern Central Atlantic off the Saharan coast, and consists of seven major islands and several islets. These islands extend about 450 km from East to West and are placed between 27° and 30° of North latitude, see Fig. 1. Due to its geographical location, in the Southern edge of Azores High, Canaries are within the fairly regular Trade Winds belt.

Las Palmas port is located at Gran Canaria island, which is over 2000 m high. The presence of this high island produces important disruption in the wind flow. However, the port is situated north of the island, under the direct influence of the Trade Winds, just partially sheltered by an small islet, as shown in the right side of Figure 1.

Data used for the analysis of wind climate were collected at the harbour by means of an anemometer placed at the 10 meters above mean sea level standard height and spanned the period from January 1984 to March 1994. Data set contains maximum daily wind speed and the corresponding direction. The time series presents several gaps and missed data represent 13.5% of the total expected data, approximately. Due

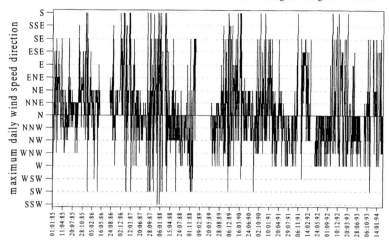

Figure 2: Temporal variability of maximum daily wind speed direction.

to the existence of gaps as large as one month no procedures to fill gaps were applied. Fortunately, data gaps are not grouped in the same month or season but are irregularly distributed in time.

3 Long term statistical analysis

Annual and seasonal behaviour of winds in a harbour location are of great importance for construction and operational considerations. Naturally, due to the vectorial character of wind velocity, directional information results of great interest. Figure 2 shows the maximum daily wind speed direction in Las Palmas harbour for the whole period of observation. It can be readily observed the predominance of winds from NNW, N, NNE and NE directions, mainly during summers. This is due to the intensification of the Azores High and the associated enhancement of the trade winds during that period. Winds from this sector remain the most frequent, representing more than the 70% of the total time, but the approaching of low pressure systems to the islands, specially from the NW during winter, and ocassionally from West or Southeast, gives rise to a considerable variability.

Furthermore, it can be observed in the frequency distribution of maximum daily wind speed direction, Figure 3, that there is a relatively important fraction of wind events from the E-SE sector. This situation usually occurs during periods of wind trades weakening and give rise to warm winds blowing from the Saharan desert, which some times carries along a large concentration of suspended dust. This phenomenon, locally named "calima", takes place once or twice per year, aproximately. Nevertheless, Figure 3 displays the clear predominance of winds blowing from the NW-NE quadrant in the study area.

Then, as expected, the wind direction distribution at Las Palmas Port reflects general atmospheric circulation, mainly during summer. Synoptic disturbances are the major determining process when synoptic circulation, i.e. Trade Winds, intensity weakens.

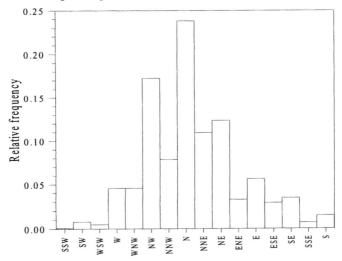

Figure 3: Relative frequency of maximum daily wind speed direction.

The mean values and its standard deviations for the maximum daily wind speeds in 1984-1995 are represented, in form of daily averages, in Figure 4. The results indicate the existence of an apparent annual course, the latter summer and the early autumn being the calmest periods and the winter the windiest season. The spring is a transitional time which varies from year to year.

Empirical probability of exceedance distributions of maximum daily wind speeds for the whole data set and for the mean year are presented in Figures 5a and 5b, respectively. It is observed, Fig. 5a, that maximum wind speeds during the observation period is about $26m/s$, with a probability lower than 0.1% of been exceeded, i.e. . The modal value of maximum daily wind speed is about $7m/s$. In average, the maximum wind speed is $13m/s$, with an exceedance probability close to 1%, that is 3.65 days by year.

3.1 Seasonal variability

The seasonal pattern commented in relation to Figure 4 is easiest visualised in Figure 6, which shows the monthly averages for the whole observational period. The monthly mean values of wind speeds are represented together with their standard deviations. It is possible to observe quantitative diferences between the variability of monthly average values during the latter spring, summer, and the early autumn period and the rest of the year. The largest inter-annual variability corresponds to the period from the late autumn to the early spring. As expected, the lowest speeds appear during the summer season, when the prevailing Trade Winds are enhanced, weaking progressively from autumn to winter and reinforcing from the spring to summer. The variability observed during the period extending from late autumn to the early spring is due to the intermittent intrusion of cyclonic systems, particularly from the Northwest Atlantic.

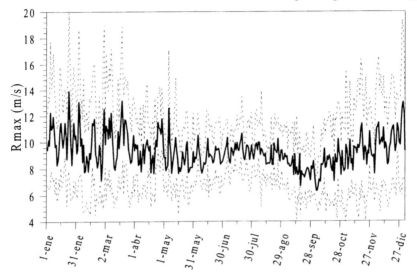

Figure 4: Mean year as daily averaged and standard deviation of maximum daily wind speeds.

Figure 7 shows the probability distribution of exceedance estimated from observation for each season. Observation of these figures clearly reflects the seasonal beaviour of wind speeds. It is observed that larger speeds are observed during winter, Fig. 7d, with maximum speed values over $25m/s$ and probabilities of exceedance for $20m/s$ about 2%. Note that the maximum wind speed occuring during spring, Figure 7a, and summer, Fig. 7b, is below this value, which is also reached during autumn but with a significantly lower probability. A simple observation of the falling slope for wind speeds larger than the modal value for each season reveals a decrease of wind speed from winter to summer, with similar intermediate values during spring and autumn.

4 Extreme value analysis

A traditional extreme value model used in wind speed studies is the Gumbel, or Ficher-Tippett I, distribution. It can be shown that this distribution is a special case of the generalised extreme value and the generalised Pareto distributions, which have been extensively applied during recent years in extreme value statistics. However, most researchers have used the Gumbel distribution for modelling extreme wind speeds, mainly for temperate latitudes [5]. The daily maximum wind speed data set observed at Las Palmas Port has been fitted to various extreme value distributions commonly used in practice. The best results have been obtained for the Gumbel distribution.

The two parameters Gumbel probability density function is given by

$$p(x) = \frac{1}{b} \exp\left(-\frac{x-a}{b}\right) \exp\left[-\exp\left(-\frac{x-a}{b}\right)\right] \qquad (1)$$

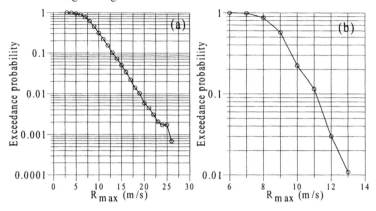

Figure 5: Probability of exceedance for the whole data set (a) and the mean year (b).

where a and b are the location and scale parameters, respectively. The corresponding distribution function takes the following expression

$$P(x) = \exp\left[-\exp\left(-\frac{x-a}{b}\right)\right] \qquad (2)$$

Taking natural logarithms twice and after some algebraic manipulations, the Gumbel distribution adopts the form of an straight line,

$$y = \ln\left(-\ln\left(P(x)\right)\right) = -\frac{1}{b}x + \frac{a}{b} = \hat{b}x + \hat{a} \qquad (3)$$

Gumbel [3] sugessted a simple and robust procedure for extreme value analysis that can be summarised as follows [4]. Given a set of N data values which represent, (say the annual largest values of the hourly mean wind speed at a particular site, the values are ranked in ascending order of size, i.e. the smallets is accorded rank $m = 1$, and the largest rank $m = N$. Each of the wind speed values is plotted versus the variable y derived from its rank

$$y = \ln\left(-\ln\left(P(x)\right)\right) = \ln\left(-\ln\left(\frac{m}{N+1}\right)\right) \qquad (4)$$

Then, a straight line is fitted to the plot, from which the slope and the intercept on the windspeed axis are obtained. Note that the values of $m/(N+1)$ are identified with the probability of the corresponding wind speed not being exceeded in one year.

Figure 8 shows the probability distributions of daily maximum wind speeds for the whole data set (a) the mean year (b) and the seasons, spring (c), summer (d), autumn (e) and winter (f), fitted to the Gumbel distribution by means of the above procedure. The parameters model have estimated by the least squares method and are shown in the right lower side of each picture jointly with the correlation coefficient between the observations and the model. It can be observed that, in general, the Gumbel distribution produces an adequate fit to empirical observations. Both, the whole data set and the mean year values, as well as each of the seasons reveals a good agreement with the Gumbel distribution.

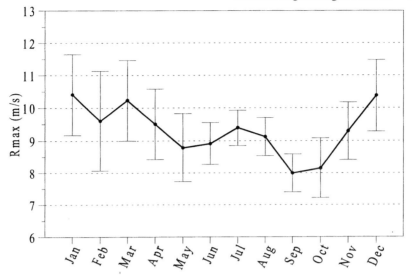

Figure 6: Monthly average of wind speed and standard deviation.

It is interesting to note that most important deviations are observed during summer and winter. In the latter case, notable deviations are observed for high wind speeds, probably due to storm invasions from the Northwest North Atlantic. This deviations are clearly reflected in the statistical behaviour of the whole data set.

5 Time-frequency analysis

Classical spectral analysis can not be applied for the analysis of time series spanning over very large periods because of the basic hypothesis of stationarity is not fulfilled. However, time-frequency methods of signal analysis make possible the description of a nonstationary signal in terms of its frequency composition as a function of time. One of the most commonly used time-frequency methods in time series analysis during the last decade is the Wavelet Transform (WT) analysis.

The WT can be considered as the correlation between the analysed time series, $x(t)$, and a set of functions called wavelets. Each wavelet, also called daughter wavelet, is generated by scaling and translating one initial wavelet, called mother wavelet, ψ. Scaling implies a dilation or compression of the mother wavelet and translation implies its shifting in the time domain. The Continuous Wavelet Transform for a real signal is given by

$$W_{a,b} = \frac{1}{\sqrt{|a|}} \int_{-\infty}^{\infty} x(t)\psi^* \left(\frac{t-b}{a} \right) dt \tag{5}$$

where $\psi^*(t)$ denotes the complex conjugate of the mother wavelet and a and b are the dilation and translation parameters, respectively. The scale parameter is proportional

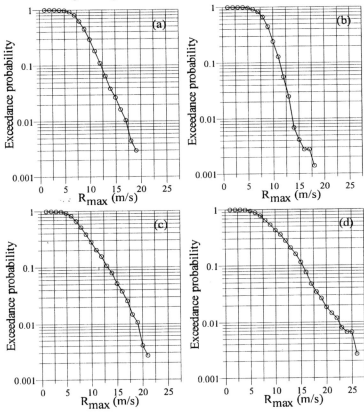

Figure 7: Distribution of exceedance of maximum daily wind speeds for seasons, (a) Spring, (b) Summer, (c) Autumn, (d) Winter.

to the reciprocal of frequency and the translation parameter stands for time. A detailed description of wavelet transform analysis can be found in a large number of review papers and books, e.g. [6] [7].

The wavelet spectrum for a segment of the maximum daily wind speed time series is presented in Figure 9. The continuous wavelet transform has been evaluated by using the well-known morlet wavelet. Visual inspection of the wavelet spectrum reveals the nonstationary character of the process, with its frequency composition varying with time. It can be observed the persistence of the semi-annual and seasonal periods, while bi-monthly, monthly, bi-weekly and weekly periodicities present a large intermittency which increases with the frequency.

6 Discussion and conclusion

The knowledge of wind climate, including mean windspeeds and directions throughout the year, seasonal variations, and extreme winds that may occur at the structure site, results vital for the adequate design and for the operational purposes in harbours.

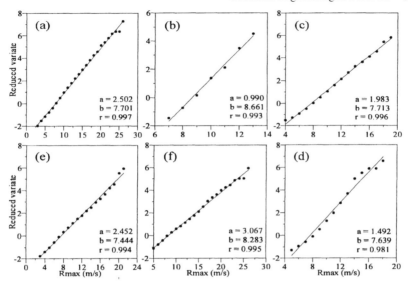

Figure 8: Fit to Gumbel probability distribution of maximum daily wind speed for the whole period (1984-1994), annual average and seasons.

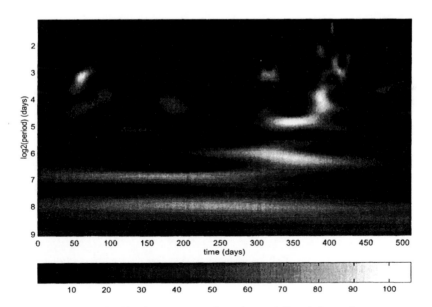

Figure 9: Wavelet spectrum of maximum daily wind speeds.

Long-term statistical characteristics of daily maximum wind speed observations recorded at Las Palmas Port, Canary islands, during a period of 10 years have been examined. Due to their geographical location the Canary archipelago is under the direct influence of the prevailing trade winds during the main part of the year. It has been observed that the predominant direction of winds reaching the port is the sector NW-NE, accounting for more than the 70% of the observations, reflecting the pre-vailing character of the trade winds, particularly during summer. In relation to wind speeds, it has been recealed the existence of an apparent annual periodicity with the calmest period spanning from the latter summer to the early autumn, while the windi-est season is the winter. In average, maximum daily wind speed is about $13m/s$ with a probability of being exceeded close to 1%.

Maximum daily wind speed long-term statistical behaviour, as well as annual aver-age and seasonal values, are adequately characterised by means of the two-parameter Gumbel distribution. Furthermore, time-frequency analysis of the maximum daily wind speeds at Las Palmas Port, by using the continuous wavelet transform reveals the nonstationary character of this physical process, and the significant persistence of semi-annual and seasonal variabilities, while smaller periodicities present a substan-tially intermittent character.

While interesting results on the long-term climate at Las Palmas Port have been obtained, it should be desireable the use of larger time series and with smaller sam-pling period, hourly or less, to reduce the uncertainty on the probability of occurrence of extreme events, as well as small time scale effects.

Acknowledgements

The author would like to thank Professor Carlos Brebbia his offer to present this study as an invited paper. This research has been undertaken within project VETERANO, which was financed by the Spanish Ministry of Science and Technology under contract No REN2000-1503-C02-02. The author also wish to thank Jos Miguel Pintado, Port Authority of Las Palmas, for providing the data used in this study.

References

[1] Simiu, E., & R.H. Scanlan. *Wind Effects on Structures: An Introduction to Wind Engineering*, Wiley: New York, 1978.

[2] Fossen, T.I. *Guidance and Control of Ocean Vehicles*, John Wiley & Sons: Chichester, 1999.

[3] Gumbel, E.J. *Statistics of Extremes*, Columbia University Press, 1958.

[4] Harris, R.I. Gumbel re-visited - a new look at extreme value statistics applied to wind speeds. *J. of Wind Engineering and Industrial Aerodynamics*, **59**, pp. 1-22, 1996.

[5] Brabson, B.B. & Palutikof, J.P. Tests of the Generalized Pareto Distribution for predicting extreme wind speeds. *J. of Applied Meteorology*, **39**, pp. 1627-1640, 2000.

[6] Torrence, C. & Compo, G.P. A practical guide to wavelet analysis. *Bulletin of the American Meteorological Society*, **79**, pp. 61-78, 1998.

[7] Percival, D.B. & Walden, A.Y. *Wavelet Methods for Time Series Analysis*, Cam-bridge University Press, 2000.

Section 4
Construction and design
of ports

Klaipeda Port entrance rehabilitation project

C. M. Steenberg[1] & J. Kriauciuniene[2]
[1]Training and Ports Division, Danish Maritime Institute, Denmark.
[2] Lithuanian Energy Institute, Lithuania.

Abstract

The Klaipeda Seaport is located on the eastern coast of the Baltic Sea inside the Klaipeda Strait, which joins the sea with the Kursiu Lagoon. Recently the Klaipeda Port Entrance Rehabilitation Project has been carried into effect including dredging of the navigational channel to cater for increasing ship sizes and extensions of the existing breakwater protecting the port from waves from the Baltic Sea. The abrupt change in bathymetry and the extension of the breakwaters affect both wave propagation and current conditions in the entrance. Considering this fact together with the hydrological correlation between the Kursiu Lagoon and the Baltic Sea make the Klaipeda Seaport complex when considering wave and current conditions. To determine the wave and current conditions in the final layout of the port entrance the hydrodynamic model MIKE21 was used for numerical simulations. The environmental data were subsequently implemented in the Danish Maritime Institute real-time simulator for the purpose of evaluating the new entrance layout and provide training of the pilots under the changed environmental and structural conditions.

1 Introduction

Klaipeda State Seaport is an ice-free port in the Eastern coast of the Baltic Sea. The port is located in the narrow Strait that joins the Baltic Sea with the Kursiu lagoon.

The present project has been carried out as a part of the Klaipeda Port Entrance Rehabilitation Project funded/sponsored by the World Bank, which aims at reducing the downtime due to inclement weather as well as improving the safety of navigation. These objectives are achieved by extending the outer breakwaters while reducing the width of the entrance to 150m. Furthermore excavation of the existing entrance channel has been carried out to a depth of 14.5m.

Investigation of navigational safety, access channels, turning basins, position of buoys and marks, tug requirement and the estimation of the environmental conditions are important issues, which require realistic modelling of

- Behaviour of representative vessel
- Environmental Conditions
- Harbour Layout

With extension of the existing breakwaters and dredging of the entrance channel, changes in the Klaipeda Strait flow structure, the wave pattern, sediment processes, and the water exchange between Kursiu Lagoon and the Baltic Sea, are expected in the port. It is important to investigate these activities as dredging increases the permeability of Strait while the extension of the breakwaters has a reverse effect. However, these hydrodynamic changes will along with the structural changes have an effect on the navigational safety.

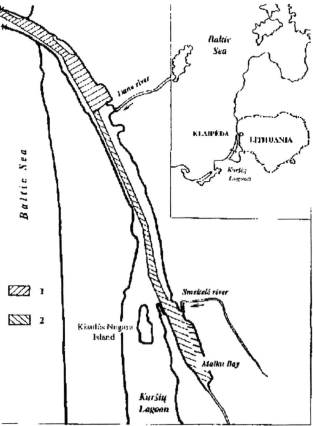

Figure 1: Geographical location of Klaipeda Strait

At the premises of Danish Maritime Institute real-time simulations were carried out in the full-mission simulator partly to evaluate the future harbour layout regarding navigation safety and partly to familiarise with the new layout and the limiting conditions by training of the pilots. The evaluation included all phases of maritime operations including approaching and departure, tug boat assistance, manoeuvring and docking within the port areas. Wind, waves and currents had to be included in the simulations to reproduce realistic physical conditions, as they would exist in real life. Numerical modelling of current and waves were carried out at the Lithuanian energy Institute by use of the hydrodynamic model MIKE21.

2 Environmental conditions

The water level differences between the Baltic Sea and the Kursiu Lagoon characterize the quantity and direction of discharge along Klaipeda Strait (positive water level difference – current flows from Kursiu Lagoon to the Baltic Sea, negative – from the Baltic Sea to Kursiu Lagoon). During the year the currents of salt water can be noticed about 53 times and last for 74 days. Mostly it lasts for 1 day, and very rarely for 6 days. In the remaining days of the year water flows from Kursiu Lagoon into the Baltic Sea.

In Klaipeda Strait two different flow regimes can be observed. During the floods the flow is directed from the Lagoon to the Baltic Sea. When the difference of the levels of the Kursiu Lagoon and the Baltic Sea is 0,8 m, the discharge is 3250 m³/s. The maximum permeability of Klaipeda Strait reaches 5000 m³/s. Then the difference of levels is 1 – 1,4 m and the average flow velocity in the canal is 1,2 m/s. Such velocities can be noticed very rarely, approximately once per 70 years. Mostly the discharge in the Strait is 1300 m³/s, and then the difference of levels is 15 cm. When the flow is directed to the Lagoon, and the difference of levels is 0.5 – 0.6 m and it flows 3500 m³/s, the average velocities in the canal are 1 m/s. Mostly the observed discharge to the Lagoon is 850 m³/s. Sometimes there is the intervening stream between these regimes of flow. Then in the surface level fresh water flows from the Lagoon and in the bottom level – salt water to the Lagoon. The discharge of such compensations is little and the velocity is up to 0.2 m/s.

The wave pattern in the Baltic Sea is recognised by relatively short waves due to the rather limited free fetch.. The waves are sometimes heard mentioned as "crab waves". Due to the orientation of the port, the dominating wind and wave conditions comes from westerly directions.

2.1 Modelling cases of currents and waves in Klaipeda Port entrance

The difference of the levels between the Baltic Sea and the Kursiu Lagoon determines the water exchange through the Klaipeda Strait. The directions and velocities of current in Klaipeda Strait depend on the weather conditions. The analysis of Klaipeda meteorological observations of the last 6 years showed the prevailing stormy wind direction and velocity meanings, which characterize the wave and current processes in Baltic nearshore. It was determined that the sector of southwest winds clearly differs among strong winds: SW winds make 23.8%, W —14,9%, SSW —11,2%, S and WSW —10,8 % each. So, according to the prevailing wind directions, the modelling of currents and waves was done for the following cases:

- N, S and SW wind directions up to 20 m/s, current of Klaipeda Strait flows from Kursiu Lagoon to the Baltic Sea.
- WSW wind directions up to 20 m/s, current of Klaipeda Strait flows to the Baltic Sea or in the opposite direction.
- W and NW wind directions up to 20 m/s, current of Klaipeda Strait flows from the Baltic Sea to Kursiu Lagoon.
- High water level in Kursiu Lagoon (flood), small wind speed, big current of Klaipeda Strait flows from Kursiu Lagoon to the Baltic Sea.

2.2 Hydrodynamic modeling

MIKE21's Hydrodynamic module (MIK21HD) was used to establish hydrodynamic conditions within the study area under pre and post harbour construction stages.

The area modelled was 8.2km x 11.8 km in extent including 9 km of the Klaipeda Strait and was set up on a grid with a grid spacing of 20 m in both spatial directions.

The model boundary conditions were established through a detailed analysis of water level difference between the Baltic Sea and the Kursiu Lagoon. The model was validated for wind driven flows using near-shore current and water level measurements.

The numerical model applied for the modelling of the current field at the entrance of the Klaipėda State Seaport was the Hydrodynamic Module of DHI-Water and Environment's MIKE21 numerical model (MIKE21HD). This module simulates unsteady two-dimensional flows in one-layer (vertically homogeneous) fluids. MIKE 21 HD makes use of Alternating Direction Implicit (ADI) finite difference scheme (MIKE 21 Hydrodynamic Module. 1998.) to integrate the equations for mass and momentum conservation in the space-time domain. Water levels and currents are calculated for every grid point with consideration of bathymetry, bed roughness, wind direction and boundary conditions.

The model requires the following input:

- A digitised bathymetry (A grid spacing of $\Delta x = \Delta y = 20m$ was applied)
- Boundary data
- Wind data
- Information on the bed resistance and eddy viscosity (used as calibration parameters)

The model was calibrated against current data measured off the port entrance and measurements of water level data measured in the Baltic Sea and in the Kursiu Lagoon.

The output from the numerical model is current fields defined by speed and direction at every grid point in the bathymetry at every time step.

2.3 Results of hydrodynamic modelling

The current velocities and directions for the existing and final layout of the port were compared for all tested wind directions.

The reconstruction of Klaipeda Port Entrance will result in alternations of flow structure of the Baltic Sea and Klaipeda Strait Aquatorium. The biggest changes of current speed would be induced by wind of NW (increase of 23%) and SW directions (increase of 26%). The current speeds before and after reconstruction would be similar when wind directions are W and S. The changes of current directions would be induced by wind of SW directions.

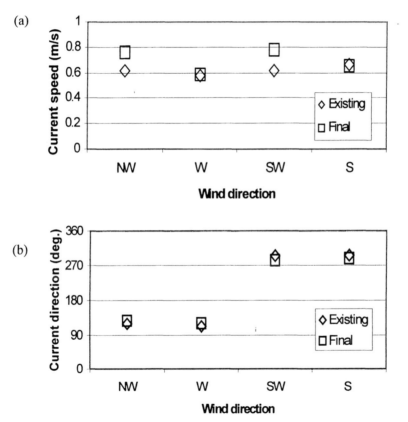

Figure 2: Current speed (a) and current direction (b) for tested wind direction for existing and final port layout.

2.4 Nearshore wave modelling

The offshore wave climate in the study area is characterized by short waves (crab waves) with mean wave periods 6s to 8s. The wave climate outside the port, approximately in the centre of the entrance channel is well established from available measurements/recordings. These data were used for calibration of the model.

The wave propagation modelling was carried out from offshore to establish the spatial variation of the wave climate close to the port entrance. For this purpose an irregular directional wave module within the MIKE21 (NSW – Near Spectral Wave) was used. The model computations were verified against simultaneous wave measurements just outside the port entrance. Through analysis of offshore wave data, wave heights for every tested wind speed and direction were determined and simulated through MIKE21 NSW model set-up to derive the wave conditions to be used in the simulator. The areas modelled were approximately 6 km x 5 km in extent and were set up on a grid with a grid spacing of 20 m in the x-direction and 80 m in the y-direction. The output from the numerical model is a wave climate defined by wave height, period, and direction at every grid point in the bathymetry.

2.5 Results of nearshore wave modelling

Significant wave heights, mean periods, and wave directions for the existing and final layout of the port were compared for all tested wind directions in the calibration point. The extension of the breakwaters at the entrance will result in some changes in the wave pattern around the entrance. Changes of wave height in the calibration point would be induced by wind from W and NW (increase of 3%). The wave heights before and after reconstruction would be similar when wind directions are SW and S.

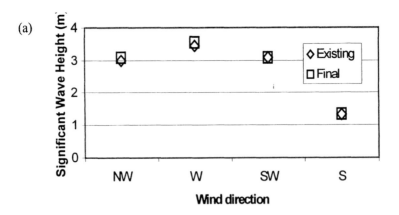

(b)

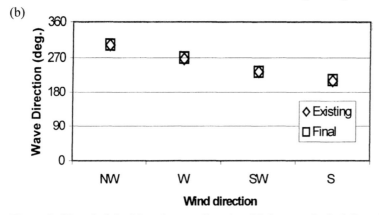

Figure 3: Wave height (a) and wave direction (b) for tested wind direction for existing and final port layout.

3 Real-time simulations

The use of real-time ship manoeuvring simulators provides a realistic tool for verification of navigational safety under specific environmental conditions and structural layout, preventing unexpected port operation problems in the future.

The simulations were carried out by the Klaipeda pilots at DMI's full mission simulator, which have a 360 deg. visual view. The bridge is a full version of a real bridge, with radars, electronic sea charts etc. Captains with more than 25 years of experience with the chosen ship types were conducting the training of the Klaipeda Pilots.

The objective was to evaluate the port entrance with emphasis on the width of the entrance including the hydrodynamic changes in flow structure and wave pattern. Waves were included in simulations by defining several wave areas in which the random nature of wave height and period was modelled by a PM spectrum with no directional spreading. The simulations used constant wind velocity and wind direction. The current was defined by its speed and direction and constant in time. The environmental conditions represented the limiting conditions for the port.

5 ships of different type and sizes were used in the simulations. See Table 1. The 35.000 DWT Tanker represents the traffic that the Klaipeda State Seaport already receives today together with the Ro-Ro, which is arriving and departing on daily basis, while the 60.000 DWT Tanker represents the traffic the port expects to receive in the future. These ships were navigated in and out of the entrance as well as berthing at the NAFTOS Terminals and at the ferry terminal.

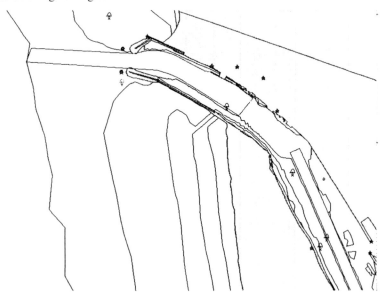

Figure 4: Buoys, marks, and depth contours for the proposed final layout of the entrance of the port.

Table 1: Main Particulars of Ship Models.

Ship Number	Ship Type/Loading Condition	Lpp (m)	Beam (m)	Draught Fore/Aft (m)	Displacement (m³)	Shaft Power (kW)
3079	Tanker/Loaded	173.0	27.5	10.5/10.5	38364	5280
3080	Tanker/Ballasted	173.0	27.5	5.0/7.0	20781	5280
3189	Tanker/Loaded	206.0	36.0	12.5/12.5	75100	9500
3192	Tanker/Ballasted	206.0	36.0	6.5/8.0	43000	9500
3207	Ro-Ro/Loaded	173.0	26.0	6.14/6.86	19636	4x2650

Tugs were provided from the beginning of the entrance channel and until berthing and were connected to the ship either as pull tugs or as push tugs as recommended by the pilots.

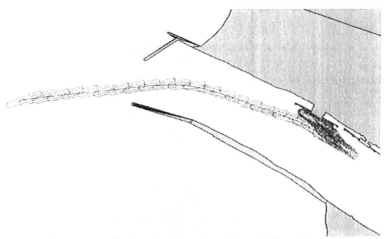

Figure 5: Track plot of on run from the real time simulations.

3.1 Recommendations

During the simulations it became clear that in order to support navigation on arrival it was recommended to establish a second leading light as shown in Figure 3.1.

To support navigation on departure with deep draught ships it was recommended to place 2 light buoys to mark the new 14.5 meter curve outside the harbour, as shown on above mentioned chart.

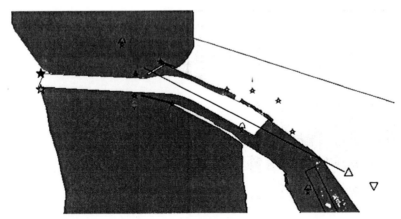

Figure 6: Suggested positions of additional light buoys and leading light marked by stars and triangles, respectively.

For handling of the bigger ships expected to arrive in the "new port" better tugs are recommended, preferable strong tugs of tractor type.

As the port can expect larger ships in the future it is important to ensure that the pilots receive the necessary training on a regular basis. Thus ensuring that they at all times have the necessary skills and experience in handling the additional challenges of a large vessel. Such training can be provided in many manners, e.g. by establishing a part-task simulator within the realm of the port effectively enabling the port to provide regular training but also to investigate the possibility of handling other vessels requiring special needs and handling skills.

Generally, it can be concluded that in the final layout, investigated in the study, the navigational conditions are fully acceptable considering the limiting environmental conditions.

4 Conclusions

A fairly extensive training program has been carried out in relation to familiarize the local pilots with the new harbour layout. Furthermore the navigational safety has be verified and evaluated with minor recommendations to follow.

References

[1] Klaipeda Port Entrance Rehabilitation Project – Evaluation of the New Port Entrance and Training of the Pilots, Phase 1 and 2, 2001
[2] Gailiusis, B., Kovalenkoviene, M. & Kriauciuniene, J., The Hydrological Problems caused by the Development of Klaipeda Seaport, Pp. 466-475

The development of a breakwater design at Caleta La Mision Port, Argentina

L. A. Mohammad & O. J. Jensen
COWI A/S, Lyngby, Denmark.

Abstract

The new generation of Concrete Armouring Units, CORE-LOC[TM], as a single layer armour has been in use for less than a decade with only a handful of breakwaters built. CORE-LOCs have been subjected by researchers and designers to stability tests. There are however still many possibilities for the use of CORE-LOCs in design to be covered and verified by physical modelling.

This work deals with design of the Caleta La Mision Breakwater, Argentina, and presents the conclusions from the design process supported by extensive physical model testing in both wave flume and basin for verification and optimisation. CORE-LOC units have been employed in armouring the breakwater in many different arrangements and combinations. The breakwater is very exposed with a design wave of, Hs = 7.5 m, situated on a reef at level 0.0 m and slightly above. The site has about 9.0 m tidal range, so the breakwater toe is dry at low tide.

The paper deals with the design of the front face, special toe hold blocks, overtopping and rear side stability as well as special roundhead features. On the reclamation behind the structure special trench for drainage of overtopping water was introduced as special structural element.

1 Introduction

Port Caleta La Mision, Rio Grande, is a new port development project in the Province of Tierra del Fuego. The plan is to construct new marine infrastructure on the east coast of Tierra del Fuego, to meet the future cargo transport needs as well as for supporting industrial development in the province having offshore natural gas resources.

The original project, designed by other consultants, includes a piled trestle to the offshore berth that was to be protected by a berm breakwater. Construction of this project commenced in April 1998. Work at the site of the port was suspended in Sept 1999 due to several problems including difficulties with the yield of large rocks in the quarry and concerns raised by a new study that indicated an increase in the design wave height at the port from 6.0 to 7.5 m. At the time the work was suspended the first 600 m of an approximately 1600 m access trestle had been completed and a berm breakwater progressed approximately 100 m with placement of approximately 6000 m^3 of armour stones.

2 Hydrographic and Topographic Conditions

Caleta La Mision is going to be one of the rare ports that has a tidal fluctuation of more than 9.0 m, where LLW is -0.2 m and HHW is +9.2 m. This, together with frequent high wind and high waves presents a great challenge to establish a port terminal.

The wave climate for the project was established by another consultant. At the beginning of the project a preliminary assessment of existing data was made, concluding that the 50 year Return Period significant wave height was, H_s= 6.0 m. This formed the basis of the initial design of the port and its structures. Further analysis based on recent wave measurements changed the assessment to a design wave height of, H_s = 7.5 m. This change has drastically altered the design concept of the breakwater. Wave analysis also revealed that the principal approach directions for the waves are NNE, NE and ENE.

Joint statistical analysis of tidal levels and wave heights were carried out to assess the crest elevation of the breakwater, CE, which can be expressed as:

$$CE = WL + \alpha \Box H_s$$

where WL is the sum for the tidal level and increases associated with storm surge and sea level rise due to global warming. The coefficient α $\Box$will be in the order of 1.5 for rubble mound breakwaters. The joint probability is shown in Fig.(1). From which it appears that for, P= 3 hours/ 50 years (0.00068%), the necessary crest elevation is +19.0 m.

The location and the orientation of the breakwater have been dictated by the natural topography of the area, as shown in Fig.(2), where the reef has a protrusion of about 500 m long. This has definitely provided an excellent opportunity to take advantage of this solid and shallow foundation to the breakwater.

3 Initial Design - Berm Breakwater

A berm breakwater concept was chosen by another consultant based upon that the required stones would be available. A physical hydraulic study was also conducted to finalise the breakwater design for a design wave height of, H_s = 6.0 m. The result was a berm breakwater with a berm width of 30 m, crest elevation

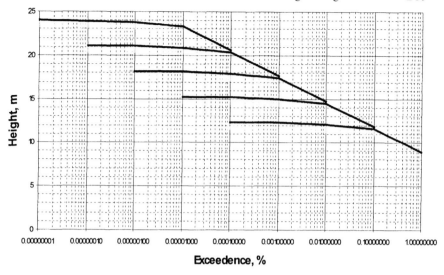

Figure 1: Joint probability of wave heights and water levels

of +17.0 m at the NRH (Northern Round Head) to +14.0 m at SRH(Southern Round Head), armoured with 0.6-5.0 t stones. The increase in the design wave height, i.e. H_s = 7.5 m, means that it would be necessary to increase significantly the stone size in the northern sector and on the roundheads. Preliminary assessments indicated that stones with approximately twice the weight would be required. The available quarry, on the other hand, proved to yield significantly less large stones. Thus an alternative solution had to be developed.

4 New Design- CAU (CORE-LOC™) Breakwater

Two alternative designs were found feasible among many alternative ideas and designs. Both are using Concrete Armouring Units (CAU). One (Type A) is with a relatively higher crest than the other (Type B). Both are shown in Fig.(3). This figure is showing sections from the northern sector of the breakwater, i.e. the most exposed sector. Then, Type (BA) as shown also in Fig.(3), was developed from the first two types to be the final section.

The location of the port and that of the breakwater, as shown in Fig.(2),has already been delineated by the reef configuration, because placing the breakwater on the reef provides the most feasible and cheapest solution. The alternative, i.e. extending the breakwater further north down the steep bed leading to the deep water, represents many problems and would be very costly. But even by placing the breakwater entirely on the reef, the total height of the breakwater will be around 19.0 m.   This height still allows for a sizeable overtopping discharge. This will be collected in the drainage area behind the breakwater, allowing only minimal spill to reach the reclamation area except in the most sever conditions happening very rarely.

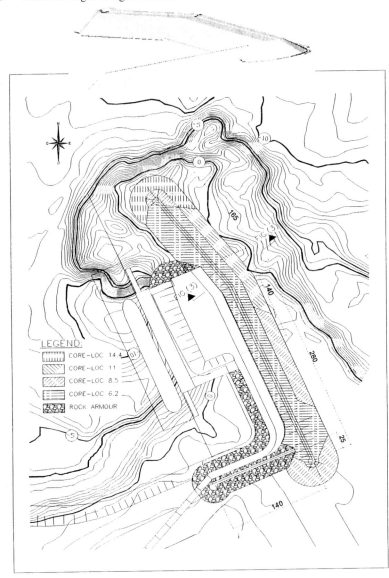

Figure 2: Bathymetry, Layout, Armour distribution and 3D CAD model

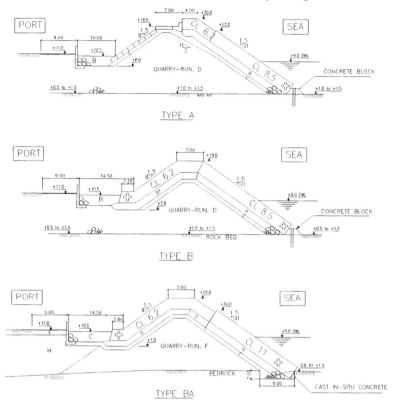

Figure 3: Type A, B and BA profiles

5 2D Flume Model Tests

A model, at a linear scale of 1:43.2, was used to study the alternatives. Tests were started with Type B, using CORE-LOC size of 8.5 m³ to armour the front side   (K_D = 13.5) and of 6.2 m³ for the crest and the rear side. A side slope of 1:1.5 was selected to achieve a reduction of about 10% in armour weight. Precast concrete toe blocks were used to hold the armour layer in place. These toe blocks are to be keyed to each other and fixed into the bedrock. The first two rows of the CORE-LOCs behind the toe blocks were placed randomly without further measures to ensure fixity between the toe blocks and the CORE-LOCs. Random placement is normally the recommended practice when the CORE-LOCs are to be placed upon a toe protection constructed of stones.

The main armour was adequately   stable as it survived several design conditions, however settlement of the armour layer occurred during the tests creating small openings in the armour layer and minor settlement in the crest. These settlements are judged to be slightly over the normal settlement experienced with having the toe CORE-LOC units embedded in the toe protection stones.

Further adjustment to the design section were also carried out with respect to the crest elevation and the width and stone sizes of the drainage area behind the breakwater.

The tests were run at water levels +0.0, +4.8, +9.0 and +10.0 m CD, with wave heights ranging from, H_s= 4.7 to 8.3 m corresponding to Return Periods from 2 to over 100 years.

The second series of flume tests was conducted on Type A, as shown in Fig.(5), with a crown wall and CORE-LOCs of sizes 8.5m³ and 6.2m³ armour on the front side and revetment blocks on the rear side. Toe blocks were also employed with the lowest two rows of CORE-LOCs placed in a patterned manner, i.e. canon method, see Turk and Melby [1]. This type of toe units placement requires in reality good working conditions and thorough inspection, which is the case at the present site where nearly the entire breakwater is above water level at low tide. The main armour was adequately stable during the tests and the armour layer settlement was significantly smaller than for Type B.

The tests were run at water levels +9.0 and +10.0 m CD with wave heights ranging from 4.7 to 8.2 m, which corresponds to return periods from 2 to over 100 years.

Based on the above stability results for Types A and B, and on the measured overtopping discharges, as given in Fig.(4), a third alternative section was developed, Type BA, which is a combination of the first two types. The stone size for the drainage trench behind the breakwater will be in the range 1.0-2.1 ton to avoid excessive erosion during design conditions. Type BA was used to construct the 3D physical model, with the replacement of the 8.5m³ with 11.0m³ CORE-LOCs at the northern sector of the breakwater.

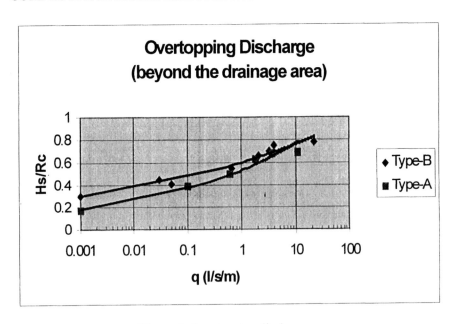

Figure 4: Overtopping discharge

Figure 5: 2D Physical model showing Type A with toe blocks

6 3D Physical Model Tests

A model, at a linear scale of 1:58 as shown in Fig.(6), was set up to test, develop and evaluate the performance of the breakwater with respect to wave agitation inside the harbour and along the trestle, movements of the moored ships at the berths and the stability of the two breakwater roundheads, part of the northern trunk, the spur breakwater and the revetment of the reclamation area.

Stability tests were carried out with a design water level of +9.0 m CD, and wave heights ranging from, H_s= 5.0 to 8.5 m, corresponding to Return Periods of 4 to over 100 years, approaching from two principle directions, NE and ENE.

A different toe arrangement than the toe block used in the 2D flume tests, was employed in the 3D model having the lowest row of the CORE-LOCs founded in a trench, as shown in Fig.(3) of Type BA. This is basically carried out to explore the possibility of both options. CORE-LOC toe units were placed by the canon method at the trunk section, and as this method cannot be employed at the roundheads, so CORE-LOCs were placed there at random, all the 14.4m^3 units at the NRH and the 8.5m^3 units at the SRH.

- The first stability test series was conducted by employing 11m^3 CORE-LOC to armour the NRH (with K_D = 10.6) and 6.2m^3 for the SRH (with K_D = 12.8 for H_s = 6.6 m at the SRH). Excessive settlement was observed on the sea side face at the transition zone from the trunk to NRH, followed by loss of interlocking between the CORE-LOC units and complete displacement of some units at the design wave height, i.e. H_s = 7.5m. There were very few rocking units at the water level and at the toe. The SRH however was adequately stable with minor settlement to the armour layer. The toe units were placed randomly at the roundheads and by the canon method at the trunk. All toe units were not fixed firmly in place during this stability tests series.

- The second tests series was then planned and performed by using 14.4 m^3 CORE-LOC at the NRH, which is 1.3 times heavier than the 11m^3 unit and with K_D = 8.1, but still with no fixing to the toe units. Further the transition from the trunk armour of 11m^3 units to the NRH armour of 14.4m^3 units being shifted back a distance of 25m, i.e. to move this critical transition away form the failure region of the previous test series. The use of smaller stone sizes than what is recommended under the CORE-LOCs at the crest and the rearside has been verified to be acceptable with no effects have been   shown   on   the   stability   of   the   CORE-LOCs.

The stability of the $14.4m^3$ CORE-LOCs was not any better than that of the $11m^3$ units. Large settlements were encountered at the design wave height, i.e. $H_s = 7.5m$, leading to complete displacement of the armour units at a wave height of $H_s = 8.5m$. The failure took place exactly at the same zone. No other weak points have been observed with all the transition zones from one CORE-LOC size to another being very stable, and further there were no rocking units. This was very closely watched to ensure the safety of the CORE-LOC units against breakage as the $14.4m^3$ size has never been used before, and there is always the concern of being fragile to breakage if it become too large, similarly Tetrapods and Dolosse, van der Meer [2]. The conclusion reached is that the cause of the excessive settlements of the armour layer is due to the movement of the toe units. Therefore a stable armour layer cannot be achieved without fixing firmly the toe units and preventing or limiting their ability to move.

- The third tests series used exactly the same armour as in the second test series, but fixing of the toe units by mortar. As a result, minor settlements were observed with an adequately stable armour layer. This confirms the conclusion of the second stability tests series, namely that the critical part of the breakwater is the toe, and the use of in- situ concrete to fix the toe units is a necessity in order to achieve a stable roundhead and adjacent trunk section.

Figure 6: 3D physical model showing the northern round head and trunk with trenched toe

7 Conclusions

- CORE-LOC's interlocking, longitudinally/diagonally between two consecutive sizes and vertically between consecutive sizes or even at a difference of two sizes, proved to be good with no sign of weakness.

- It is generally an accepted practice at sections not considered to be critical to use filter/underlayer stones corresponding to one size up/down of the CORE-LOC armouring units. This practice has been extended by using stone sizes corresponding to two sizes down of the CORE-LOC. But in areas which are not regularly exposed to high hydraulic loading, i.e. the crest and the rear side of the breakwater.

- Placement of CORE-LOC toe units in a patterned (canon) method has been confirmed as being more stable than the random placement. This is not only true for the toe units but also extended for the whole of the armour layer as it will suffer much less settlement, specially if the CORE-LOC toe units are placed on bedrock. Therefore CORE-LOC toe units have to be restrained from movement (nesting movement and rocking) in order to minimise armour settlement and eventual failure. This is normally achieved if the units are embedded in a rock toe protection, but if they are resting on bedrock in a high exposed level, then fixing firmly in place is required by means of grouting. With random placement of CORE-LOC toe units, the amount of grouting material needed will be more than what is needed for the canon placed units.

- Longitudinal transition from one CORE-LOC size to another should preferably be kept at some distance away from the roundhead.

- Wave forces acting on breakwater armour units has been studied before by many researchers but their findings never interpreted into a useful design guidelines. Most of them however, have a common understanding that the hydraulic loading is concentrated at and around the water level, i.e. WL $\pm$ H_s. This finding has been widely used in the introduction of a berm at an appropriate depth below the water level. The main armour is used down to the berm, and there after smaller stones are employed for the berm and downwards. Another result of this understanding is the use of reduced armour size a region strating at a distance above the water level. The reduction was in the present case in the order of 40% by weight. In Ref.[3] are presented a number of examples of breakwaters where the same principle is used with the heavy armour units used only where they are really needed.

References

[1] Turk,G.F. and Melby, J.A."CORE-LOC^{TM} Concrete Armour Units: Technical Guidelines", US Army Corps of Engineers, Miscellaneous paper CHL-97-6, 1997.

[2] van der Meer, J.W."Design of concrete armour layers", Proc. of Int. Conf. Coastal Structures'99, Santander/Spain/7-10 June1999.

[3] Jensen, O.Juul, "A Monograph on Rubble Mound Breakwaters" Danish Hydraulic Institute, 1984.

Section 5
Marine engineering works

Spreadsheet modeling of optimum maintenance strategy for marine machinery in wear-out phase subject to distance between ports as one of the maintenance constraints

K. B. Artana[1], K. Ishida[2]

[1]*Graduate student, Kobe University of Mercantile Marine, Japan*
[2]*Department of Electro Mechanical and Energy Engineering,*
Kobe University of Mercantile Marine, Japan

Abstract

This paper addresses a method in determining the optimum maintenance schedule for components in wear-out phase. The optimum interval between maintenance for a certain component is optimized based upon the minimum total cost (the objective function) resulted by decision on either that component needs to be replaced by a new one or only requires a preventive maintenance action. That decision is determined by verifying the reliability and availability index of that component at each maintenance time. Premium Solver Platform (PSP) is utilized to model the optimization problem. The model takes a finite and equal interval between maintenance, and the increase of operation cost and maintenance cost due to deterioration of components is taken into account. An analysis on a liquid ring primer (LRP) of a bilge system of a ship is taken as the study case. The optimum preventive maintenance schedule is directed to bring into agreement with the decision that has been taken on the ship's general survey schedule.

1 Introduction

The emergence on practical method to set an optimum marine machinery maintenance program is becoming crucial with the trend of many small shipping companies buying second hand ships, doing minimum modification to comply with the modern regulation, and treating the machinery as if they are new ones. As a result, an impressive increase on the operating cost as well as the maintenance cost become apparent.

The optimization of maintenance decision making can be defined as an attempt to resolve the conflicts of a decision situation in such a way that the variables under the control of the decision-maker take their best possible value [1]. One of the controllable variables in the case of machinery maintenance is the interval between maintenance. The optimum value is achieved when the working area of the optimization problem, which is set by constraints, is satisfied. Chiang [2] and Zhang [3] employ MARKOV model to set the reliability and availability as the constraints on determination of the optimal maintenance policy and failure frequency. This approach is only applicable to system or components having constant hazard rate, wherein the probability of making transition between two states remains constant. In the case of wear out components, the reliability of the component hardly achieves the same performance as the condition of the previous maintenance. It is not a wise decision, therefore, to disregard the decreasing performance of the component in the optimization model.

In the case where there is uncertainty in the value of the distribution parameter, a Bayesian approach could be used to formally express the uncertain parameters as proposed by Sheu [4] and Apeland [5]. If the random variable of analyzed data is on hand, the Maximum Likelihood Estimation (MLE) can be used to obtain the distribution parameter, as used in this paper on the liquid ring primer of a bilge system of a ship.

This paper is aimed to provide a practical method in constructing an optimum marine machinery maintenance schedule. Spreadsheet modeling is one of the alternatives, and will be adopted in this paper. This method needs no painful and exhaustive effort to produce programming codes, especially when the problem and optimization model have been well defined [6]. In this paper, non linear programming (NLP) can express the problem, and Generalized Reduced Gradient (GRG) method can be effectively used to work with the NLPs problems, as used by the Premium Solver Platform (PSP).

2 Problem description

Liquid Ring Primer (LRP), as seen in Figure 1, is one of the components that are used in ballast or bilge system of the Ship's machinery system. This kind of pump is very popular in marine work due to their non-contacting working surfaces. They are usually either of single or double lobe construction. It is required to determine an equally spaced maintenance schedule (decision variables) of the LRP of a ship which has voyage from Port A to B, B to C, C to D, and then the same voyage in the way back to port A, as shown in Figure. 2. The trip distances are 3500, 2600 and 2500 miles, respectively for trip A-B, B-C and C-D. The average ship speed is 14.5 knot. It is assumed that maintenance action can only be executed in ports (yard). As the result, an extra penalty cost is charged for additional operation exceeding the optimal interval (see Figure. 3a and 3b).

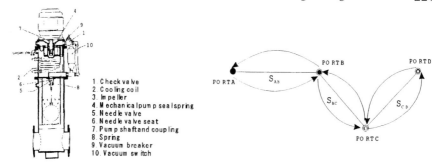

1. Check valve
2. Cooling coil
3. Impeller
4. Mechanical pump seal spring
5. Needle valve
6. Needle valve seat
7. Pump shaft and coupling
8. Spring
9. Vacuum breaker
10. Vacuum switch

Figure 1: Liquid ring primer (LRP)   Figure 2: Ship's route

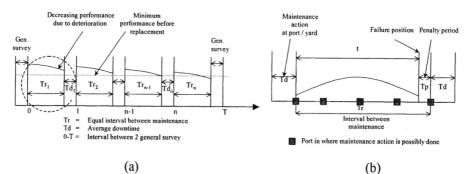

(a)   (b)

Figure 3: Detail of the optimization problem

The determination of minimum total cost (objective function), which covers: maintenance cost, operating cost, downtime cost and penalty cost, will be directed in such a way that the optimum reliability index (RI) and availability index (AI) are not less than the minimum RI of 0.95 and AI of 0.995. The determination of availability and reliability index is based on the maintenance/failure record of the LRP.

It must be carefully thought that after maintenance action the component will not be at the same performance level as the starting point of the previous maintenance. To express this condition, an assumption is taken in that every maintenance action is subject to a 0.5% decrease of reliability index due to deterioration of the components. Furthermore, a replacement decision must be carried out when the component has reached the minimum RI of 0.95.

Hence the global expression of the optimization problem can be expressed in the same way as used by Lasdon [7, 8]: find X=[number of maintenance between two general surveys/two major docking for component i (X_{1i}) (i=1,2,....,m), interval between maintenance (X_{2i}), reliability of each component (X_{3i}), availability of each component (X_{4i})], which minimize $f(X)$, the total resulted cost due to maintenance (Cm), operation (Co), downtime (Cd) and penalty due to extra operation to reach the subsequent port for maintenance (Cp), subject to:

$$\text{Minimum } X_{1i} \leq \text{optimum } X_{1i} \leq \text{Maximum } X_{1i} \qquad (1a)$$

$$\text{Minimum } X_{2i} \leq \text{optimum } X_{2i} \leq \text{Maximum } X_{2i} \tag{1b}$$
$$\text{Minimum } X_{3i} \leq \text{optimum } X_{3i} \leq \text{Maximum } X_{3i} \tag{1c}$$
$$\text{Minimum } X_{4i} \leq \text{optimum } X_{4i} \leq \text{Maximum } X_{4i} \tag{1d}$$
$$X_{1i} = \text{Integer} \tag{1e}$$

The total cost between two general surveys will be a function of the interval between maintenance $(C(Tr))$ and can be written as

$$C(Tr) = Cm + Co + Cd + Cp \tag{2}$$

where Cm, Co, Cd and Cp are the total maintenance cost, total operating cost, total cost as result of downtime and total penalty cost respectively, for all components under evaluation as a function of Tr, between two general surveys.

$$Cm = \sum_{i=1}^{m} n_i \cdot \int_0^{Tr} Cum_i(t)dt \tag{3}$$

$$Co = \sum_{i=1}^{m} (n_i + 1) \cdot \int_0^{Tr} Cuo_i(t)dt \tag{4}$$

n_i = number of maintenance of ith component between two general survey

$Cum_i(t)$ = maintenance cost of ith component per unit time (hour) at time t after the last maintenance

$n_i + 1$ = number of interval between two general surveys

$Cuo_i(t)$ = operating cost of ith component per unit time (hour) at time t after the last maintenance

$$Cd = \sum_{i=1}^{m} n_i \cdot Cud_i \tag{5}$$

Cud_i = cost as a result of downtime of ith component between two general surveys

$$Cp = \sum_{i=1}^{m} Tp_i \cdot Cup_i \tag{6}$$

Tp_i = accumulation of extra operating time of ith component to reach the subsequent port for maintenance within two general surveys

Cup_i = unit penalty cost of ith component

Equation (2) therefore can be written as

$$C(Tr) = \sum_{i=1}^{m} n_i \cdot \int_0^{Tr} Cum_i(t)dt + (n_i + 1) \cdot \int_0^{Tr} Cuo_i(t)dt + n_i \cdot Cud_i + tTp_i \cdot Cup_i \tag{7}$$

Due to component's deterioration, the maintenance cost and operating cost per hour are assumed increase exponentially with use of the form of:

$$Cum_i(t) = A_i - B_i \cdot \exp(-k_i \cdot t) \tag{8}$$
$$Cuo_i(t) = E_i - F_i \cdot \exp(-l_i \cdot t) \tag{9}$$

where $(A-B)$, $(E-F)$ may be interpreted as the maintenance cost and operating cost per unit time (hour) if no deterioration occurs. k, l are growth factor/constant which specifies the shape of the curve. Substituting equation (8) and (9) to (7) gives the complete declaration of the total cost (objective f unction) as below:

$$C(Tr) = \sum_{i=1}^{m} n_i A_i Tr_i + \frac{n_i B_i}{k_i}\left(\exp(-k_i Tr_i)-1\right)+(n_i +1)E_i Tr_i +$$
$$\frac{(n_i +1)F_i}{l_i}\left(\exp(-l_i Tr_i)-1\right)+n_i.Cud_i + Tp_i.Cup_i$$

$$(10)$$

where the output/decision variable n_i can be expressed by (see Figure. 3a):

$$n_i = \frac{T - Tr_i}{Tr_i + Td_i} \qquad (11)$$

If it is assumed that the component's downtime *(Td)* is constant, then the problem becomes minimization of total cost *(C(Tr))* by applying the optimum equally interval maintenance program *(Tr)*.

3 Model construction

The basic format of the offered optimization process can be seen in Figure. 4. Input consists of all parameters, which will be used in the entirely of the optimization process. For a very complex problem, those parameters can be classified into several directories so as to make the fault identification easier. Moreover, the use of directories will also make the optimization process easier, since it will design the optimization process and the relationship between each directory become clearer. In this particular problem, input comprises distance between port, average ship speed, unit downtime cost, unit penalty cost, reliability reduction factor, component's failure rate, etc.

All basic calculations for the optimization process (eqn (3-9)) are located in the "equation folder". The results of each equation were continuously updated since the optimization process in the "constraints" and "output" will always affect the variables employed on the equation. The equation covers determination of operating cost, maintenance cost, number of repair before replacement, replacement schedule, position of maintenance, position of end trip, penalty time, etc.

Constraints, which are the considerations to be fulfilled (eqn (1b-1e)), become the director of this optimization process. A minimum or maximum value is set to give the working area of the optimization process. The optimum values are located in the center of the form and it will change, as the constraints are changed. Determination of the minimum or maximum value absolutely depends on the characteristic of the constraints.

Output (equation (1a)) has characteristics, which are nearly the same as the constraints except that the output are set from decision variables (optimization result), which are different with the equation that adopted in the constraints. The maximum and minimum values are also set to direct the optimization process.

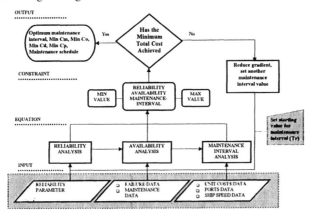

Figure 4: Basic format of the optimization process

All optimization methods have the same pattern in which they formed to find either a maximum or minimum solution of the objective function. Equation (10) shows the expression of the total cost that is the objective function of this particular problem.

There are several strategies in transferring the model into spreadsheet form. Ragsdale [9] and Monahan [10] can be referred for detail information on this matter.

4 Data analysis

The maximum likelihood estimate (MLE) method is widely used to obtain parameters of certain distribution if a set of random variable of the analyzed data is available. This paper only considers four distributions: 2-parameter exponential distribution, normal distribution, 2-parameter Weibull distribution and 3-parameter Weibull distribution. The normal distribution is chosen based upon central limit theorem assumption. The exponential distribution is selected due to its failure characteristic represent the useful life period in a bath-up curve. While the Weibull distribution is selected due to the flexibility of the determination of the parameter that can well described the failure pattern of the data that might be laid either on useful life period or wear out period. These four alternatives are examined to ensure that the LRP's components being analyzed operate at wear-out phase, and relevant reliability function can be applied accordingly.

The input of failure modeling of the LRP is time to failure (TTF), and recorded based upon its maintenance record. The parameters for each distribution are determined by using MLE method. PC-based software was used to speed up the calculation for obtaining the parameters. The distributions resulted from a set of LRP time to failure are then compared to choose the fittest one based upon the likelihood value of the MLE. Table 1 shows the results of MLE analysis and the value of parameters of each distribution that represents each set TTF data of the LRP and Figure. 6 shows the Reliability and *pdf* curve of the 5(five) first components of the liquid ring primer (LRP).

Table 1. MLE evaluation results and Weibull parameter

Components	Likelihood value for each distribution under evaluation				Weibull parameter values		
	normal	Exp.	Weibull	Weibull	Beta	Eta (hrs)	Gamma
1. Check valve	-921.24	-867.5	-866.99	**-866.95**	4.1661	5747.46	-554.446
2. Cooling coil	-894.19	-861.7	-861.04	**-860.45**	2.9047	3974.25	-529.675
3. Impeller	-819.43	-772.3	**-771.96**	-771.99	3.939	2162.15	0
4. Mech. pump seal spr.	-848.46	-847.5	**-835.93**	-836.07	1.6172	2,039.86	0
5. Needle valve	-952.92	-937.1	**-932.53**	-932.65	2.0326	6236.13	0
6. Needle valve seat	-892.26	-880.2	-875.83	**-875.71**	2.092	3605.09	-283.27
7. Pump shaft & coupl.	-1001.93	-1021.4	**-1000.2**	-1000.25	1.2511	9031.01	0
8. Spring	-976.23	-963.6	**-957.61**	-957.63	1.9885	7935.05	0
9. Vacuum breaker	-1029.46	-1041.9	**-1023.7**	-1024.64	1.4478	12482.50	0
10. Vacuum switch	-1024.49	-983.71	-983.89	**-981.98**	3.0503	13799.61	-1156.38

As shown in Table 1, the components are clearly in the wear-out periods, since their likelihood values lean toward either 2-parameter Weibull distribution or 3-parameter Weibull distribution (bold type values mean preferred distribution) and their shape parameter are greater than 1 ($\beta>1$) [11, 12]. Figure. 5 shows that for components having value $\beta>1$, then the *pdf* is zero at $t=\gamma$ increases as t toward the mean life and decrease thereafter. It is also shown that the Weibull reliability function starts at the value of 1 at $t=\gamma$, and decreases thereafter for $t>\gamma$. As t tends toward infinity, then the reliability function headed for 0. For wear-out cases the $R(t)$ decreases as t increases, and for the same value of β, component having greater η decreases less sharply than the one having smaller value of η.

The Weibull distribution, in which all of the LRP's components fit with, is one of the most widely used distributions in reliability engineering. It is because the distribution is able to model a great variety of data by adjusting the value of shape parameter β. The *pdf* of three-parameter of Weibull distribution is given by

$$f(t) = \frac{\beta}{\eta}\left(\frac{t-\gamma}{\eta}\right)^{\beta-1} e^{-\left(\frac{t-\gamma}{\eta}\right)^{\beta}} \qquad (12)$$

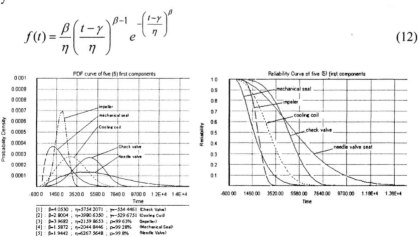

Figure 5: Reliability curve and *pdf* curve of five (5) first components of LRP

where
β = shape parameter, $\beta > 0$
η = scale parameter, $\eta > 0$
γ = location parameter, $\gamma <$ first time to failure
The reliability function of the Weibull distribution can be written as

$$R(t) = e^{-\left(\frac{t-\gamma}{\eta}\right)^{\beta}} \tag{13}$$

and its failure rate can be written as

$$z(t) = \frac{\beta}{\eta}\left(\frac{t-\gamma}{\eta}\right)^{\beta-1} \tag{14}$$

If $\gamma = 0$, then the two-parameter of Weibull distribution is obtained.
The mean time to failure (MTTF) of Weibull pdf is given by

$$MTTF = \gamma + \eta\Gamma\left(\frac{1}{\beta}+1\right) \tag{15}$$

where $\Gamma[(1/\beta)+1]$ is the gamma function evaluated at the value of $[(1/\beta)+1]$.
The availability of the component then can be expressed as

$$Availability = \frac{MTTF}{MTTF + MTTR} \tag{16}$$

Aside from the failure (TTF) data, cost data also need further verification. Based on the data collection process, only the maintenance cost and operation cost of the LRP are available. Due to the fact that it is required to find the effect of the each component's deterioration to the total cost, then we adopt weighting method to distribute the total cost into its component's cost constituents [13, 14].

5 Model analysis

5 (five) models are set and feed into the optimization program. Each model has different interval between two general surveys (T): 1.0, 1.5, 2.0, 2.5 and 3 yearly interval, and named as model 1 to model 5 respectively. The results are obtained by solving each model many times, using different decision variable initial value, and without changing the value of the constraints. If the optimization results remain the same, then we could consider that the optimization program is stable. This also proves the consistency of the model to keep a certain convergence solution. When the first message, "Solver found a solution" appears, it means that the optimal solution has found. This convince us that there is no other set of values for the decision variable close to the current value which yields a better value for the objective, or in other words, we found a peak, if maximizing, or valley, if minimizing. The input parameters and the optimization result are given in Table.2. As shown in Table.2, model 4 provides the lowest average total cost. This minimum value mainly provides by the minimum downtime and penalty time. It means that the component characteristics, which are represented by their distribution parameters, have a

better agreement with the equally-interval between maintenance for a 2.5 yearly general survey.

Table 2. Cost recapitulation for each model

INPUT			reliability decrease factor			0.995
minimum req. availability index		0.95	port c-port d distance		miles	2500
minimum req. reliability index		0.995	average ship speed		knot	14.5
port a-port b distance	miles	3500	unit cost of downtime		$	150
port b-port c distance	miles	2600	unit ext. cost for ext. utilization		$/hrs	0.1

	interval between 2 surveys	total operating cost	total maint. cost	total downtime cost	total Penalty cost	total cost	Ave. total cost
	(years)	($)	($)	($)	($)	($)	($/mth)
model 1	1.0	1559.73	160.50	450.00	379.43	2,549.	212.47
model 2	1.5	2506.10	215.41	750.00	533.69	4,005.	222.51
model 3	2.0	3122.65	453.51	1500.00	780.72	5,856.	244.04
model 4	2.5	3938.08	577.08	900.00	866.53	6,281.	209.39
model 5	3.0	4504.48	856.54	2850.00	1503.17	9,714.	269.84

Table 3. Optimization results for model 4

Components	interval between maint.	optimum reliability	optimum availability	Maint. position	No. of maint. Before Repl.	Repl. schedule (from next Ts)*
1. Check valve	4380.0	0.9801	0.9968	B-C-D-C	6	26280
2. Cooling coil	4380.0	0.9779	0.9966	B-C-D-C	6	26280
3. Impeller	7300.0	0.9764	0.9992	A-A	5	36500
4. Mech. pump seal spring	4380.0	0.9642	0.9975	B-C-D-C	3	13140
5. needle valve	4380.0	0.9667	0.9964	B-C-D-C	3	13140
6. needle valve seat	4380.0	0.9667	0.9968	B-C-D-C	3	13140
7. pump shaft and coupling	4380.0	0.9582	0.9959	B-C-D-C	2	8760
8. Spring	4380.0	0.9771	0.9975	B-C-D-C	6	26280
9. Vacuum breaker	4380.0	0.9725	0.9973	B-C-D-C	5	21900
10. Vacuum switch	4380.0	0.9801	0.9973	B-C-D-C	6	26280

* Ts = the beginning of the next general survey period (hours)

The interval between maintenance and the optimum maintenance schedule of each component can be seen in Table.3. It is shown that the optimization program directs the model to produce almost similar interval between maintenance for most of the components to guarantee that minimal downtime cost will be achieved. The model also directs interval between maintenance as close as possible to the actual time of ship approaching the port, where the maintenance action can be possibly done. Table.3 also shows that, for example, all components except impeller have the same maintenance interval, and their maintenance position for the next four intervals (one interval between two general surveys) would be in port B, C, D and C respectively.

The sixth and seventh columns of Table 3 shows the rest useful life of each component before replacement action. The check valve, for example, will have another 6 maintenance before replacing the present component with the new one. It means that the replacement will be held in Port D. The values of these two columns are obtained by the consideration that the components can not fulfil the minimum reliability requirement of 0.95, due to deterioration and the existence of reliability decrease factor of 0.5 % for every interval between maintenance. By using this information, ship operator can predict the logistic support accordingly. The other general feature of the optimization result is that the increase in interval between maintenance result in the increase of the operating cost, and at the same time reduces the maintenance cost. The increase in interval between maintenance will then be limited by the requirement to perform a minimum value of reliability index for each component.

As shown in Figure.6, minimum total cost is achieved when number of maintenance within interval between two general surveys is an even number, except for the mechanical pump seal spring. The reason behind this phenomenon is that by dividing the interval between two general surveys with the even number, the penalty cost and downtime cost will be minimized. This becomes possible since the exact time of the ship approaching the port are become nearly coincide with the interval between maintenance. Hence, change in model's port distance scenario might produce different result.

So far, the ship speed is assumed constant at 14.5 knot. Practically, it is absolutely an unwise assumption. Therefore, in order to understand the significance of the ship's speed to the model, ship's speed is then taken as another decision variable. It is also assumed that the allowable speed range is 12 knots to 14.5 knots. The result is presented in Figure.7. It is shown that the minimum total cost is obtained when the service speed is set to around 13.25 knot.

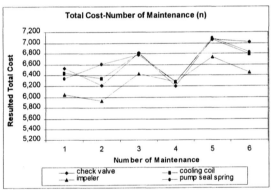

Figure 6: Effect of varying number of maintenance to the total cost of model 4

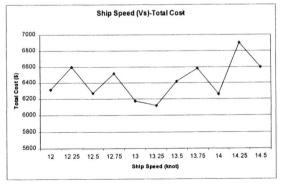

Figure 7: Effect of varying ship's service speed (Vs) to the total cost of model 4

Having known the general behavior of the model, we will then try to examine the model sensitivity to several different parameters. Those parameters are unit downtime cost and unit extra cost for extended utilization. Table 4 shows the several cost compositions according to various units downtime cost. At glance we see that by varying the unit downtime cost, the optimum number of maintenance within 2 general surveys shifts from 4 to 3 and back to mostly 4 maintenance, before arriving at a constant number at the last three downtime values. We then can conclude that for this particular case the model is very sensitive to unit downtime cost in changing the optimum interval between maintenance, especially when the unit cost range is 50 to 150. This result also proves that the optimum interval between maintenance can not merely be based on the component characteristic (distribution parameters) but also based on the unit cost compositions. For a unit downtime cost of more than 150, the model becomes insensitive. It is proved by either the same optimum interval between maintenance or relatively constant value of marginal downtime cost to total cost.

Table 4. Optimization results of model 4 for various units downtime cost

Unit downtime cost ($)	50	100	150	200	250	300
Number of maintenance of 10 components under evaluation	4-4-4-4- 4-4-4-4- 4-4	3-3-3-3- 3-3-3-3- 3-3	4-4-2-4- 4-4-4-4- 4-4	3-3-3-3- 3-3-3-3- 3-4	3-3-3-3- 3-3-3-3- 3-4	3-3-3-3- 3-3-3-3- 3-4
Cost Constituents						
maintenance cost	586.01	464.07	577.08	478.07	478.07	478.07
operating cost	3909.10	4142.27	3938.08	4135.32	4135.32	4135.32
downtime cost	200.00	300.00	900.00	1400.00	1750.00	2100.00
penalty cost	829.45	1305.29	866.53	1253.20	1253.20	1208.19
total cost	5524.56	6211.62	6281.69	7266.59	7616.59	7921.58
average	184.15	207.05	209.39	242.22	253.89	264.05
delta downtime cost	-	50	100	150	200	250
delta total cost	-	687.06	757.13	1742.03	2092.03	2397.02
marginal value	-	0.07	0.13	0.09	0.10	0.10

By varying the unit extra cost for extended utilization while keeping the other variables constant, some features is obtained as shown in Table 5. Unit extra cost becomes very sensitive for value less than 0.1. The cost compositions also remain constant except the penalty cost, which directly affected by the unit extra cost.

Table 5. Optimization results of model 4 for various units extra cost caused by **extended utilization**

Unit extra cost ($)/hr	0.05	0.1	0.2	0.3	0.4	0.5
Number of maintenance of 10 parts under evaluation	3-3-3-3- 3-3-3-3- 3-4	4-4-2-4- 4-4-4-4- 4-4	4-4-2-4- 4-4-4-4- 4-4	4-4-4-4- 4-4-4-4- 4-4	4-4-4-4- 4-4-4-4- 4-4	4-4-4-4- 4-4-4-4- 4-4
Cost constituents						
maintenance cost	478.07	577.08	577.08	586.01	586.01	586.01
operating cost	4135.32	3938.08	3938.08	3909.10	3909.10	3909.10
downtime cost	1050.00	900.00	900.00	600.00	600.00	600.00
penalty cost	581.59	866.53	1761.90	2488.34	3317.78	4147.23
total cost	6244.98	6281.69	7177.06	7583.45	8412.90	9242.34
average	208.17	209.39	239.24	252.78	280.43	308.08
delta d/t cost	-	0.05	0.15	0.25	0.35	0.45
delta total cost	-	36.71	932.08	1338.47	2167.92	2997.36
marginal value	-	0.0014	0.0002	0.0002	0.0002	0.0002

6 Conclusion

In the present article, a spreadsheet model has been developed and used to determine the optimum maintenance schedule for several liquid ring primer components of a ballast system of ships, which has been entering a wear-out phase. The PSP is employed to simulate 5 models having different interval between two general surveys. The optimal policy is defined as the one that minimize the total cost which comprises maintenance cost, operating cost, downtime cost and penalty cost.

The simulation results show that with the existing condition of the components, as represented by their Weibull distribution parameters, the 2.5 yearly interval between two surveys is the scenario that provides minimum total cost. Sensitivity analysis on the effect of unit downtime cost and unit penalty cost shows that the equally interval maintenance scheme can not be decided by considering the components characteristics only, but also must take the operation condition into account. In this paper, the operating condition comprises ship route, technical maintenance policy, and unit cost composition that are adopted within the model. Effect of the decrease of components performance and reliability index due to deterioration has also been considered in the model. Therefore, spare parts and other logistic supports can be prepared accordingly.

Generally speaking, the difficulty of using spreadsheet model to solve optimization problem does not come into spreadsheet construction viewpoint, but lay on the way to express every optimization problem and condition into mathematical expression that can be executed by the spreadsheet. In this particular study case, since the unit downtime cost and unit penalty cost effect the optimization result sensitively, the attention must be paid on the way to determine those unit costs that reflect the actual ship's and machinery operation condition.

Likewise, it is difficult to accurately express the time dependent function of operating and maintenance cost as simplified by equation (8) and (9). As these two cost constituents are the main cost components of this particular problem, then we must focus the attention on the preciseness of each constant, or if possible, express those two equations in different way, that resembling the real condition.

References

[1]   Jardine, A.K.S., *Maintenance, Replacement and Reliability*. Great Britain, Pitman Publishing, 1973.

[2]   Chiang, J.H., Yuan, J., Optimal maintenance policy for a Markovian system under periodic inspection. *Reliability Engineering and System Safety*, 2001;71:165-172.

[3]   Zhang, T., Hiranuma, K., Sato, Y., Horigome, M., Failure frequency and availability of 3-out of –4 G warm standby systems with non-identical components. *Proceedings of ISME Tokyo 2000*;Vol.2:805-810.

[4]   Sheu, S.H., Yeh, R.H., Lin, Y.B., Juang, M.G., A Bayesian approach to an adaptive preventive maintenance model. *Reliability Engineering and System Safety*, 2001; 71:33-44.

[5]   Apeland, S., Aven, T., Risk based maintenance optimization: foundational issues. *Reliability Engineering and System Safety*, 2000;67:285-292.

[6]   Artana, K.B., Ishida, K., Determination of ship machinery performance and its maintenance management using Markov process analysis. *Proceedings of Marine Technology 2001 Conference*.

[7]   Lasdon, L.S., Waren, A.D., Jain, A., Ratner, M., Design and testing of a generalized reduced gradient code for nonlinear programming. *ACM Transactions on Mathematical Software*, 1978; 4: 34-49.

[8]   Lasdon, L.S., Smith, S., Solving large sparse nonlinear programs using GRG. *ORSA Journal on Computing*, 1992; 4: 2-15.

[9]   Monahan, G.E., *Management Decision Making: Spreadsheet Modeling, Analysis, and Applications*. Cambridge Univ. Press, Jan 2000.

[10] Ragsdale, C., *Spreadsheet Modeling and Decision Analysis*. South-Western College Publishing, 2000.

[11] Hoyland, A., Rausan, M.. *System Reliability Theory*. John Willey & Sons Inc., 1994.

[12] Kececioglu, D., *Reliability Engineering Handbook Volume 2*. New Jersey: Prentice-Hall Inc. 1991.

[13] Yang, J.B., Sen, P., A General multi-level evaluation process for hybrid MADM with uncertainty. *IEEE Trans. On System, Man, and Cybernetics*, 1994; 24: 1459-1473.

[14] Sen, P., Yang, J.B., Combining objective and subjective factors in multiple criteria marine design. *Proceedings of 5th International Marine Design Conference*,1994: 505-519.

UK port mitre gates - time for modernisation

M Cullen
Glasgow Caledonian University, UK

Abstract

Mitre gates remain an important element of ports throughout the world and will remain so for the foreseeable future. For ports around the coast of the United Kingdom the design and details use for replacement mitre gates have changed little in the 43 years since the publication of Cornick's *Dock and Harbour Engineering, Volume 1 The Design of Dock Gates*. Indeed, many port engineers still regard this as the manual with which all mitre gates should comply.

These views are not shared in other countries that depend on maritime transport and continue to use mitre gates, such as the United States of America. However, not all mitre gates in UK ports have stuck to the established details for the three key areas of watertight seals, heel, mitre and sill, and yet these developments are generally unpublished. As a result of the lack of communication, combined with the relatively low frequency for replacement, engineers who are about to engage on a replacement gate project tend to stick to the "tried and test" principles of Cornick's book. Although the established details are not incorrect they are often based on inaccurate design assumptions. The objective of this paper is to draw the attention of port engineers, principally in the UK, to the developments in mitre gate details that have taken place, not only in other countries but also in UK ports where innovations been introduced. In addition, a more appropriate design methodology will be presented to improve effective water retention for mitre gates.

1.   What is Cornick's book?

Since the publication of Cornick's[1] book in 1958 there have been significant changes in the maritime transport industry of the UK. The use of small vessels for commercial transportation of goods around the coast has been increasingly replaced by of road transport. In addition, although seaborne transport to the UK continues to be an important part of the national economy, the form of dock facilities for sea-going vessels has progressively transferred from the enclosed impound dock to deep-water sites, such as Felixstowe, to cope with the larger vessels.

In his book *The Major seaports of the United Kingdom* Bird [2] gives a historical view of the situation in 1969. The majority of the ports discussed in this book have experienced significant changes. For example, major areas of industry and commerce such as Glasgow and London no longer have a port within the city limits and depend on road and rail links to make use of a number of larger centralised ports that are remote from the city. Although most ports are now servicing different customer today from those they had in 1969 a number of impound docks are still in operation.

These developments in the transportation system have resulted in the core impound dock utilities, such as the quay wall and the dock gates of these ports, functioning with very few new developments. New mitre gates in UK ports have been predominantly replacement gates as part of a maintenance strategy. Often gates would be replaced because of leakage passing around, or through, the gate was such that the efficiency of the impound dock was being compromised. Such an event would not be suitable for innovation. It is not unreasonable to assume that the port management's main concern would be to have the facility operational as soon as possible with a minimum level of risk.

To assess the number of ports that continue to use mitre gates, a questionnaire survey to collect associated data was posted to 60 ports in 1996. The chosen ports were those listed in *Lloyd's Ports of the World* [3] which appeared to be have an impound dock, therefore, which might have mitre gates.

There was a response from 35 ports (58.3%), which is a significant response to an unsolicited questionnaire. Of the 35 that responded, 21 had impound docks but two did not have mitre gates. Therefore, 54.3% of the 35 respondents used mitre gates. This shows the importance of these gates to the seaborne transport system.

Of those ports that did have operational mitre gates, the average expected life of the heel/mitre post was approximately 28 year and the structural steelwork just over 60 years. Therefore, it is reasonable to assume that it is probable that a port engineer may have responsibility for 1 replacement gate project in the whole of their working life. With such statistics it is understandable that port engineers, tend not to be innovative when specifying replacement mitre gates. As a number of ports are independent single commercial units, such as the Port of Sunderland that is owned by the City of Sunderland, the port engineer may not have the opportunity to discuss his/her specific situation with other port engineers. With commercial pressures of modern ports it is also unlikely a port engineer would willing seek assistance from an engineer based at a rival port. Communication on technical developments in mitre gates between those who have an interest has therefore been scarce.

2.   Source of leakage

In the questionnaire previously referred to in section 0, port engineers were asked to identify areas of leakage in the mitre gates they have at their port. The three areas of potential leakage, i.e. the heel, the mitre and the sill, were separated to help categorise not just the leakage as an effect but also to help identify the cause. The collated responses are listed in Table 1.

Table 1 Percentage of all mitre gates surveyed that have significant leakage in particular zones

Location	Abbreviation	
Lower heel	LH	78.9%
Upper heel	UH	31.6%
Lower mitre	LM	63.2%
Upper mitre	UM	26.3%
Sill at heel	SH	68.4%
Sill at mitre	SM	73.7%

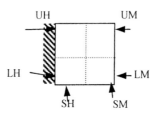

Clearly there is a predominance of problems in the lower heel, lower mitre and sill areas which are not functioning satisfactorily. Discounting damage as a cause of leakage, given the design principle of mitre gates as defined by Cornick's book, and accepted by most port engineers, these zones should be the most effective due to the high hydrostatic pressure and not the worst. To assess the cause of these leaks it is necessary to consider the details and assumptions made for these areas of the standard mitre gate.

2.1   Heel post

Heel posts of mitre gates have two objectives in the operation of a mitre gate; load bearing and watertight seal. In addition the detail is required to allow the gate to swing freely during the opening/closing process. To achieve these objectives heel posts have traditionally been constructed using a hardwood, such as greenheart or ekki, and fixed to the gate in a manner similar to that indicated in Figure 1.

The detail show is that used for the construction of the replacement gates for Granville Dock at Dover in 1943. The same detail was used in 1998 when the gate was modified for a change of use in the dock. Traditional heel post details are generally perceived to have the advantages of:

• Being tried and tested
• The effectiveness of the post as a watertight seal increases as the hydrostatic pressure increases, and
• Hardwoods such as greenheart and ekki are resistant to marine borers and other form of decay.

However, for the gate to function as perceived there are a number of disadvantages that should be considered.

- The ability of the heel post to act as a watertight seal requires direct contact with the masonry hollow quoin, but clearance is necessary to allow the gate to swing open or closed.

- Once installed the gate has no allowance for adjustment that would be required to address wear on the heel post during normal opening and closing. The wear on the heel post tends to be uneven due to the load caused by the swinging weight of the gate being concentrated on the area adjacent to the lower gudgeon.

- Environmental issues that could argue the use of such hardwoods are more beneficial by encouraging a managed form of felling for sustainability than the alternative of using a manmade material. Unfortunately, due to the limited quantity of such hardwoods, and the long time period for maturity, it could be argued that their use should be limited to such a level to maintain the originating forests.

- To achieve the quality of product that can best satisfy the requirements of a mitre gate, skilled personnel is required. With the reduced frequency of new or replacement gates, this resource base is declining and is likely to reach an unsatisfactory level within the foreseeable future.

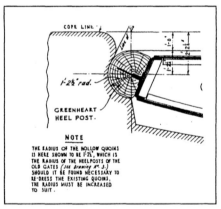

Figure 1 Typical Heel post Design Detail

2.2   Mitre post

As with the heel post, the mitre post has the same two objectives, load bearing and a watertight seal. Traditional mitre post design details made use of greenheart or ekki as is shown in Figure 2. This detail is of Tilbury lock gate, which Cornick [4] described as "new" in 1958. These were replacement gates that were installed post World War II and are an example of the UK "state of the art" mitre gate design in the 1950's.

Given the arrangement of a typical mitre post it was on occasions possible to make use of a single log rather than the two or more necessary for the heel post.

In addition the shaping of the contact face of the mitre post, which is angled but flat, was less involved than the cylindrical surface of the heel post. However, given the accepted design principle of a three-pin arch, the design loading on the mitre post was the same as the heel post. Traditional mitre post details are generally perceived to have the same advantages as the heel post, however there are a number of additional points of concern specific to mitre posts that should be considered by the design engineer.

- As previously stated the accepted design principle of the mitre gate is that the meeting face of the mitre posts will act as a hinge. This would require the facility of rotation therefore the face pressure cannot be consistent.
- The flat contact face of the mitre post should be sufficient indication if the gate leaves misalign but the detail does not ensure a satisfactory alignment. In practice misalignment, although small, is normal, therefore a point contact will result rather than the perceived full-face contact.
- The faces are manufactured to meet at the appropriate angle but this depends on the gates being the correct length. Of a gate leaf is short than the pair will either not meet, or if they do, the mitre face contact will be at a point on the dock side of the gate. A similar but opposite affect would result if the gate leaf is manufactured longer than necessary.
- There is no facility to make maintenance adjustments to the mitre to allow for wear and tear due to normal operation of the gate.

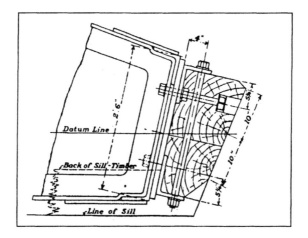

Figure 2 Traditional Mitre post Detail

2.3   Sill seal

The sill seal has a single objective: to provide a watertight seal. Traditionally, the design detail of the sill seal was to use a large section, e.g. 30cm x 30cm, or larger, of a hardwood such as greenheart, ekki, oak or elm. Figure 3 shows the detail of the sill seal used for the replacement mitre gate for Granville Dock in

Dover in 1944. This detail is typical of sill seals that have been used over a long period for new or replacement mitre gates. The perceived advantages of the traditional hardwood sill seal are:

- the hardwood is robust and will deal will debris that may become trapped between the gate and the standing sill;
- misalignment of the gate's steel structure that is to support the timber sill seal can be allowed for in trimming of the timber to suit;
- timber sill seal can be cost effective.

Unfortunately, the operational reality of timber sill seals does not support these views and there is a points of concern that should be considered by the design engineer. The design principle of the gate acting as an arch to retain water assumes the water loading will be distributed in line with the hydrostatic pressure (ρgh), therefore, the thrust loading through the gate will be minimum at the higher levels of the gate and maximum at the lower levels of the gate.

Given the elastic response of the gate the stress experienced by the main structure will produce a directly proportional strain. As the gate will be experiencing compressive stress the effective length of the gate will be reduced. It would be reasonable to assume that if the length of the two leaves of the gate are shortened the location of the mitre must move forward from the dock in line with the loading applied, i.e. the lower level moves more than the higher level. As the timber sill seal is selected for its robust nature against the stationary standing sill the lower level of the gate cannot move, but the higher level of the gate can move. This can result in the loading on the gate can be the reverse of the assumed distribution.

The extent of this phenomenon is dependent on the initial unloaded length of gate. If the gate leaves are is longer than necessary, the gate will respond as designed until the sill seal makes contact with the standing sill when loading will be redistributed in line with the extent of strain available to the gate.

The specialist contractor who have experience of mitre gates often allow extra length to ensure the initial wear on the heel and mitre post is provided for by the gate responding in this manner. As the gate timbers wear the redistribution of loading increases to reach the full inverse of the design model.

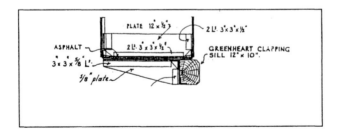

Figure 3 Typical sill seal detail

This effect is evident from the figures listed in table 1 that shows the high percentage of leakage at the lower levels of both heel and mitre post. The long-term effect of the torsional stress that results from the redistribution of loading on the gate structure is the connection of the heel post to the gate becomes loose and gaps develop. Often the gaps are sufficient to allow water to leak into the buoyancy chamber, therefore the swinging weight of the gate increases accelerating wear on the heel post.

3.   Developments in mitre gate seal detail

The observations made in Section 2 may appear to be innovative and the result of modern structural analysis but this is not so. Cornick [5] refers to paper produced by Cooper of work completed for the Wilson Dam, Florence, Alabama, but implies the proposals should be discounted as too complex. In his 1926 paper Cooper [6] acknowledges the influence of the sill seal detail and produces an alternative seal design to act more in line with the perceived view of sill seals. As can be seen in Figure 4, this detail provides the facility for the gate to respond to the stress/strain by moving forward and the location of the rubber section forming the seal can vary, thus allowing for wear of the heel and mitre.

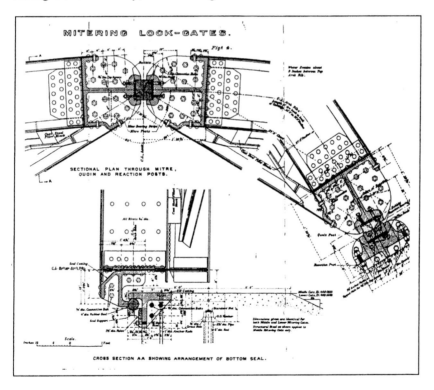

Figure 4 Innovative gate details as presented by Cooper[5]

Figure 4 also shows that the heel (referred to by Cooper as quoin and reaction) and mitre post are also non-traditional. However, the two objectives of load-bearing and watertight seal are still served by the same units as the traditional details but there is a form of adjustment to allow maintenance to take place without removal of the gate.

Despite there being a gap of 32 years between Cornick's book and Cooper's paper, there is no evidence of such details being adopted in the construction of new or replacement mitre gates in the UK. As for the USA, where mitre gates used in the inland waterway system are designed, installed and maintained by the US Corp of Engineers, the design details presented by Cooper have been maintained and developed further as can be seen in the details contained in Figure 5.

The Corp's web site www.usace.army.mil is available to all and gives many examples of the diverse work that the Corp has completed and those that are in progress. For those that have an interest in design of mitre gates there are many details used successfully by the Corp.

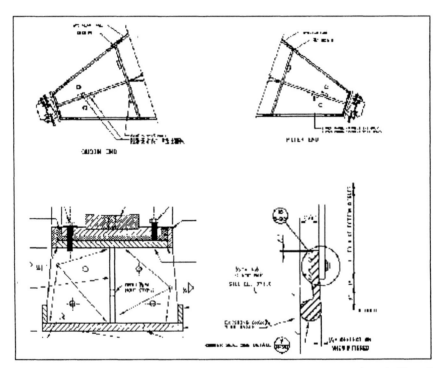

Figure 5 US Corp of engineers details of quoin, miter, quoin block and sill seal

This does not mean there have been no developments in UK mitre gate construction. Rubber sill seals have been used in a number of locations but progress has been slow. Early examples of solid, rectangular synthetic rubber blocks were designed and incorporated into new and replacement mitre gates by

Head, Wrightson Teesdale Ltd., in the 1960's. Yet the use of synthetic rubber for the sill seal is only recently being accepted by of port engineers in the UK as normal for dock gates, but there still remains a few to be convinced.

At about the same time, Head, Wrightson Teesdale Ltd were showing further innovation by introducing a thrust block at the mitre on both gate leaves to carry the thrust loading and a separate, but closely located, shaped synthetic rubber block to act as the watertight seal. Both the seal and the load bearing blocks had provisions for adjustment that allowed for operational maintenance without the need to remove the gate. Examples of these details from the Falmouth N°3 Dry Dock replacement gates, which were constructed in 1968, are show in Figure 6. The main commercial competitor of Head, Wrightson Teesdale Ltd. was Sir William Arrol Ltd., latterly part of Rolls Royce plc and they also introduced synthetic rubber sill seal details. The first rubber section sill seal detail used by Sir William Arrol Ltd. was that of the widely available neoprene 'D' shaped fender. This detail was used in replacement gates for Burntisland dock in Fife and has proven to be a reliable sill seal that give some freedom for the gate to strain as assumed in the design process.

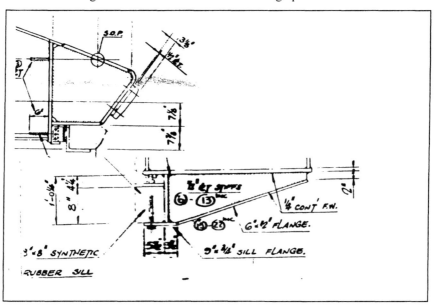

Figure 6 Head, Wrightson Teesdale Ltd. details of mitre and sill seal

Unfortunately neither company is still in existence. However, perhaps the most significant development of gate seal design was the work of the prestigious consulting engineering organisation, Rendell Palmer & Tritton for Royal Royal Portbury Dock near Bristol. The gates were constructed by Fairfield Mabey Ltd. and installed in 1978. Innovative detail for the heel, the mitre and the sill were introduced for the large mitre gates that have to contend with the largest tidal range of any UK port. In the main, the design engineers considered each of the objectives of each location and provided a solution to each objective. Perhaps the most significant change from traditional gate design was to separate the heel post's role as a watertight seal and its load-bearing objective. During the swinging action of the gate during opening and closing the heel post is not in contact with the quoin. Once mitred and the hydrostatic loading takes effect a system of spring supports are compressed to engage the heel post with the hollow quoin and the gate as a whole adopts a seating to function to the best advantage to retain water in the impound dock.

The heel post is not constructed of timber but makes use of the manmade engineering bearing material ORKOT from San Diego Plastics, Inc. mounted on a machined cast steel heel section. Similarly the mitre load-bearing objective and watertight seal objective are dealt with separately. Manmade material has also been used for thrust pads located at levels corresponding to the deck positions in the gate to deal with the load transfer and a separate, but closely located, composite rubber section to provide a water barrier. The composite rubber section continues from the mitre to the sill to ensure a continuity to create a watertight seal. The system is in regular use and the extent of leakage passed the gates is minimal.

4.   What of the future?

The example of Royal Portbury Dock shows what can be achieved in mitre gate design, but in answer to the paper *Design considerations for impound dock mitre gates* [7] there was one response that suggested the standing sill should be replaced by a horizontal, flat sealing face. It was proposed that a sufficiently flexible yet robust synthetic rubber seal be used in conjunction with a stainless steel plate. The restraint imposed by the standing sill would no longer apply and the gate would be able to stain as assumed by the design procedure. In addition the likelihood of debris being trapped between the swinging gate and the standing sill would be minimal.

To date there is no evidence of such a detail being installed, or planned to be installed, in a mitre gate entrance to a port in the UK. The US Corp of Engineers has used approximately similar details but there are sufficient differences to reduce the likelihood of installation in a UK port.

To influence port engineers, the benefits of such a proposal would need to be proven by full scale testing over a significant period of time. The capital expenditure of such a test is likely to be prohibitive, therefore the use of such a design detail in the future is unlikely, but not impossible.

5.   Conclusion

Mitre gates continue to be an important item on the itinerary of a port engineer who has an impound dock. Excessive leakage can result in the dock not functioning, which results in a loss of revenue. Despite the importance of these gates there has been limited development undertaken, or encouraged, in the UK. From the early dock gate developments of Cooper, the UK has lagged behind the

USA in applying the principles modern engineering to construct better gates with the one notable exception at Royal Portbury Dock.

To construct a new or replacement mitre gate the designer should separate and engineer a solution for each individual objective of the heel, the mitre and the sill seal. A number of good examples of how this was achieved in the past are available for engineers to witness. Unfortunately, engineers are often unaware of what these developments are, or where they are.

Communication by papers such as this paper of the developments in mitre gates that have proven to be successful (and those that have been unsuccessful) is essential to ensure their advancement in the future.

References

[1] CONRNICK H F *Dock and Harbour Engineering: Volume 1 the Design of Docks,* Giffen, London, 1958

[2] BIRD *The Major Ports of the United Kingdom,* Hutchinson, London, 1969

[3] Lloyd's Register of Shipping *Lloyd's Ports of the World,* Lloyd's of London Press, London, 1987

[4] CONRNICK H F *Dock and Harbour Engineering: Volume 1 the Design of Docks,* Giffen, London, pp 284 & 285, 1958

[5] CONRNICK H F *Dock and Harbour Engineering: Volume 1 the Design of Docks,* Giffen, London, pp 284, 1958

[6] COOPER H L, Mitering lock gates *Proceeding of the Institution of Civil Engineers,* London, **114**, 1931

[7] CULLEN M, Design considerations for impound dock mitre gates, *Proceedings of the Institution of Civil Engineers Water, Maritime and Energy,* London, **136**, 1999

Impounding gates for marina and harbour navigation use

K. Grubb
Kenneth Grubb Associates Ltd

Abstract

There are a range of design options available when choosing to impound water in a harbour.   The choice of gate type will depend on a wide range of considerations.   This paper attempts to briefly review the various issues to be considered and gate options available.

1. Introduction

With the increase in leisure activities in recent times, there has been much investment in Marinas, whether within existing harbours or as stand alone facilities.   The purpose of this paper is to review the various gate designs often employed for marinas and leisure related harbours.   Also, to cover some of the factors that influences their application.   Common criteria for such gates are that they seal in one (closed) position and are navigable when open.

Considerations as to the type of gate to employ will depend on a number of performance criteria including

- The tidal range
- The speed of operation required
- The consequences of failure
- A requirement to navigate at varying tide levels

2. Design basis

The design basis for impounding gates for harbour and marina navigation is an intriguing one.   At one level they have been employed for hundreds of years and everyone is familiar with their use.   At another level, British Standards or Codes of Practice poorly cover these installations and many areas are in effect a 'black art'.

In addition, there has been a general reduction in the number of 'specialist design and build' Contractors with in-depth knowledge and experience in this field. Similarly the number of 'expert' Consultants has also reduced in recent years.

The combination of the increasing use of functional specifications for 'design and build' contracts, the absence of Standards and codes of practice and reducing Contractor knowledge has led to a number of problem installations in recent years.

3. Design standards applicable

The design of dock gates is covered within BS 6349 part 3. This represents the only British Standard reference work relating to the design of water control gates of any type.

Unfortunately users will find that it is difficult to obtain practicable guidance on many of the elemental loads involved. In particular advice on ship impact and friction often leaves the Designer uncertain as to the values to be adopted.

Thereafter, calculations are performed, based on either BS5950 or BS 5400. Thus in the United Kingdom, a gate has to be considered as a building or a bridge, though it is patently neither of these structures. In any case many gates are designed for deflection criteria rather than stress.

BS 6349 also provides no useful assistance on the design of gate details such as bearings, rollers, seals etc, i.e. those details that effectively turn a structure into a gate.

A more specific standard is DIN 19704, which was re-issued in 1998 in the 'limit-states' format. This is a useful and specific reference covering hydraulic structures. Specifiers should note that this standard lays a great deal of emphasis on the Client for specifying design requirements. DIN 19705 also provides good guidance on specific gate details.

Elsewhere there are reasonable standards from the United States of America, India and Japan.

4   Functionality considerations

4.1 Consequences of failure

Each site is different and engineers must evaluate the causes and consequences of operational failure when determining the type of gate to be employed and the design specification to be developed. In most harbour/marina installations, the consequences of a failure of the gates to close would mean the eventual emptying of the harbour. The financial consequences of damage to vessels could in these circumstances be severe.

Whilst many larger installations can financially justify an effective team of lock keepers and maintenance staff to deal with emergencies, smaller harbours cannot economically sustain twenty-four hour personnel cover and call out. In the former it may be appropriate to include alarm dial-out facilities and manual intervention equipment.   In the latter cases a simpler system would be appropriate, perhaps float operated or based on occasional gate operation. Other harbours have adopted a duplicated gate approach to increase the probability of correct functioning.

Wherever possible duplicated operating systems should be considered, so that no single failure can cause the gate to be inoperable. Where appropriate, a considerably higher level of redundancy needs to be employed.

4.2 Vibration

All gates are prone to vibration due to the passage of high velocity water flowing past the structure. Special consideration needs to be given to ensure that vibration is designed-out at the detailing stage. Design to avoid vibration is an essential part of the gate development process.

4.3 Speed of operation

There are two distinctly separate aspects of the speed of operation of a gate. How fast does it open and close and, in the case of navigable locks, how fast does it allow water equalisation.

Typically, power operated gates open and close in around one to two minutes, though there are no rules in this area and wide variations exist.

Intelligent sluicing is beginning to be adopted in some marinas so as to vary the sluicing area in proportion to the differential head of the water levels. This enables a near constant throughput of water.

4.4 Control options

The development of control options is very site-dependent and only general advice can be given within a paper such as this.

Control systems should be designed so as to fail-safe where-ever possible.

Consideration should be given to the inclusion of back-up systems; appropriate to the implications of gate failure. Such provisions can include:
- Duplicated electric motors;
- Auxiliary power supplies;
- Manually operated valves so as to overcome electrical control failures;
- Trolley mounted emergency hydraulic systems with snap-on connectors.

Provision is required for navigation lights. Advice should be sought from the Harbour Master and Trinity House. Generally they will favour the standards adopted by the International Association of Lighthouse Authorities (I.A.L.A.). Whilst these are very appropriate for large installations, smaller marinas may wish to adopt a simpler system of red or green lights, which may be better understood by 'week-end sailors'.

Marinas with a permanent lock keeper may require manual control. Small installations without manual intervention may rely on a simple timer controlling the direction of access to the harbour entrance.

Larger marinas are now providing event logging equipment so as to protect them from false litigation in the event that a vessel becomes damaged.

4.5 Free flow

Many harbours work on the basis of a period of free flow (gates fully open when the tide levels match the range of operating levels within the harbour/marina). This is particularly so around the top of the tide. When this can occur, special considerations relating to loading and controls come into play.

Great care should be taken to evaluate the maximum water velocity that may be present when the harbour empties or fills under such conditions. Larger harbours cannot usually adopt such a regime.

4.6 Flood defence

Some gate installations are required to provide a flood defence for the immediate inland area. Such gates must be capable of reverse loading.

In addition, detailed consideration needs to be given to ensuring that the gates are capable of closure even under the most advanced levels of component failure such as electrical power failure, motor failure, transmission failure, hydraulic pipeline bursts, etc.

4.7 Water leakage

In most harbour installations the degree of water leakage is not an especially big issue as later high tides can be used to top them up. In some places this is not the case and the cost of impounding pumps is a significant operating cost.

There is, however, a maintenance cost associated with specifying a low-leakage seal as the Contractor response is usually to jack the seals hard onto their respective sealing faces leading to accelerated wear.

5   Gate types

5.1 Mitre gates

5.1.1 Introduction
Mitre gates are the traditional means of impounding water within a commercial harbour. Large gates are normally floated into position and allowed to settle in position over a pintle pin, by opening tidal chambers. Such gates typically incorporate a combination of tidal and buoyancy chambers so as to regulate the net forces on the pintle.

Access to the internal parts of the gates bring into play issues relating to confined spaces which require minimum dimensions and safe means of ingress and egress, as well as facilities for air injection.

The larger gates are arranged with a timber heelpost, which fits within a civil engineering quoin and forms a three-point arch when closed.

Smaller mitre gates can be designed with traditional bearings and incorporate neoprene seals against a stainless-steel frame.

Mitre gates are simple, well proven and are the traditional means of impounding water in harbours.   Typically they incorporate sluice valves to enable water levels to be equalised across the gate prior to their operation.

Problems with mitre gates are well documented and include a vulnerability to trapping submerged debris between the lower clapping seal and it's mating face.

In addition, mitre gates cannot operate against reverse heads, hence there is a range of tides for which the gates must be open and a limitation on the range at which the gates may be opened or closed.   The lack of resistance to reverse loading also makes them vulnerable to severe wave loading in their standard form.

5.1.2 Operating Systems

Historically, mitre gates were opened and closed using chain systems driven by capstans.   Many gates remain today using variations of this system, however most modern gates have moved over to an oil hydraulic system.

Larger gates often employ a hydraulic cylinder running on a cross-head system with a separate strut linked to the gate leaf.   This system limits the vulnerability of the cylinder to damage from ship impact.

Mitre gates normally incorporate sluices/penstocks that can be used to equalise water levels across the gate prior to operation.   Alternatively such equipment is built into the civil engineering which allows water to bypass the gates.

5.2 Vertical Sector gates

5.2.1 Introduction

Sector gates have become very popular in the United Kingdom for marina use, mostly because of their ability to operate against a maximum unbalanced head from either side.   As such, these gates can provide locked access to a marina for all navigable tide levels.

The gates are relatively expensive because they require accurate fabrication jigs and the general construction detail is of a more complex nature.   However, they give the maximum flexibility to marina operation.

Water levels are synchronised by partially opening the gate leaves so that water flows around the recess.   A secondary seal system prevents flow through the centre of the gates, which may be dangerous to boats within the lock and would promote vibration.

Sector gates are normally based on a pair of gates; however it is possible to base the installation on a single gate in the event that the design vessel width is small.   This saves considerable cost and space in terms of recess construction.

As a consequence of the ability to withstand a load from either direction, the sealing systems are more complex.   The seals for Sector gates need to be set very accurately.   Unfortunately modern extruded neoprene seals cannot be manufactured to tight tolerances.   For this reason the best designs incorporate seal sub-frames which can be finely adjusted by jacking in at least two planes.

A design that simply mounts the seal onto a surface that can be jacked in and out in one plane is unlikely to provide good service in the long term.

The design of the seal mounting frame also requires careful thought as the seals need to be protected from fast moving flotsam during sluicing.

5.2.2 Operating Systems
Sector gates can be operated by winch or by hydraulic cylinder. Cylinders have tended to predominate in the last decade in view of their direct action, ability to accelerate and decelerate a load and their general robustness.

The design of the cylinder construction is important and the installed position needs to take tide levels into consideration, as there may be occasions when it is immersed.

The design of load control valves for Sector Gate use is of significance because there are considerable fluctuations of pressure in the cylinder during an opening/sluicing cycle, which can lead to hydraulic instability.

Recent Sector gates have included 'intelligent sluicing' equipment.   This system senses the water level difference across the gate leaf and automatically adjusts the gate position to increase the sluice opening as the differential falls. This system can maintain a relatively even rate of water transfer and thus substantially reduces the time required to lock through the system.

5.3   Horizontal Rising Sector gates

5.3.1 Introduction
A rising sector gate can also be used to impound water and be navigable. Such arrangements are similar to the Thames Barrier in principle (see figure 3).

The gates are capable of accepting a hydraulic load from either direction and have the advantage that they take up a smaller 'footprint' than conventional Sector gates.

The turbulence caused when such gates are equalising water and their cost when compared to a tilting gate has generally meant that their take-up has been restricted.   However they do have some advantages within certain limited site constraints and should not be immediately discounted when first considering options.

In view of the need to design an underwater recess to lower the gates into, some thought needs to be given to the incidence of siltation. In general, gates which open and close on each tide tend to stay untroubled from an accumulation of silt. Where this may not be the case, provision can be made for a means of fluidising the silt via air or water pipeline systems.

5.3.2 Operating Systems
Sector gates can be operated by winch or by hydraulic cylinder. Cylinders have tended to predominate in the last decade in view of their direct action. Also the

use of a winch requires careful design of the centre of gravity and buoyancy so that the rope remains in tension through all points of operation.

5.4 Delta gates

5.4.1 Introduction
Delta gates are similar in principle to Vertical Sector gates. They differ in so far as the gate leaf is flat.

Delta gates offer the advantage that the gate leaves are cheaper to manufacture because they can be made on the fabrication workshop floor and thus do not require special jigs. They have one major disadvantage in that the bottom seals have a part sweeping and part scuffing action and experience has tended to show that failure rates are high. For this reason they have not been widely adopted.

5.4.2 Operating systems
Because Delta gates operate in a similar manner to Sector gates, the points previously raised, apply identically here.

5.5 Tilting gates

5.5.1 Introduction
Tilting gates are normally flat structures, hinged along their lower edge and are raised or lowered when the tide level equates to the natural gate impoundment level. In so doing the gate is effectively operated under near balanced head conditions.

This being the case, Tilting Gates provide the cheapest form of gate impoundment. This is so because the gate leaf is flat and the operating equipment does not have to be rated for large differentials.

In view of their design, simple Tilting Gates cannot take a high degree of reverse loading and it is necessary to open and close them at specific water levels over the tidal cycle.

Tilting gates can provide an element of wave or flood protection by introducing mechanical latches at the top outside edges. Special attention should be given with such devices, as they are located¡ at a position where flotsam can be a problem.

Care needs to be taken when applying Tilting Gates to large Harbours as high water velocities may be engendered at certain phases of the tide.

On large tilting gates it is often cost effective to build some measure of buoyancy into the structure; this has the advantage of reducing the forces necessary for articulation.

Special attention needs to be paid to protecting the bottom edge of the gate. Tilting gates are vulnerable to debris falling down the leaf as it is raised and becoming jammed between the gate leaf and frame, where the considerable mechanical advantage of the operating equipment can cause structural damage.

Typically this problem is addressed by the introduction of a flap, which spans the gap between the gate and its sealing frame.

The Designer should take steps to protect vessels during gate operation as they may be unaware of a large structure rising just below the water level. In this respect a Tilting gate is at a disadvantage to say a Sector Gate in that the gate leaf is often invisible to mariners.

Tilting gates can be arranged to include pedestrian walkways along the top edge. Special risk assessment needs to be undertaken as there are often difficulties in clearing the structure prior to operation, particularly with the need to regulate the precise time at which such a gate is operated.

In view of the need to design an underwater recess to lower the gates into, some thought needs to be given to the incidence of siltation. In general, gates which open and close on each tide tend to stay untroubled from an accumulation of silt. Where this may not be the case, provision can be made for a means of fluidising the silt via air or water pipelines.

Because tilting gate bearings are permanently immersed it is wise to ensure that they are sealed from silt ingress. In addition, provision may be necessary to be able to change the bearings with the gates insitu.

5.5.2 Operating systems

The two principle means of operating an impounding tilting gate is by wire rope winch or hydraulic cylinder.

The wire rope arrangement is relatively cheap and consists of the dead ended rope on one side of the civil works passing over a number of pullies mounted on the gate leaf and finally onto a winch.

Winch pullies should be arranged so that the wire rope cannot disengage from a pulley in the event of a slack rope condition.

Consideration should be given to the means by which a rope can be changed in an emergency.

Limit switch arrangements need to consider the effect of long-term rope stretch.

Hydraulic arrangements can employ either one or two cylinders.

A single cylinder can be used for gate operation provided that sufficient torsional stiffness is built into the gate structure. Such stiffness usually takes the form of a box type structure. A single cylinder is cheaper and avoids the need to synchronise hydraulic operation. In addition it can also mean that the hydraulic system does not need to be routed across the lock and this avoids potential pollution hazards.

Where the lock is too wide, it may be necessary to use two cylinders. This arrangement can also have the advantage of providing an element of cylinder redundancy for emergency use.

On small harbour entrances, it may be possible to employ a displacer-operated gate. These have been used successfully over a number of years and their simplicity helps to reduce the risk of a failure to operate at the appropriate time.

One small problem with such installations is that since the gate operates according to tide level, it is not possible to print a definitive timetable as to when the gate will operate. Also the relative uncertainty as to the specific operating point leads to navigation being curtailed sooner than would be the case for powered systems.

5.6 Caisson Gates

5.6.1 Introduction
A caisson gate is a large single span structure, sometimes referred to as a free-floating gate. The gate is flooded with water to sink it into position or pumped out to enable it to float. Once floating, it is possible to winch the caisson out of the way.

When in the closed position, the gate seals against vertical sealing faces and a lower sill.

Caisson gates are seldom used for access purposes because they are expensive to manufacture and only effectively operate under controlled opening and closing conditions associated around a single tidal condition.   In most cases Caisson gates are employed to act as dry or wet dock entrance gates, however there are notable exceptions to this.

5.6.2 Operating Systems
The conventional Caisson gate is winched in a lateral direction so as to clear the dock entrance. Under these circumstances the arrangement often employs guide rails to ensure that the gate is delivered and retrieved in a controlled manner.

It is possible to arrange for a Caisson gate to be hinged at one end so as to enable opening and closing via winch systems. Such an arrangement is being successfully employed at Milford Haven to enable regular access to the harbour by pleasure craft.

6   Relative Costs

It is not possible to provide consistently accurate comparisons for the costs of impounding gates. Typical cost per tonne type rates have not been found to be a good guide to project costing. Some designs are cheaper in view of their relative occurrence, which leads to some design savings.

Similarly we are all aware of 'special prices' given by Contractors who are either short of work or who have simply made mistakes in their estimating.

As a generalism, the following typical cost comparators has been assembled for a mythical gated entrance, 10 m wide, and having an 'average' level of control equipment requirements. Inevitably such an exercise is fraught with assumptions and the figures should be used for very early project assumptions only.

Note that gates which only impound water are generally shorter than those that are required to hold back the full tidal cycle.

Gate Type	Arrangement	Assumed gate size	Typical Cost £000's
Mitre Gates	Single set	10 m wide x 8 m high	£500
Vertical Sector Gates	Single Pair	10 m wide x 8 m high	£650
Horizontal Rising Sector Gates	Single Gate	10 m wide x 3 m high	£350
Delta Gates	Single Pair	10 m wide x 8 m high	£550
Tilting Gates	Single Gate	10 m wide x 3 m high	£250
Caisson Gates	Single Gate	10 m wide x 8 m high	£1000

7 Conclusions

There are a number of choices when considering the type of gate to use for marina or harbour impoundment purposes. There is a great deal of experience of all types and each has advantages and disadvantages in particular circumstances.

The best choice will depend on a myriad of criteria relating to the project and its budget. The answer to almost any question relating to water control gates seems to start with the words 'it all depends.........'.

Designers and Specifiers need to make a comprehensive and systematic assessment of the various operating requirements and constraints in order to determine the most appropriate type and functionality. Purchasing an impounding gate on a design and build basis using a simple functional specification is unwise due to the lack of detail within most standards.

In spite of their relatively mature technology, great care needs to be taken in designing gated installations as it is usually difficult to modify the equipment once installed. Purchasers should carefully consider the experience and track record of the Professionals and Contractors that they employ on such schemes.

Monitoring of marina construction, Gulf of Suez, Egypt

K. A. Rakha and A. G. Abul-Azm
Irrigation and Hydraulics Dept., Faculty of Eng., Cairo University, Egypt.

Abstract

The wave conditions inside a marina are an important factor to be considered when planning and designing a marina. This paper provides a study for a marina in the Gulf of Suez where the design layout was not properly executed, resulting in high wave conditions during southerly storms. The REF/DIF model is used to study the wave conditions inside the marina for the actual and the design layouts. Finally, two alternatives for alleviating the existing conditions are suggested.

1 Introduction

Many marinas are being constructed along the Red Sea coasts of Egypt. These marinas will accommodate pleasure boats and should be properly designed to protect these boats during high wave conditions. This paper presents a case study for a marina (Dome marina) constructed along the Gulf of Suez in Egypt (Figure 1).

In 1996 and 1997 wave modelling was performed to plan and design the Dome marina. After the construction and operation of the marina in 1999, high wave conditions were observed inside the marina during a southerly storm. A recent survey for the actual marina constructed showed that the entrance of the marina was not constructed as proposed in the design (Figure 2). The marina entrance was wider than that proposed in the original design. Furthermore, the main breakwater was found to be shorter than the length proposed in the design.

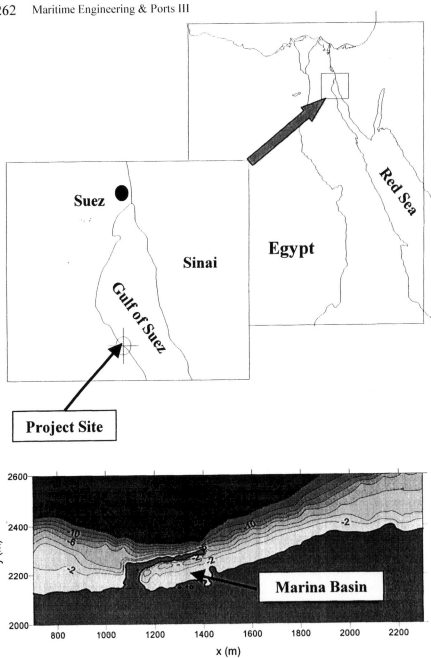

Figure 1:Location of Project Site and Marina Layout.

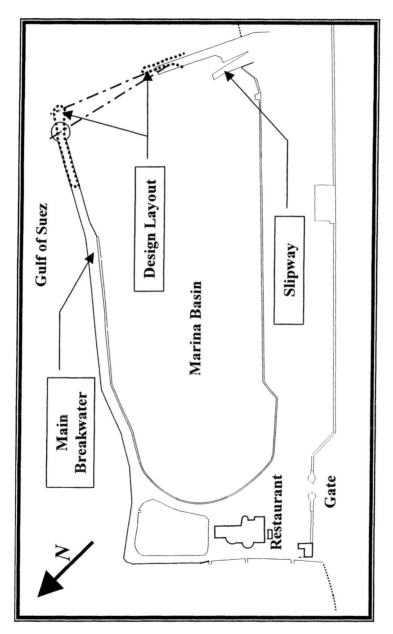

Figure 2: Marina layout

In this study the wave conditions inside the marina are calculated using the REF/DIF model [1] to determine the wave conditions for the existing marina layout. The model is also applied to demonstrate the effect of not constructing the marina layout as proposed during the design stage. Finally, different solutions to reduce the wave conditions inside the marina are studied and discussed.

2 Project Description

The Dome marina is located at Latitude 29° 26'N and Longitude 32° 30'E 80 km South of Suez City along the Gulf of Suez in Egypt (Figure, 1). The marina was constructed to accommodate @ 100 boats of different sizes ranging between 12 m and 30 m length. The marina consists of two rubble mound breakwaters designed to provide suitable wave conditions for mooring inside the marina basin (Figure 2).

The nearshore bathymetry was surveyed in 1996 and 1997 before the construction of the marina. A recent survey in 2001 was conducted after the construction of the marina.

3 Model Description

The REF/DIF model was developed by [1] and solves the Parabolic Mild Slope Equations PMSE [2]. The MSE are valid for bed slopes up to 1:3 [3]. The model includes the effects of wave refraction, diffraction, shoaling, and wave breaking.

The Parabolic Mild Slope Equations PMSE considers wave diffraction in the direction of wave propagation only and neglects wave diffraction in the direction of propagation. This is a reasonable approximation only when the solution marches in the direction of propagation (wave rays are in the direction of x-axis). The angle between the wave direction and the direction of propagation should not exceed 30° [4]. This limit was not exceeded in this study.

3.1 Model Setup and Input Data

The bathymetric survey performed in 2001 together with the surveys performed in 1996 and 1997 were used to produce the bathymetric files required for the numerical model. The older bathymetric data (from 1996 and 1997) was used to provide data in areas that were not surveyed during the 2001 survey. The simulations were performed for the MSL condition for the tides (the maximum tidal range for the project site was reported to be about 2.15 m according to [5]).

The grid spacing used was 5.0 m in the x-direction (onshore) and the y-direction. The wave conditions covering the range from 50 to 90 degrees with the north were considered. The 90-degree provides the limit for waves to directly reach the marina (due to the protection from the southern headland). The 50-degree limit was determined as explained below.

Ship wave measurements at a location approximately 12.5 km southwest the Dome Marina site with a water depth of 60 m were used [see 5]. The annual average percentage frequency of occurrence of the offshore significant wave height from all directions (Table 1) showed that about 15 % of the waves arrive from the Northerly direction. Only about 4 % of the waves arrive from the Easterly or the Southern directions. The southern waves will not directly reach the project site.

Table 1: Frequency of occurrence for offshore wave data

Dir.	Wave Height (m)						Total
	0-0.6	0.6-1.2	1.2-1.8	1.8-2.4	2.4-3.0	3.0-3.6	
N	5.8	5.1	1.5	0.2	0.0	0.0	12.6
NE	1.1	0.7	0.0	0.0	0.0	0.0	1.8
E	1.1	0.1	0.0	0.0	0.0	0.0	1.2
SE	2.1	0.6	0.0	0.0	0.0	0.0	2.7
S	1.3	0.3	0.0	0.0	0.0	0.0	1.6
SW	1.5	0.1	0.0	0.0	0.0	0.0	2.6
W	3.1	1.4	0.1	0.0	0.0	0.0	4.6
NW	13.9	21.6	20.2	10.3	4.0	5.0	70.6
Calm							3.3

The maximum wave height for the Easterly waves was found to be 1.0 m with a period of 4.0 seconds. This wave condition is used throughout the simulations provided below. Thus the results provided can be considered as the refraction-diffraction coefficients for the nearshore area (unit offshore wave height considered).

4 Model Results

In this section the model results for the existing layout, the design layout and two proposed layouts are provided. The results are presented in the form of wave height contour maps showing the direction of wave propagation.

4.1 Existing Layout

For the existing situation, the window for waves directly entering the marina was found to cover the range from 50 to 90 degrees with the North direction. Trail and error was used to determine these limits by simulating different angles and determining the limiting angle for waves directly entering the marina. Figure 3 provides the results obtained for these two wave directions.

As shown in Figure 3, only the area at the slipway will experience higher wave conditions for this sector. For the 90° sector, the wave conditions will be high at the entrance of the marina and along the berths just North of the slipway.

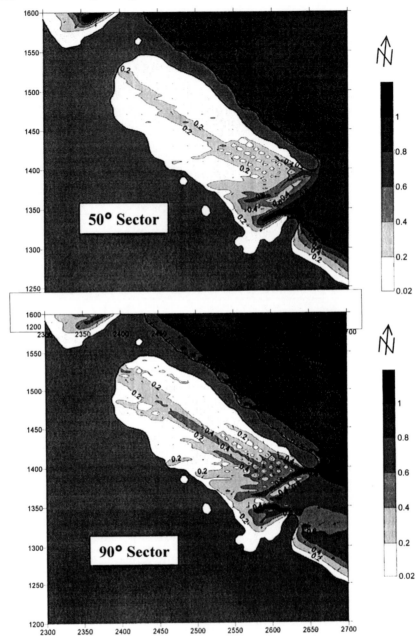

Figure 3: Waves Inside Marina for Existing Layout

4.2   Design Layout

Figure 4 provides the limits for waves directly entering the marina based on the design layout. The limits for this case were found to be from 70 to 90 degrees. For the 90° sector, the wave conditions inside the marina are slightly lower than the corresponding values for the existing situation. Again, only the area at the slipway will experience higher wave conditions for the 70° sector.

Thus, the number of days with waves directly entering the marina for the current situation is about double the number of days for the original design layout. Also for the current existing layout, the wave conditions inside the marina will be higher than those for the original design layout.

4.3   Proposed Remediation

Two different alternatives were considered for reducing the wave heights inside the marina. The first alternative includes increasing the length of the main breakwater by 10.0 m compared to the design length. Thus the extension proposed will be about 22.0 m with respect to the existing layout. This length was determined by trail and error to provide sufficient protection for the marina basin.

The second alternative proposes constructing an extension to the secondary breakwater perpendicular to the existing breakwater and extending inside the marina basin by 25.0 m. This length was also determined by trail and error.

In order to evaluate the effectiveness of these alternatives the 90 degree angle of approach was used for the different simulations.

Figure 5 provides the results obtained for Alternatives 1 and 2. The suggested extension for the main breakwater indeed provides sufficient protection for the marina basin for all wave directions.

Furthermore, the proposed Alternative 2 also provides sufficient protection for the marina basin. For this alternative however, the manoeuvrability of the boats next to the slipway will be very difficult.

5 Summary and Conclusions

The present study showed that due to the fact that the marina entrance was constructed with a layout different from the design layout, the wave conditions inside the marina entrance and near the slipway could be relatively high.

Two alternatives were suggested for alleviating this problem. The first alternative proposes to extend the main breakwater towards the south by 22 m. The second alternative consists of creating an L shaped secondary breakwater to protect the area near the slipway. Although the cost for constructing the second alternative is less than the second, it might introduce other problems for boats approaching the slipway.

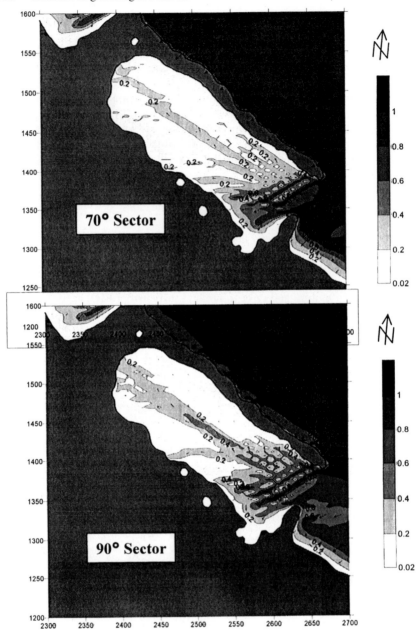

Figure 4: Waves Inside Marina for Design Layout

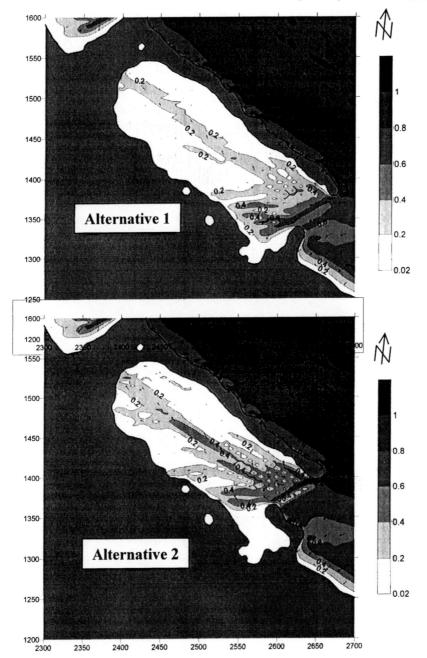

Figure 5: Waves Inside Marina for Alternative Layouts

This study also showed the importance of using mathematical models in the assessment of solutions for such problems and the importance of executing the projects as designed.

References

[1] Kirby, J.T. and Dalrymple, R.A. (1991). User's Manual – Combined Refraction/Diffraction Model: REF/DIF 1 Version 2.3. Center for Applied Coastal Research. University of Delaware. Newark, Delaware.

[2] Radder, A.C. (1979). On the parabolic equation method for water wave propagation. Journal of Fluid Mech., Vol. 95, part 1, pp.159-176.

[3] Booij, N. (1983). A note on the accuracy of the mild slope equations. Coastal Eng., Vol. 7, pp. 191-203.

[4] Dodd, N. (1988). Parabolic approximations in water wave refraction and diffraction. Ph.D. Thesis, University of Bristol, 104 p.

[5] Abul-Azm, A.G., and Rakha, K.A., (2000). Environmental concerns for marina planning in the gulf of Suez. Journal of Coastal Conservation, Issue 6.1, pp. 51-56.

A jacket turning procedure applied to dock construction

F. Pérez Arribas, L. Pérez Rojas
Naval Architecture School, Polytechnic University of Madrid, Spain.

Abstract

In the field of civil engineering for ships moorings, the use of big concrete cases is limited due to the size of the construction tools.

Due to that, the size of the actual piers or docks built with cases is limited to approximately 20 meters depth.

In this paper an alternative to the aforementioned problem is presented. The basis of this alternative consists in turning the prismatic cases so that the length is transformed into depth and depth into length. An example of the turning of a case is presented and a physical and mathematical model for turning the case and how to calculate the trajectory of the case during the turning is described.

1. Introduction

In civil technology of ships mooring, the use of big concrete boxes is limited by the forms of construction of these boxes. Although if these are constructed in floating, dry docks or syncrolift platforms, height is the limiting factor and so, the height of the boxes is also limited, that means a reduction in the size of the piers or docks that will be constructed with them.

Due to these limitations, mooring docks constructed by concrete boxes do not use to have more than 20 meters of depth. For this reason, ships such as big tankers or some chemical tankers have to discharge far from the shore, in buoys or floating platforms that are not fixed to the seabed. These devices can be affected by severe waves, making discharge possible only in fair weather conditions.

For floating platforms fixed to the seabed, construction is possible only if the sea ground is not composed of rock. In this case, the price of fixing the platform is quite expensive.

If the boxes are constructed on the horizontal plane (solving construction problems) turning height into length, and using appropriate internal compartments, it is possible to turn the box from horizontal to vertical position and then, sink the box in its final place at the dock under construction. Flooding some internal compartments with concrete when the box is floating on the water can make this.

This turning technique is frequently used in metal jackets of oil platforms and allows to duplicate the depth of the cases without using expensive construction devices that sometimes cannot be implemented due to the limited depth of some ports.

In this paper, the numerical results of the simulation in the turning of a box and validation through experiments with a physical model are presented [1]. The tests were carried out in the towing tank of the Naval Architecture School in Madrid in co-operation with the offshore division of the Spanish Company DRAGADOS S.A.

2. Modelling the problem

A plot of the box section with the different internal compartments can be seen in figure 1. The box is divided in the construction process in 49 longitudinal compartments or and a limiting wall parallel to the square side, creates seven new compartments, 1 to 7 in the picture. Transversal division is broken for these seven new tanks, so, A, B, ...H cells are joined, but only for these seven tanks.

An appropriate filling of these new compartments with concrete when the box is floating on the water produces the turning. Once compartment 3 is full, compartment 4 begins to be filled, and so on. But other factors such us stability and initial and final positions have to be considered.

Controlling stability is the most important factor and final draft sets the limit of the water depth where the process can be successfully made without grounding. After some tests, the distance of the limiting wall from the box side was taken 2.7 m, and a ballast weight L was placed on the opposite side of the limiting wall.

This way, once the box is constructed, it can float on the water with a zero trim angle, solving some construction limitations, and it has a good transversal stability that allows working over it with safety. The ballast weight L can be obtained using a symmetrical wall of the limiting wall that forms new compartments that are equivalent to 1, ...7 of Fig. 1, but on the opposite side, or with a removable sea water tank that is taken out when the box turning is finished.

The initial situation of the box has compartments 1 and 2 of Fig. 1 completely filled with concrete, and the sea water ballast allows zero trim and good transversal stability. Water ballast begins to be extracted at the maximum values of the stability curves, as will be seen later, while compartments 3 to 7 are still being flooded with concrete. So, the turning can be safely made with positive transversal and longitudinal stability.

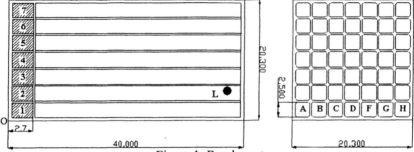

Figure 1: Box layout

2.1 Mathematical modelling

Equilibrium of forces (Eq. 1) and moments (Eq. 2 referenced to point O of Fig. 1) have to be obtained at every time step. The problem is modelled assuming successive equilibrium stages, that works if the flooding of the compartments is slow enough. This way, inertia moments and dynamical forces that are difficult to obtain are not considered.

The different forces acting on the problem and their points of application referenced to O point of Fig. 1, are now presented.

- Box weight (constant): Q, Xq, Yq
- Weight of the limiting wall (constant): M, Xm, Ym
- Concrete weight on compartments 3 to 7 (variable): P^*, Xp^*, Yp^*
- Salt water ballast (variable): L, Xl, Yl
- Box buoyancy (variable): E, X_E, Y_E

According to this nomenclature, equilibrium equations are:

$$\sum F = 0 \Rightarrow E = Q + P^* + M + L \tag{1}$$

$$\sum M_o = 0 \Rightarrow \tag{2}$$
$$\Rightarrow E \cdot (Sin(\alpha) \cdot Y_E - Cos(\alpha) \cdot X_E) =$$
$$= Q \cdot (Sin(\alpha) \cdot Yq - Cos(\alpha) \cdot Xq) + P^* \cdot (Sin(\alpha) \cdot Yp^* - Cos(\alpha) \cdot Xp^*) +$$
$$+ M \cdot (Sin(\alpha) \cdot Ym - Cos(\alpha) \cdot Xm) + \cdots$$
$$+ L \cdot (Sin(\alpha) \cdot Yl - Cos(\alpha) \cdot Xl)$$

In Eq. 2, α is the trim angle, that is unknown and buoyancy E is a function of this value as far as the box shape changes accordingly α. A non linear equation system is solved to obtain α [2], and so, for every value of the added concrete weight, P^*, and subtracted weight, L, a new value of the trim angle is obtained and the turning of the box is obtained.

During the process, longitudinal and transversal metacentrical heights have to be obtained to control stability in both motions. This will be a function of the box waterplane area and of the height of the centre of gravity of the system that varies according concrete is added and salt water ballast is removed.

2.2 Concrete inside the compartments

Concrete weight P* that is added, floods tanks 3 to 7 until every tank is completely flooded. A low viscosity fluid will maintain its free surface parallel to outside water level (Fig. 2, left), but a high viscosity fluid, that can be considered as a kind of solid, will have its "free" surface parallel to tank base (Fig. 2, right). This assumptions will affect to the centre of gravity of P*, (Xp*, Yp*) that also affects to Eq. 2 solution.

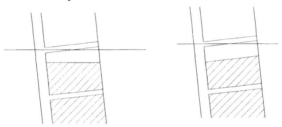

Figure 2: Concrete modelization inside the compartments

The concrete, when is not solid, will maintain and intermediate behaviour, so both situations have to be solved assuming the real behaviour between them. Differences obtained are small as can be seen in Fig. 3. Inertia moment of the concrete free surface inside the compartments affects stability [3], but in this case, the small size of these compartments allows to neglect this effect.

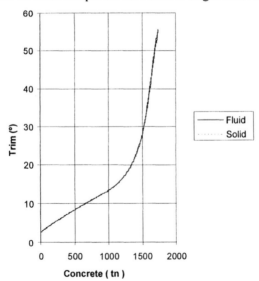

Figure 3: Concrete as perfect fluid or solid

3. Results

Trim angle vs. added concrete (ρ = 2500 kg/m^3) in tanks 3 to 7 (permeability 95%) is shown in Fig. 4. In this case, the concrete inside the tanks is modelled as a solid. At the end, the box is completely vertical with a draft of 33.53 m.

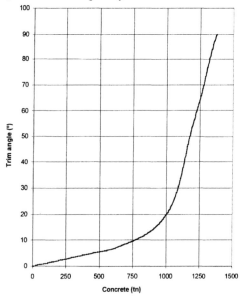

Figure 4: Trim angle vs. added concrete

In order to control the turning stability, longitudinal and transversal metacentrical heights were calculated and are shown in Fig. 5. In the maximum values of these curves, the salt-water ballast begins to be subtracted.

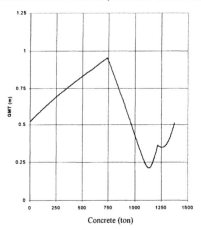 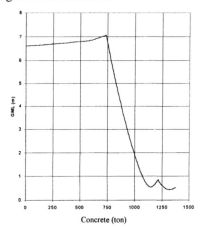

Figure 5: Stability Curves (transversal at the left)

4. Validation

A 1:75 scale model of the box was constructed and tested (Fig. 6). The modelization of the flooding of the compartments was not possible to make with concrete due to scale factor and viability to make different tests, so, lead slices were used to reproduce the concrete that should be added in the compartments 3 to 7, and the water ballast weight.

Figure 6: Pictures of the model

A system to control the vertical position of these slices was installed in the model, and changing the number of the slices and its vertical position, different stages of the turning procedure were reproduced and compared with the numerical results that were calculated (Fig. 7). Moving the lead slices, the scaled position of the system centre of gravity is obtained, and an equilibrium position is obtained.

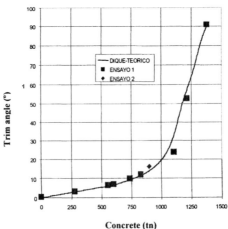

Figure 7: Validation of the numerical results

5. Conclusions

- Once solved construction problems, the turning of a concrete box can be made in a safe way by filling internal compartments with concrete and considering some ballast to control initial trim and stability; then, the box is towed to its final position at the dock and sunken. So, deeper docks can be constructed with this procedure.
- In this case, initial transversal stability of GMT = 0.5 m was obtained with an appropriate combination of initial filled compartments (1 and 2) and initial water ballast.
- The dimension of the internal compartments was chosen to obtain a final GMT = 0.5 m. Initial and final positions of the turning procedure are showed in Fig. 8. Once the box is in vertical position, it can be sunken by filling the rest of compartments with concrete.
- Water ballast is retired at the maximum values of the stability curves at the same speed that concrete is added. This way, stability is positive during the turning and no violent turning is produced.
- In this case, turning can be made without grounding in a minimum water depth of 37 m.

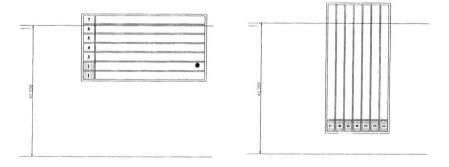

Figure 8: Initial and final position

Acknowledgements

We would like to thank Dragados Construcción S.A. for its kind permission in publishing the results, and the contribution in the numerical calculations of Mr. Iván Artime Díaz.

References

[1] Towing tank of ETSIN, *Proyecto de I+D Cajón Volteado para Dragados y Construcciones*, 2000.
[2] Press, W.H. et all, *The art of scientific computing*, Cambridge University Press. pp. 340- 386, 1994.
[3] E.V. Lewis, *Principles of Naval Architecture, Vol. I Stability and Strength*. SNAME, pp. 93, 1989

Section 6
Container systems

The effects of the market concentration in the maritime transport on the strategies of the container terminal operators

R. Midoro & F. Parola
Dipartimento di Tecnica ed Economia delle Aziende,
Genoa University, Italy.

Abstract

The aim of the present paper is to show the first results of our research about the strategic behaviour of the global stevedoring companies over the last few years. Our investigation will particularly focused on the strategic decisions of the top management of the main container terminal operators such as Hutchison Port Holdings, PSA Corporation, AP Moeller Terminals and P&O Ports.

We will try to evaluate the impact of the strategies of the global terminal operators in the different markets and geographical areas, highlighting on the one hand the burden of investment in assets, focused on the increase in productivity and in the terminal capacity, and on the other hand the influence on the traffic flows, especially referred to the transhipment terminals.

As regards the main container terminals we will also underline weak and strength points related to the operating activities and to the management problems.

Moreover a particular attention will be dedicated to the study of the vertical integration of some global carriers along the transport chain.

1 The strategic alliances

During the last few years, thanks to the advent of the globalisation, the market of the sea transport has shown radical changes largely due, on the one hand, to the formation of the strategic alliances among the top carriers and on the other hand to the achievement of growing economies of scale, referred both to organisational aspects (mergers and acquisitions) and to the "vessel" as technical asset.

The global alliances can be considered as a breakthrough with the previous forms of co-operation as they are not limited to a single trade lane but aim to cover every major routes, as well as a number of relevant north-south trades and regional feeder links. At the same time alliances extend their area of influence beyond vessel operations towards the shared use of container terminals, joint equipment management, intermodal transport, logistics and joint purchasing and procurement [1].

The factors that drove lines together 30 years ago, namely the need for risk sharing, cost control, and a capability to increase service frequencies, have to be re-analysed in conformity with the new needs of mobility induced by the globalisation and, in a different point of view, by the protracted poor profitability of the market.

During the 1990's the economic system changed, passing from a multitude of distinct markets separated by trade barriers, distances, time and culture, to one that is increasingly converging and integrating. In particular two main factors underline this trend towards globalisation: the decline in barriers to the free flow of goods, services and capitals and in the last two decades the dramatic development in communications, information and transportation technology.

This means a substantial growth in the scope of activities performed by carriers, in terms of extended geographic coverage, higher frequency of services, faster transit times, supply chain management and provision of value added services.

The second force pushing container carriers towards new forms of co-operations is the protracted unsatisfactory financial performance of the maritime industry as a whole. The demands for massive investments required by the globalisation are unfortunately not met by shipping rates. On the contrary, rates on every major routes have dropped faster than have gained in productivity.

Since 1993, the average index for major trades has fallen by more than 35% and, consequently, 1996 financial results of the leading carriers showed poor returns on investments, with ROI's unlikely to exceed 7-8%.

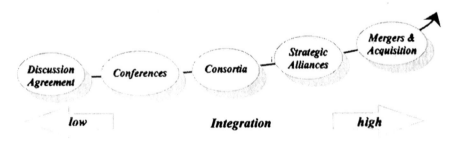

Figure 1: The evolution of the forms of co-operations.

These circumstances have generated the need of new forms of co-operation which, differently from the experiences of conferences and consortia (Figure 1), are agreements not only referred to a single trade lane but, as mentioned above, they include all major east-west routes, in certain cases extending to feeder links and to other phases of the intermodal chain (container terminal management, inland transport, joint ship purchasing, etc.).

Over the last few years, together with the advent of global alliances, we have seen a multitude of mergers and acquisitions which have caused a further supply concentration in the sea transport.

2 The market concentration in the sea transport

The need of financial resources required by the pressure of the competition arranges that container maritime transport is referable to a market based on services volume, in which the control of high market shares and the acquisition of traffic quotas represent the main tool of competition among global carriers.

On the basis of these considerations we can analyse and explain the advent of the increasing market concentration [2]. In fact over the last few years merger and acquisition operations have been several.

In particular, in the European environment, there have been numerous cases of mergers and acquisitions among liner operators; Hapag Llyod is born from the merger between Hamburg America Line and Norddeutscher Llyod, while DSR/Senator from the merger between Senator Linie and Deutsche Sereederei Rostock. P&O Container Lines, recently merged with Nedllyod, is born from the merger between P&O and OT&T.

Certainly the most famous event is represented by the acquisition of the American Sea Land on the part of the Danish Maersk which, thanks to this financial operation, has consolidated its world leadership in terms of offered slots.

The majority of top 20 carriers is born either from the merger or the acquisition of pre-existent companies.

In a competitive market like liner shipping, where the control of freight rates is almost impossible, the opportunity of profit or, in the worst cases, of survival, has to be looked for in the area of cost control. It is necessary the achievement of economies of scale, in finance, logistics, organisation, and technology, related to the use of ultra large container vessels and information technology resources, and this is the main cause of the growth of the market concentration [3].

Moreover the market of carriers is global and it imposes a good organisation and the ability to act on a world-wide scale. The acquisition of other companies answers the need to enter in new markets, previously ignored.

Over the last decade the market concentration has grown, choosing as parameter the fleet capacity in terms of TEUs. Top 20 carriers have considerably increased their quota passing in the last ten years from 39,6% to 62,2%, as regards the slot capacity of the world fleet, and from 74,6% to 83%, as regards the capacity of the cellular one (Figure 2).

This has implied an increase in the contractual strength of carriers against the other players of the transport chain and, in particular, of shippers and stevedoring operators, partially balancing the impact of the freight rebate induced by fleet overcapacity.

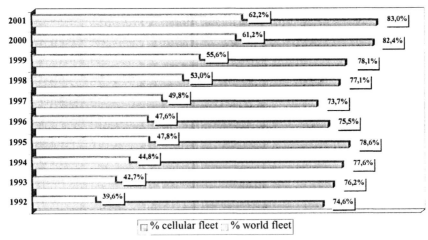

	% cellular fleet	% world fleet
2001	62,2%	83,0%
2000	61,2%	82,4%
1999	55,6%	78,1%
1998	53,0%	77,1%
1997	49,8%	73,7%
1996	47,6%	75,5%
1995	47,8%	78,6%
1994	44,8%	77,6%
1993	42,7%	76,2%
1992	39,6%	74,6%

Figure 2: The concentration of sea transport market; source: Drewry Shipping Consultants.

3 The birth of the "global stevedores"

The advent of the so-called "global stevedores" in the 1980's has had a fundamental impact on port facility financing and management. Terminal operators have focused their activities from a national basis to an international one. Port privatisation in particular has encouraged this course to the adoption of strategies which have induced some "top players" to hold stakes (usually majority) in the share capital of several terminals in their strategic portfolio [4].

This trend has obtained further strength from the advent of the globalisation of the production systems, from the relentless pursuit of economies of scale within the container shipping industry and, consequently, from the increased contractual strength of global carriers caused by market concentration [5].

The introduction of Post-Panamax vessels in the 6.000 to 8.000 TEUs range and the probable use, in a near future, of over 10.000 TEUs full-containerships, requires larger scale port facilities, more onerous and difficult to manage.

Global stevedores are increasingly meeting these requirements and the "landlord" port model is becoming the model that the public sector is adopting within the international port community.

The first stevedores, still today among the top players, which have expanded their operations on a geographical basis, have been able to catch the opportunities offered by the boom of port privatisation. These companies are Hutchison Port Holdings, the Australian P&O Ports and the American Stevedoring Services of America.

PSA Corporation, nowadays the second operator in the world and owner of some Mediterranean terminals, belongs to the so-called "second wave", together with the German BLG and the American CSX.

These companies have basically been attracted to the international theatre of operations after witnessing the success of the investment made by their predecessors in the first wave and by the growing momentum of port privatisation worldwide.

In 1999 BLG of Bremen has merged with Eurokai of Hamburg, creating the most important European stevedore, Eurogate, while CSX after the acquisition of Sea Land by Maersk emerged as e new market force, as some Sea Land terminals remained to the parent company CSX Corporation.

The third wave of terminal operators is composed by some "ocean carriers", entered the port business as part of an effort to support their core activity, i.e. shipping operations. These players, such as the Danish AP Moeller Terminals associated company of Maersk-Sea Land, Evergreen, the Chinese COSCO, APL-NOL, thus represent an example of vertical integration along the transport chain. On the one hand these operators try to catch the important opportunities offered by this business, as potential profit margins in the international port sector are much higher, on the other hand this strategy represents a tool to strengthen their competitive position against global stevedores of the previous waves.

4 The present competitive scenario

Nowadays the stevedoring market shows the leadership of four great global operators namely HPH, PSA Corporation, APM Terminals and P&O Ports which move 31,1% of the world throughput (Figure 3). In the last five years the market concentration has been increasing after some acquisitions, such as for example that of ICTSI by Hutchison in 2001, and thanks to the entry of a new operator, that is AP Moeller, which has passed from 7,5 million TEUs handled in 1999 to 18 million in 2001. Graph 1 clearly shows the evolution of this trend which, in accordance with a research made by the company West LB Panmure, should lead the top four operators to move about 43% of the world throughput in a 2010 vision [6].

It is clear the gap between 1999 and 2000, period during which AP Moeller almost doubled its throughput and Hutchison acquired further container terminals in the world. According to the carried out evaluations, AP Moeller is destined to become, in some years time, the second operator in the world, overcoming PSA Corporation, market leader until 1998.

Interesting considerations could be made analysing the geographical positioning of the terminals of these operators (Table 1). Both PSA and Hutchison have their core business in a port, respectively Singapore and Honk Kong, where handle the greatest part of their overall volumes. In particular PSA, realises in the Asian port of Singapore over 80% of its throughput, handling in only one terminal about 25% of containers transhipped in the world. Hutchison is not so bounded to a single terminal, as it owns several facilities in other areas of Asia, in Europe and, differently from PSA, in America too [7].

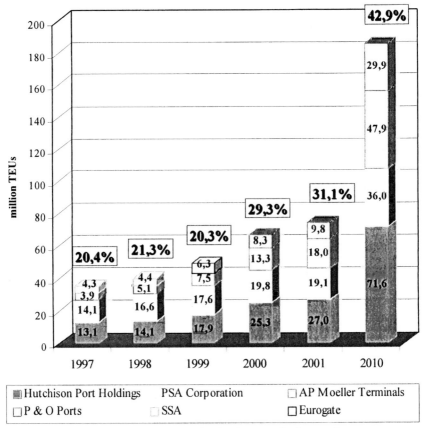

Figure 3: The concentration in the stevedoring market.

Global Stevedore	Asia	Europe	Africa	America	Austr. - New Zel.	**Total**
Hutchison Port Holdings	21	4	1	7	-	**33**
PSA Corporation	9	4	5	-	-	**18**
AP Moeller Terminals	6	4	8	22	-	**40**
P & O Ports	7	5	1	4	4	**21**

Table 1: The geographical distribution of terminals (2001).

P&O Ports is the only operator to be present in all continents and, particularly, it shows a strong activity in three countries, namely Great Britain, Australia and Indonesia, where it handles about 45% of the overall throughput. Differently from other "top players" this company is not present in any hub port of the Far-East [8].

Over the last few years AP Moeller Group has been protagonist of a process of vertical integration which has caused the born of a new entity, Maersk Ports, with the aim of managing and moving containers of the associated company Marsk-Sea Land. Two years later, keeping its captive market, it became an independent operator, with the focus to work for other carriers too.

Thus we can foresee a revolution which will lead AP Moeller Terminals to hold a greater market share, with probable disappointment not only of the stevedoring operators but also of the other global carriers which, to escape from Maersk attack, in a future could fight to obtain further port concessions. Nowadays Maersk-Sea Land represents about 90% of volumes handled by this company of the group and in the next ten years this quota should probably decrease up to 80%.

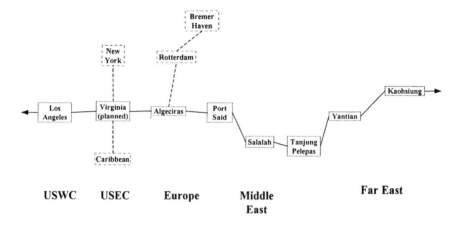

Figure 4: AP Moeller terminals on east-west route.

This strategy of vertical integration has implied the escape from Singapore and the consequent acquisition of a quota of 30% in the Malesian terminal of Tanjung Pelapas and of 49% in that of Salalah, in Oman. As we can see in Figure 4, at the moment AP Moeller has at its disposal a group of hub terminals, strategically located along the east-west route, which permits to manage operations of hub and spoke, relay and interlining. Consequently the advantages deriving from this policy are several, both in terms of economies of scale, thanks to the introduction of over 6.000 TEUs vessels, and in terms of efficacy of the service offered to customers.

References

[1] R. Midoro, A. Pitto, *A Critical Evaluation of Strategic Alliances in Liner Shipping*, Maritime Policy and Management, vol. 27 pp. 31-40, 2000.
[2] R. Midoro, *Le Strategie degli Operatori Transpotistici Globali*, ECIG: Genoa, pp. 109-177, 1997

[3] Drewry Shipping Consultants, *Annual Container Market Review and Forecast*, 2001.

[4] Hans. J. F. Peters, *Development in Global Seatrade and Container Shipping Markets: Their effects on the Port Industry and Private Sector*, International Journal of Maritime Economics, vol. III n.1, 2001.

[5] Drewry Shipping Consultants, *World Container Terminals: Global Growth and Private Profits*, 1998

[6] Containerisation International, *The Big Four*, March 2002.

[7] Containerisation International, *Big Three on Global Trail*, March 2001.

[8] Containerisation International, *Big in the World*, July 2001.

Life cycle feasibility of a new type of container handling system

M. W. Ludema
Department of Transport Policy and Logistical Organisation, Faculty of Technology, Policy and Management, Delft University of Technology, Delft, The Netherlands.

Abstract

Container handling at container terminals can be done with several old and new types of container handling systems, like straddle carriers or Automated Guided Vehicles and Automatic Stacking Cranes. A third type is introduced, based on units with a frame and a belt that runs around this frame by two rolls. This study investigates the economic feasibility of the new system by comparing it with the other two by means of a cost effectiveness analysis over a 20 year period. It was found that the new system is a feasible alternative, so the development of this system should be continued.

1 Introduction

Traditionally the logistic process of handling containers at a deep-sea container terminal starts with quay cranes that put the containers on the quay for further transport into a containers stack with for instance straddle carriers. A more advanced and also proven container handling system uses Automated Guided Vehicles that each will position itself under the quay crane and automatically transport the container towards a stack lane, where an Automatic Stacking Crane will place the container in the container stack. In this study a third type of container handling system is introduced, based on several units that consists out of a frame and a transport belt, that runs around this frame by two rolls. The quay crane puts the container on the transport belt that will roll the container into a stack lane, where a special designed Automatic Stacking Crane will place the container in the container stack. The aim of this study is to investigate the economic feasibility of this new container handling system by comparing these three systems by means of a cost effectiveness study for a period of 20 years. ECT (Europe Combined Terminals) the largest container handling company in the Port of Rotterdam agreed to provide the necessary data for the two existing systems. The engineering company (ILS) that designed the transport belt system provided the other input data.

2 Container handling systems

The container as a containing unit makes it possible to transport cargo around the world in a unified way, and container handling systems are put in operation to facilitate the de-coupling point in the world wide cargo flow. Containers vessels, with a carrying capacity up to 6000 Twenty-foot Equivalent Units (expressed in TEU's) travel in line-services over the world. A container vessel stores containers (generally 40 feet containers) in the holds between vertical guides that provide sea-fastening of the cargo without special means and also guide the containers when being loaded and unloaded. This latter is done in a vertical sense either by cranes mounted in board or, more general, by special container quay cranes. Also above deck special cells that can hold containers are available, which make the stowing of the cargo much faster (Atkins, et.al.[1])

The sizing of container vessels is important for the right scale-advantages. On routes like those from Europe to Singapore or New York very large container vessels travel in line-services. During their stay in Europe vessels will only stop at one or two deep-sea ports, otherwise they will loose to much time in a port. To reach this very short turn time in a container terminal, loading and unloading is limited to one or two days at the most. Container vessels are relative fast and the loading and unloading time in a port is often the bottle-neck in the total logistic and transport process of these container vessels. To load and unload large container ships in a very short service time is one of the competitive advantages a container port can have. The above situation makes it clear that innovation in container handling systems and the materials and equipment they are made off, is essential for container liners, ports and its stevedores. All the equipment infrastructure and services provided are focused towards achieving maximum efficiency when handling these containers.

The container stack is the de-coupling point in the loading and unloading process, and can be seen as a separate part of the container handling system. But if the equipment at both sides of the container stack is the same, sometimes scaling advantages can be made. Currently the following four types of container handling systems are most widely used in the port of Rotterdam: (1) Container Handling Systems with Reach-Stackers, (2) Container Handling Systems with Straddle Carriers, (3) Container Handling Systems with a Multi Trailer System (MTS) & Straddle Carriers, and (4) Container Handling Systems with Automated Guided Vehicles and Automatic Stacking Cranes. Besides a new type of container handling system only the two last systems will be compared and briefly discussed.

3 Innovations in container handling systems

Competitive advantages between container terminal operators is on speed and cost. Ocean liners only choose one of several container ports on a continent and want as less disturbance as possible. Innovations are of the utmost importance for container terminal operators. Some operators belief in flexibility and operate container terminals with straddle carriers, other believe in automation, also driven by the high wages of container terminals personnel in the Western seaports and experiment with fully automated container handling systems for loading and unloading container vessels with capacities of 8.000 TEU and 10.000 TEU in a reasonable time slot are analyzed, such as FAMAS (First, All Modes, All Sizes).

In 1997 Intermodal Logistic Solutions (ILS) a small firm specialized in new maritime and logistic engineering solutions, designed a container handling system under the name of Promoteus. Promoteus is a fully automated system for the transport of containers from a quay under a portal crane to its designated positions in the stack. Transport from the quay position is performed by putting a container on special units that consists a construction frame and a special designed transport belt, that rolls around the construction frame, like a conveyer one might know from baggage handling systems on airports. The units are put in-line with each other in lanes in several directions. When the container is in the stack, a special designed Automated Stacking Crane will take the container from the belt to place it at their designated stack-position. Normally (in the case of the AGV-ASC system) containers are stacked in the length direction. With the ASC needed for the Promoteus system, containers are stacked in the opposed direction. Each of the transport belts is operated by an electromotor. The length of a transport belt is 40 feet, for a 40" container, but can also hold smaller containers. The concept is extendable to very large container terminals and probably useful when large volumes and personnel costs are high.

4 Economic feasibility study based on life-cycle costing

The research question is: *"Is the Promoteus container handling system a feasible alternative compared with the straddle carriers system and the AGV-ASC system?"* The inbound flows and the way the containers enter the process, as well as the outbound flows and the way the containers leave the process are kept the same. In reality the three systems have their own characteristics, and advantages and disadvantages in the way the inter-modal handling is organized, but these are set aside in the analysis.

In this research an economic feasibility study of the Promoteus system was performed by making a Cost Effectiveness and/or Life Cycle Cost comparison between this Container Handling System and those based on Straddle Carriers and Automated Guided Vehicles together with Automatic Stacking Cranes. As is often the case with durable exquipment, see for example Blanchard [2], the investment costs in container handling systems are very high, but the operating and maintenance costs of the container handling systems are much higher, especially when both are considered during the time these systems are planned to operate, namely for a period between 10 and 30 year. In such a case, a life cycle cost calculation will provide better results than a simple calculation based on return of investment. The cost-effectiveness of the three systems is compared for several realistic yearly throughputs. The results give a clear, but of course not a very detailed picture of the competitiveness of the three container handling systems.

After several discussions with the initiators, it was decided, that Promoteus was to be compared with two container handling systems already operational with container terminal operators in the port of Rotterdam.

Straddle Carriers (gasoline/electric): (1) Transport from the container vessel with a portal crane with a theoretical maximum capacity of 60 containers per hour; (2) Transport between the vessel/quay and the container stack with straddle carriers; (3) Transport in the container stack for repositioning if necessary and to different non-quay side modalities (land or water) with straddle carriers.

AGV-ASC: (1) Transport from the container vessel with a portal crane with a theoretical maximum capacity of 60 containers per hour; (2) Transport between the vessel/quay and the container stack with unmanned (pre-scheduled) Automated Guided Vehicles and a transponder grid; (3) Transport in the container stack for repositioning (if necessary) and to different non-quay side modalities (land or water) with standard Automatic Stacking Cranes.

Promoteus: (1) Transport from the container vessel with a portal crane with a theoretical maximum capacity of 60 containers per hour; (2) Transport between the vessel/quay and the container stack with transport belts (units); (3) Transport in the container stack for repositioning (if necessary) and to different non-quay side modalities (land or water) with heavy Automatic Stacking Cranes.

5 Life cycle cost model

5.1 Building the LCC-model

The life cycle costs of the container handling system are defined as: *"All costs that may be caused by the container handling system or all the costs that may arise for the organization by operating the container handling system, to keep the container handling system in a desired state, during the whole life cycle of the system from the first conceptual ideas of the system till the system's end of life."* For the economic feasibility study a life-cycle costing tool is developed tool for the necessary calculations. During the development of the Life Cycle Cost Model the following six steps were performed:

1   Divide the container handling process in the following activities:
-        transport activities from quay to stack;
-        positioning the container in the designated stack position;
-        taking the container from its stack position;

<table>
<tr><td>-</td><td>transport and placement of containers on outbound modalities.</td></tr>
</table>

2   Make a Hard Ware Breakdown Structure (HBS) of the system;
3   Model the HBS for all the life cycle phases in the LCC-model:
4   Define the cost equations for all distinguished parts of the LCC-model;
5   Gather all date necessary for the variables for use in the LCC-equations;
6   Perform the necessary LCC-calculations and LCC-analysis.

5.2 Data gathering

To acquire the necessary data for the input of the LCC-model real life data was elicited from interviews and documents of two comparable container handling systems of the same organization, namely ECT in Rotterdam. For the gathering of LCC-data for the Promoteus system, design data and data of suppliers of known sub-systems was used.

5.3 Starting-points of the capacity calculation

Before a life cycle cost calculation can be made the necessary maximum capacity and the operational aspects of the process have to be defined. This means that the speed of the individual equipment items have to be calculated and the distances and heights the containers have to be transported within the container handling system have to be known. Besides the operational capacity the availability of these systems have to be known in respect to the maintenance requirements of each of the systems. Results of this calculation is a detailed configuration of number, position and capacity of the total basis container terminal and the equipment that is part of it.

Normally there is no limitation of transporting a container from the position of every portal crane to a stack-position. In this study two basis terminal were configured, each operated by four portal cranes and a container handling system that will move the container to a stack position of the container stack that is directly related to the two portal cranes. So two separately functioning basis terminals are modeled. The LCC-model and the made calculations are a combination of two of the same basis terminals. Each basis terminal has covers an area of 360 meter quay length, enough for 4.000 TEU container vessels, and 500 meter broad for container handling movements and the container stack. The strip between quay and the beginning of the stack is 90 meters. The capacity of the container stack of each basis terminal is 10.000 TEU, at least 5.000 containers (40" containers). Stacking height of the stack is three containers. The containers have maximum platform dimensions of 12 meter x 2,5 meters.

The dimensions of the each total container handling system are enough for a handling capacity of 900.000 container moves each year, for the two quay locations equally spread over the year or sequentially processed. The maximum capacity of the container handling system is operational when both portal cranes are used and operating at full capacity. In the model two basis container handling systems are dimensioned to this maximum capacity. Quay peeks and inland stack peeks are sometimes simultaneously. To make this possible the container handling system is over-dimensioned with an additional capacity between 20% and 25% depending on the configuration and capacity of the subsystems or separate equipment. In the chosen configuration two vessels can be processed simultaneously. To make this possible two times four portal cranes must be available for each basis terminal, each with a theoretical capacity of 60 container moves per hour. In the model the capacity is set to a more realistic operational capacity of 50 container moves per hour. So one container move every 72 seconds.

5.4 Basic terminal with straddle carriers

The average transport distance a straddle has to travel from the portal crane to the stack position and back is 810 meters. The average speed for covering this distance is 268 seconds. The input for the system is one container every 72 seconds. The minimum capacity is 15 straddle carriers. If an additional capacity of 25%-30% is added; the capacity should be 18 straddle carriers for each basis terminal. Due to maintenance the system needs reserve capacity. The MTBF (Mean Time Between Failure) of a Straddle Carrier is 530 moves. These Straddle Carries will be replaced immediately, and repaired during another period. The time necessary to replace the Straddle Carrier is expressed by the MTTR (Mean Time To Repair), and is 30 minutes. To keep the container handling system within the necessary additional 20% capacity an extra Straddle Carrier is needed. Total for a basis container terminal operated with straddle carriers, 19 pieces of this equipment are necessary.

5.5 Basic terminal with AGV's and standard ASC's

The theoretical minimum and maximum number of stack lanes for the basis terminal with a driving space of 90 meters, with the given dimensions and a capacity of 10.000 TEU is receptively 9 and 14. The capacity of a stack lane and its Automatic Stacking Crane is determined by the average time of the ASC to pick up a container from the AGV and put it at an average stack position. If enough AGV's are used, the ASC does not have to wait to place a container on an AGV. If the number of necessary ASC's is determined, the capacity of the 10.000 TEU determines the depth of the container stack. The average distance an ASC has to travel is determined by the depth of the container stack. Together with an additional capacity between 20%-25% all ASC's together will have to transport a container every 14.4 second. A calculation showed that 12 stack lanes are needed to reach this capacity. The MTBF of an ASC-standard is every 1.122 move. Non-functioning ASC's will be replaced within 15 minutes (= MTTR). Also with the possible extra capacity for the MTTR the 12 stack lane just stays above the additional capacity of 20%, so 12 stack lanes for each basis terminal will be sufficient. After the minimum capacity of the ASC's stack lane configuration is determined the number of necessary AGV's has to be found. The average distance an AGV has to travel is 280 meters. With the average speed, time an AGV stands still under the portal crane or ASC, this would add 20%-25% additional capacity 19 AGV's for each basis terminal will be sufficient. The MTBF is 1.480 moves. The MTTR is 12 minutes. The MTTR does not lead to an additional AGV, so 19 AGV's are sufficient for each basis container terminal.

5.6 Basic terminal with promoteus roller belts and heavy ASC's

For the Promoteus system the capacity of the heavy ASC's and its stack lane configuration have to be determined first. The available space on a basis container terminal determines the minimum and maximum possible number of stack-lanes. We can use the minimum of 3 stack lanes, if the total available depth is used and 5 stack lanes, it the total available length is used. Because an very innovative control system will be used together with the Promoteus system, the ASC only has to travel 20% of the stack length every container move. The configuration with 5 stack lanes has an additional capacity of 4,7%. The MTBF of the heavy ASC's is estimated at 1.122 moves. This situation would lead to the fact that actual 6 ASC's would be necessary, though on the hypothetical available space, there is only room for 5 ASC stack lanes, and with 6 ASC's the ASC-system would be heavily over dimensioned. Because the Promoteus is still in the preliminary design stage, another interview with the possible developer of this not yet existing ASC was held. Concluded was that the average speed could most probably increased. In the LCC-calculation the basis terminal was estimated to operate with a 5 stack lane configuration. The average speed of the transport belt system is estimated at 0.5 meter per second. On the average 175 meter have to be covered. So every container needs on average 350 second to reach its stack position (that is position under the ASC). Every 1.000.000 movers all transport belt units have to be replaced. The basis terminal configuration needs a total capacity of 663 units.

6 Life Cycle Cost Analysis

6.1 Design of the model

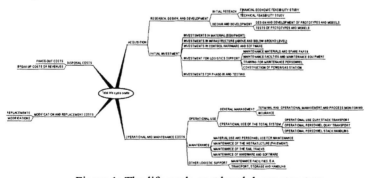

Figure 1: The life cycle cost breakdown structure

For all three alternatives; the phases, all means, all activities are part of the LCC-model. Three scenario's are included in the model, namely a 300.000, a 600.000 and a 900.000 container moves per year scenario. Also included in the model are all the necessary equipment, the necessary personnel to operate the terminal and the maintenance facilities necessary for the repair of the equipment. The figure below summarizes the costs that are included in the LCC-model. Some cost are found by the total of others, but on the lower levels in the Cost Breakdown Structure each cost-item contains an equation with several input variables, see the figure 1.

6.2 Gathering the necessary data and designing the LCC-model

The eventually designed LCC-structure represents a generic structure that can be used for all three alternatives. At the start of the study it was assumed that the availability, detail, and reliability would be much higher, than it actual was. The development of the LCC-structure and investigating the availability and quality of the necessary data turned out to become an iterative process. The iterative approach resulted in a more realistic LCC-structure and outcome of feasibility analyses than the use of a full generic LCC-model would give.

6.3 Types of LCC-analyses

After the first set of calculations it turned out that cost for operational personnel is very high, if this personnel would be available 24 ours a day the whole year. The container handling process is more a peak related process. Some days it is very busy and some days there are no vessels to handle. In reality such as is the case in the port of Rotterdam, only a part of the personnel is on the pay-roll of the container terminal company. To analyze the effects of the cost of the operational personnel, three types of calculation were performed, the last one being the most realistic.

- all operational personnel is permanent and actually on the pay-roll of the container terminal company;
- all operational personnel is flexible and will be hired if there are vessels;
- 70% of the operational personnel is permanent and 30% of the operational personnel is flexible (note that from the overall personnel costs approximately 75% is operational and 25% is supportive).

It should be emphasized that a full LCC-analysis was not performed, but only the differential costs were compared, so the real cost will be higher. The following tables show some results.

Costs per container move with 100% permanent operational personnel

Number of moves	Straddle Carrier	AGV-ASC	Promoteus
A 300.000	f 227,25	f 137,85	f 124,45
B 600.000	f 117,03	f 71,67	f 65,40
C 900.000	f 80,29	f 49,60	f 45,72

Costs per container move with 100% flexible operational personnel

Number of moves	Straddle Carrier	AGV-ASC	Promoteus
A 300.000	f 63,24	f 68,90	f 57,33
B 600.000	f 42,64	f 37,40	f 32,97
C 900.000	f 35,77	f 26,90	f 24,85

6.4 Conclusions from the LCC-calculations

From all the comparisons and analysis can be concluded that the Promoteus system has the lowest life cycle costs. The tables show the costs per container move for the 100% permanent and the 100% flexible alternatives of the three scenario's. The costs per container move are the lowest for the Promoteus system and the highest for the Straddle Carriers for the 100% permanent. If personnel cost increase the AGV-ASC and Promoteus container handling systems are better solutions. The costs per container move for the 100% flexible and 300.000 container moves per year are the lowest for the Straddle Carriers. If personnel costs are lower the Straddle Carrier alternative may also be better for 600.000 container moves per year scenario. The cost of Promoteus system are 10% lower than the cost of the AGV-ASC system. Only detailed analysis would show the real differences between these two systems.

The total throughput in containers moves per year is the main revenue driver. The cost do not increase significantly with each container move. This is certainly the case in the 100% flexible scenario.

The operational and maintenance costs cover the larger part of the life cycle cost. The acquisition costs are not significant in the 100% permanent personnel alternative, they only make up 10% to 20% of the total costs. In the 100% flexible personnel alternative they become more important. The acquisition costs of the Promoteus system are the highest. But because the system is still in its preliminary stage the possibilities to use for instance value engineering and try to redesign the system or components of the system, to make it less expensive with the same functionality, is still possible. The disposal costs of all container handling systems over the total of 20 years are of no real significançe. If the percentage of permanent personnel is high the costs of the straddle carrier system become unacceptable high. Straddle carriers are more competitive in countries with low wages.

6.5 Other comparisons

During the total research also other cost related aspects were included in the comparison of the three container handling system. The main conclusions are:
- The surface area requirements for the AGV-ASC system are the lowest;
- The Promoteus system needs 7% more space than the AGV-ASC system;
- The straddle carrier systems has the shortest through-put time;

- The through-put time of a container for the Promoteus system is three time the time needed for the straddle carrier system, but this does not influence the capacity because the transport belt functions as a moving buffer in the system;
- On-manned container handling is safer than manned container handling;
- Because of the powered by electricity and a more environmental friendly system than the other two, the straddle carriers has the highest CO_2-emmisions.

7 Conclusions & recommendations

7.1 Conclusions

The LCC-calculations showed, that the life cycle costs of the Straddle Carrier Container Handling System (above +/- 400.000 container moves per year) are the highest (for both the 100% permanent and 100% flexible personnel alternative).

The life cycle costs of Promoteus are between 8%-20% lower than the cost of the AGV-ASC container terminal. Based on calculation performed and the reliability of the input data this difference is not very significant.

Looking at the criteria for the scenario's in relation with the necessary 20%-25% percent additional capacity it can be concluded that the Promoteus system needs a quay length above the 360 meter, and an additional heavy ASC to provide the necessary capacity. With this capacity the Promoteus system may handle even more than 1.000.000 containers per year without trouble.

7.2 Recommendations

From the calculations and comparisons must be recommend to advance in the design and development of the Promoteus system. It is worthwhile to construct a test side were a small number of Promoteus transport belt units can be tested for their performance and RAMS-requirements. The results of this study were shared with ECT, the organization that provided as with the larger part of the data. It is recommendable to perform a more detailed LCC-analysis in joint research between ECT and the developers of the Promoteus system. The author sees great potentials for the Promoteus container handling system.

References

[1]   Atkins, W.H., and R.A. Boyle, Modern Marine Operations and Management, pp.28-30, 1983.
[2]   Blanchard, B.S., Logistics Engineering and Management, 3rd edition, Prentice Hall, pp.410-440, 1992.

Towards the economic operation of a to be privatized ferry system - The case of the Rozenburg-Maassluis ferry in the Port of Rotterdam

M. W. Ludema[1] & A. W. Veenstra[2]
[1]*Faculty of Technology, Policy and Management, Delft University of Technology, The Netherlands.*
[2]*Faculty of Economics, Erasmus University Rotterdam, The Netherlands.*

Abstract

Originally the Province of South Holland (the Netherlands) operated a one ferry ship system between Maassluis and Rozenburg at the New Waterway (the mouth of the Port of Rotterdam). This distance of approximately 800 meters is serviced by a car ferry between 6.00 AM and 12.00 PM. The current operator SBS BV was asked to make a proposal to operate the ferry system during a concession period of 6 years in a privatized manner. At the moment the operator earns a management fee for the management and control for the ferry system and all personnel are civil servants of the province. The authors were asked to write a proposal to commercial operate the ferry system and come up with social and financial alternatives for a time schedule of the ferry service. Several cost effectiveness analyses were performed to find the information necessary to draw up the proposal. Specifically for this project a cost effectiveness model was developed. The analysis include aspects such as actors involved, time schedule alternatives, number of ships to operate, the use of a new ship, the use of a refurbished ship, the availability of the ships due to maintenance, the tariffs to be used, the modal-split to expect, and of course all costs involved. Few data was available to evaluate on the non-commercial ferry system and had to be gathered parallel to the development of the cost effectiveness model. In advance the province's expectation was that it would be feasible to operate only a bicycle-pedestrian ferry system. This research showed that is was feasible to operate the current car-ferry system with one refurbished ship and an additional (old) ship during the rush-hours and stop the commercial ferry service after 21.00 hours. Eventually the study gave an acceptable proposal for the

Province and SBS BV, the "new" commercial operator and owner of the ferry system.

1 Introduction

1.1 Starting points and backgrounds

The Province of South Holland (The Netherlands) has been operating a number of ferry services across the New Waterway, which is the entrance channel for the Port of Rotterdam. Recently (in 2000), it has decided to privatize the ferry service between the cities of Maassluis and Rozenburg, through a six year concession, with the possibility to extend this concession with another six years. The current operator (SBS BV) was asked to hand in a proposal for the operation of this service on a commercial & viable basis. The Province also set certain standards for the service on issues such as service times and time table, legal demands regarding the right for transport, tariff system, supplemental payment, financial reporting, ownership of the vessels, infra- and superstructure, duration of the contract, environmental issues, service reliability, business-plan, current and future demand, transition period, quality of the service, reliability of the service, expertise and financial strength of the operator. With regard to the supplemental payment, these are payments by the Province to the operator because of the socio-economic role of the ferry service. However, financial feasibility was the most important criterion for the Province to decide on ferry service alternatives.

The authors were involved in the development of the economic analysis model that served as the basis for the cost-effectiveness analysis of alternatives being proposed to the operator. This paper describes the structure and analytical capabilities of this model.

1.2 Current situation, and service alternatives

In the current situation, the operator manages two vessels on the cross over between Rozenburg and Maassluis. Only one vessel can technically be operated for a longer period. The second vessel is a back-up vessel that is only used when the other is in repair. The vessels are capable of carrying an average of 35 cars, as well as foot passengers and bicycles. The current tariff structure is found to be inadequate since prices are far too low. Furthermore, it is thought that the current service could be offered with fewer personnel. Finally, the service is offered from 6.00 till 24.00 hrs, while after 21.00 hrs the demand diminishes substantially. Outside the service period, inhabitants of Rozenburg can only reach their home by an alternative route through the Benelux tunnel (a 30 km. detour). As a result of these inherent inefficiencies, the Province feels that quality of service and cost of service are no longer balanced. By shifting the commercial operation of the service to a private sector operator, the Province hopes to regain this balance.

In the request for tender, the Province asked for a comparison of several alternative service configurations. The operator decided to focus on the following three main investment alternatives:

- Operate a car-ferry with the two current vessels according to the current service situation. The two current vessels will be refurbished, so they can safely service for the period 2001-2025 (4 times the concession period of 6 years); resulting in refurbishment costs for two vessels
- Operate a car-ferry with one of the current vessels and a new vessel, in accordance with the current service situation. One vessel will be refurbished, so it can safely service together with the new vessel for the period 2001-2025 (4 time the concession period of 6 years); resulting in refurbishment costs for one vessel and investment in one new vessel
- Operate a bicycle-pedestrian ferry with one new vessel and arrange alternatives for estimable and sudden out-off service periods of the bike-pedestrian vessel. This service period is 2001-2025 (4 times the concession period of 6 years); resulting in investment costs for one new vessel

These three sets of alternatives were compared on their economic & financial feasibility. Besides the three main alternatives, the following alternatives were not taken into account:

- Operate a car-ferry with only one vessel;
- Operate a car-ferry with two new vessels;
- Operate a car-ferry (new or refurbished) together with a bicycle-pedestrian ferry as a back-up ferry;
- Operate a bicycle-pedestrian ferry (new) and modify one of the old car-ferries into a back-up bicycles-pedestrians ferry.

Within the three alternatives, the following variants were considered:

- Service form 6.00 to 24.00 hrs, with one vessel;
- Service from 6.00 to 21.00 hrs, with one vessel;
- Service from 6.00 to 24.00 hrs, with one vessel and an additional service with a second vessel from 6.30 to 9.30 hrs and from 16.00 to 19.00 hrs;
- Service from 6.00 to 21.00 hrs, with one vessel and an additional service of a second vessel from 6.30 to 9.30 hrs and from 16.00 to 19.00 hrs;

1.3 Elements of the economic analysis

In general, the economic analysis incorporates a number of variables that determine the outcome to a great extent. These are:

- Revenue generation as a result of a new tariff structure. This includes:
  - Price elasticity of the estimated demand
  - Service elasticity of the estimated demand
- Manning in relation to alternative service structure;
- Planning of assets in relation to service structure;
- Maintenance requirements of the vessels to prolong their service life;
- Supplement arrangements;

- Ownership of the vessels.

The change in tariff structure and the resulting effect on demand are discussed below. The operational issues such as manning, planning of assets, and maintenance are taken into account as if the operator were free to make any changes an optimized service required. In fact, the privatization procedure included a redundancy arrangement from the Province. For the determination of supplement payments, the tender document contained specific rules, based on what is normally in the case of subsidizing public transport, namely a supplemental payment of 1,5 time the ticket-prices for passengers. Finally, with regard to ownership, it was agreed that the operator could assume that ownership of the vessel(s) would be transferred to a new concession holder at their book value at that point in time. The Province was to agree on the depreciation method used in the proposal.

The paper continues as follows. The next section describes the new tariff structure that was suggested in the proposal with the justification of demand estimates. The section after that described the elements of the economic analysis model. The paper finishes with some conclusions and ideas for further research.

2 Tariff structure

The current tariff structure recognized the categories: foot passenger, bicycle, motorized bicycle, motorbike, car, tractor and other farming equipment, truck. All prices are inclusive the driver.

Table 1: Old & New Tariffs of the Ferry Service

Category	Type of ticket	Price '98	Price '03
Foot passenger	1 trip ticket	Fl 0.75	Fl 2.20
	10 trips ticket	Fl 5.25	Fl 14.32
	Month-ticket	Fl 11.00	Fl 28.65
	Month (school) ticket	Fl 5.00	Not sold
Bicycle	1 trip ticket	Fl 1.05	Fl 2.20
	10 trips ticket	Fl 7.50	Fl 14.32
	Month-ticket	Fl 19.00	Fl 28.65
	Month (school) ticket	Fl 12.40	Not sold
Motorized bicycle	1 trip ticket	Fl 1.40	Fl 3.31
	10 trips ticket	Fl 10.25	Fl 21.49
	Month-ticket	Fl 37.25	Fl 42.97
	Month (school) ticket	Fl 24.25	Not sold
Motor bike	1 trip ticket	Fl 3.00	Fl 5.51
	10 trips ticket	Fl 21.75	Fl 35.81
	Month-ticket	Fl 65.00	Fl 71.62
Car	1 trip ticket	Fl 6.60	Fl 6.61
	10 trips ticket	Fl 39.60	Fl 42.97
	Month-ticket	Fl 145.50	Fl 85.94
Tractor and other farming equipment	1 trip ticket	Fl 12.40	Fl 15.43
	10 trips ticket	Fl 74.40	Fl 100.27
Truck	1 trip ticket	Fl 14.00	Fl 15.43
	10 trips ticket	Fl 84.00	Fl 100.27

Table 1 contains the old and new one-way ticket prices for these categories. It is clear that the prices for foot passengers are increased, while the price for cars were kept the same. This was felt to bring more balance into the tariff system, where previously, the car was overcharged compared to the other customers. This tariff system reflects the characteristics of pricing systems for maritime infrastructure, such as ports, which are currently becoming generally accepted. These are a combination of full cost recovery, possibly combined with elements of competitive or strategic pricing (see, for instance, Haralambides et al. 2001).

The effects on demand of this change in tariff system can be grouped into two: the effects on foot passengers and cyclists, and the effects on cars. The first group is in fact a captive market. The alternative (the Benelux tunnel) results in such a substantial detour that as an alternative it is negligible. Therefore the price elasticity for this group is estimated to be zero. The price difference seems to be large, but the foot passengers are free to take their bicycle.

The price elasticity for the car customers is not zero. However, for this group the price has not changes. Furthermore, assuming that an improved service will off set the increasing attractiveness of a widened Benelux tunnel, demand is estimated at the current level. To stimulate car-pooling, car passengers are free of charge.

The model includes an adjustment period for the change in tariff system of three years (2001-2003), besides the yearly inflation correction of 3%.

The following assumptions were also included in the economic analysis model with regard to ticket sales:

- Total actual revenues from foot passengers on a bicycle-pedestrian ferry can not be higher than 30% of the actual revenues from foot passengers in case of the car ferry. This is due to the large number of estimated (paying) car-passengers in the current situation (for a better estimate additional research would be required);
- A correction of 0,96 was applied to ticket sales on all categories as a result of decreasing demand for the reduced service until 21.00 hrs;
- A correction factor of 1 is applied to ticket sales of a cycle-foot ferry with a peak service;

For the change in demand as a result of a peak service for the car ferry operating from 6:00 to 24:00 hrs, ticket sales are corrected with a factor:
- 1,15 for foot passengers,
- 1,2 for cars and trucks;

For the change in demand as a result of a peak service for the car ferry operating from 6:00 to 21:00 hrs, ticket sales are corrected with a factor:
- 1,15 for foot passengers,
- 0.96 for cycles and motors,
- 1,17 for cars and trucks;
- 0.96 for tractors and other farming equipment.

The estimated demand are not based on detailed analysis based on the potential demand area, alternatives for the current passengers, the actual demand during the peak-services and possibilities to influence this behaviors, marketing the service. Obviously, the reliability of the results can be improved considerably if more data is gathered based on additional research.

3 The economic analysis model

3.1 Components of the economic analysis model

The economic analysis model takes into account the effectiveness of several alternative ferry systems in respect to the investment, operational and maintenance costs of each alternative. This type of economic analysis refers to what is called a cost-effectiveness analysis (see for instance Blanchard, 1998).

The economic analysis model compares the alternatives as discussed above on the basis of revenue and cost comparisons during the first six year concession period in respect to a total concession period of 24 yeas, the possibility to transfer the ownership of the vessels ships against the book-value after each six year concession, and the necessary tariff-adjustment period of three years. Specific care was taken to make the economic analysis model as complete as possible in order to obtain accurate case flow and profit predictions for the alternatives over the first concession period. Over the years a 3% inflation correction was included to reflect price and cost changes over time. The components that were included in the calculations were:

- **Revenues:**
    - Supplement payments of the Province (based on a factor 1,5 for the supplement payment of the ticket-price paid by each passenger on the bicycle-foot-ferry alternatives);
    - Revenue from all ticket sales.
- **Costs:**
    - Manning costs
    - Depreciation;
    - Bunkers and lubricants;
    - Additional bunkers for deviating services;
    - Ticket sales automation
    - Housing
    - Administration
    - Investment compensation
    - Profit.

With regard to investment compensation, the current operator offers as part of the proposal to obtain all necessary financing from its parent company, Doeksen Shipping. This company operates several other Dutch ferries, as well as a port tourist service. Its financial position is sufficient to generate the necessary means for any of the alternative services.

3.2 Economic Analysis Model and data collection

The economic analysis model gives detailed calculations and outputs of the revenues and costs of several alternatives based on several variants in service-periods and frequency, with respect to the transition from the old towards a new proposed tariff structure. The main reason if comparison was to see if the ferry service can be viably and that could be commercially operated and what the yearly supplement payments where expected from the Province, next to investments in transferring the ferry service from a public service to a commercial service. The main focus was on the feasibility (revenues and costs) of operating the ferry service during the first six year concession period.

It was chosen to develop an economic analysis model as detailed as possible in respect to the available data. This means that data acquisition and model construction where performed in parallel. Gathering the necessary data on the history of the ticked sales was no problem, but it was difficult to extract the data on costs because the operational cost of the ferry service was for our purpose not or very poorly documented. After the transfer of the ownership the ferry system, accurate and periodical data gathering it highly recommended.

3.3 Comparing the results

Table 2: Summary of analysis results for 12 alternative ferry services

Refurbishing current vessels	Service period 6.00-24.00	Service period 6.00-21.00	Service period 6.00-24.00 + peak service	Service period 6.00-21.00 +peak service
Net revenues	4050	3950	4700	4500
Exploitation Costs	5700	5400	6400	6100
1,5 x supplement (slow traffic)	1500	1400	1500	1500
Net result operator	**(neg.) 150**	**(neg.) 50**	**(neg.) 200**	**(neg.) 100**
Bicycle-foot vessels + non-refurbished reserve vessel	Service period 6.00-24.00	Service period 6.00-21.00	Service period 6.00-24.00 + peak service	Service period 6.00-21.00 +peak service
Net revenues	1000	1000	1100	1100
Exploitation Costs	3800	3650	4250	4000
1,5 x supplement (slow traffic)	1450	1400	1550	1500
Net result operator	**(neg.) 1350**	**(neg.) 1250**	**(neg.) 1600**	**(neg.) 1400**
One new vessel + one refurbished vessel	Service period 6.00-24.00	Service period 6.00-21.00	Service period 6.00-24.00 + peak service	Service period 6.00-21.00 +peak service
Net revenues	4050	3900	4700	4550
Exploitation Costs	6250	5900	6900	6600
1,5 x supplement (slow traffic)	1500	1400	1500	1500
Net result operator	**(neg.) 700**	**(neg.) 600**	**(neg.) 700**	**(neg.) 550**

Table 2 shows the results for each alternative for the year 2002. The comparison of the alternatives and related variants shows that because of the relatively high investment and low revenues from ticket sales, it is not financial feasible to operate a bicycle-foot ferry. It shows that car tickets are the main revenue-driver for the service.

Due to the very high investment costs for a new car ferry, the combination of a new vessel together with a refurbished vessel is also not a financially feasibly alternative.

The most financial feasible solution seems to be the alternative of keeping the current ferry service operational with exception of ending the service at 21.00 instead of 24.00.

Because of the slightly higher cost and the increased service the most economically feasible solution is operating a ferry service until 21.00, but additionally operating a peak service. This alternative has opportunities of increasing the service in the peak, which makes the ferry service for car traffic more competitive in respect to the tunnel-alternative. For prolonging the service time till 24.00 an increase of the investment of 12,5% is necessary, possibly to be funded by the cities of Rozenburg and Maassluis.

4 Conclusions and recommendations

The economic analysis showed that to operate a commercial ferry service from 6.00 till 21.00 with one vessel, and in addition to that operate a peak service from 6.30 till 9.00 and from 16.00 till 19.00 is the most economically feasibly solution. Depending or the time the ferry service is transferred from the Province to SBS BV, lower revenues may be expected in the adjustment period until 2003. The province should compensate the difference. Because the new ferry service is operated with fewer personnel an additional release plan should be made.

We recommend improving the quality of the data and using the economic analysis model to evaluate the investment and to perform what-if scenario's to investigate the sensitivity if the results for small and large changes in revenues and costs in respect of the improvement of the tunnel alternative. Furthermore the economic analysis model could easily be adapted to evaluate very alternatives in other Dutch or European locations, thus turning the model into a tool for standard managerial decision making.

References

[1] Haralambides, H.E., Verbeke, A., Musso, E., Benacchio, M., International Journal of Maritime Economics, December-2001, Vol.3., No.4., pp. 368-386.
[2] Blanchard, B.S., Logistics Engineering and Management, fifth edition, Prentice Hall, 1998.

Author Index

High Performance Structures and Composites

Editors: *C.A. BREBBIA, Wessex Institute of Technology, UK and W.P. de WILDE, Vrije Universiteit Brussels, Belguim*

Featuring the proceedings of the First International Conference on High Performance Structures and Composites, this volume focuses on the application of computational methods to the modelling, control and management of such structures and materials. Particular emphasis is placed on intelligent smart structures.
Specific areas covered include: GENERAL TOPICS: Optimal Design; Analysis and Testing; Damage and Fracture Mechanics; Modelling Errors; Industrial Applications; Environmental Impact; Emerging Technologies; Sustainable Technologies; Fire Performance. HIGH PERFORMANCE STRUCTURES: Properties of Smart Materials; Intelligent Systems; Sensor and Actuator Technologies; Active and Passive Control Systems; Health of Structures; Fault Tolerance Structures; Seismic Design. COMPOSITES: Composite Structures; Material Characterisation; Process Simulation; Modelling Fabrics; Joining and Bonding; Structural Identification; Fibre Reinforced Concrete; and Active Materials.
Series: High Performance Structures and Materials, Vol 4
ISBN: 1-85312-904-6   2002   apx 600pp
apx £198.00/US$307.00/€322.00

All prices correct at time of going to press but subject to change.
WIT Press books are available through your bookseller or direct from the publisher.

Coastal Engineering V
Computer Modelling of Seas and Coastal Regions

Editor: *C.A. BREBBIA, Wessex Institute of Technology, UK*

Computer models now provide an efficient and economic tool for the analysis of coastal engineering problems. In particular, they are increasingly being used in conjunction with measuring techniques to determine the extent of environmental problems and to take action when a disaster occurs, determining its extent and consequence, and optimizing available resources.
Highlighting the most recent advances in the field, this book contains papers presented at the Fifth International Conference on Computer Modelling of Seas and Coastal Regions. The contributions come from scientists working in many different countries, and span a multitude of topics and techniques in such areas as coastal erosion, sediment transport, coastal evolution and environment, coastal lakes and lagoons, harbours and marinas, shallow water tidal models, wave studies, pollution studies and coastal risk.
Series: Environmental Studies, Vol 6
ISBN: 1-85312-879-1   2001   344pp
£125.00/US$194.00/€203.00

WIT Press is a major publisher of engineering research. The company prides itself on producing books by leading researchers and scientists at the cutting edge of their specialities, thus enabling readers to remain at the forefront of scientific developments. Our list presently includes monographs, edited volumes, books on disk, and software in areas such as: Acoustics, Advanced Computing, Architecture and Structures, Biomedicine, Boundary Elements, Earthquake Engineering, Environmental Engineering, Fluid Mechanics, Fracture Mechanics, Heat Transfer, Marine and Offshore Engineering and Transport Engineering.

Computer Aided Optimum Design of Structures VII

Editors: *S. HERNÁNDEZ, Universidad de La Coruña, Spain* and *C.A. BREBBIA, Wessex Institute of Technology, UK*

Demonstrating the high level of maturity reached in design optimisation methodologies, this book contains most of the papers presented at the Seventh International Conference on Computer Aided Optimum Design of Structures. Contributions from specialists working throughout the world at universities, research centres and in industry are included, and these cover state-of-the-art advances in research together with a broad variety of practical applications in engineering practice.

An important reference of direct relevance to all scientists and engineers interested in this area, the book features over forty papers divided under the following headings: Applications in Mechanical Engineering; Applications in Structural Engineering; Nonlinear Structural Behaviour; Shape and Topology Optimisation; Computational Methods; Optimal Control; Optimisation of Composites; Computer Packages.

Series: Structures and Materials, Vol 10
ISBN: 1-85312-868-6   2001   464pp
£153.00/US$237.00/€248.00

We are now able to supply you with details of new WIT Press titles via E-Mail. To subscribe to this free service, or for information on any of our titles, please contact the Marketing Department, WIT Press, Ashurst Lodge, Ashurst, Southampton, SO40 7AA, UK
Tel: +44 (0) 238 029 3223
Fax: +44 (0) 238 029 2853
E-mail: marketing@witpress.com

Marine Technology IV

Editor: *WESSEX INSTITUTE OF TECHNOLOGY, UK*

Marine technology is experiencing rapid change and new technologies not only have to be developed but also rapidly incorporated and put into use in order for all organisations involved to remain competitive.

This volume includes papers from the Fourth International Conference on Marine Technology. It reviews both traditional and improved techniques in many different areas including: Navigation and Ship Operation; Shipbuilding and Design; Materials and Fabrication in Shipbuilding; Ship Propulsion, Equipment and Automation; Management Aspects; Reliability and Safety in Marine Technology; and Deep Sea Systems and Vehicles. Over forty contributions from specialists working in many different countries are featured.

Series: Marine and Maritime, Vol 2
ISBN: 1-85312-867-8   2001   464pp
£155.00/US$239.00/€250.00

Marine Technology III

Editors: *T. GRACZYK and T. JASTRZEBSKI, Technical University of Szczecin, Poland* and *C.A. BREBBIA, Wessex Institute of Technology, UK*

Contains some of the reviewed papers presented at the third international conference on this subject. Held in Szczecin, Poland, an important centre of shipbuilding and research, the meeting attracted participants from a wide variety of organisations.

Series: Marine and Maritime, Vol 1
ISBN: 1-85312-699-3   1999   720pp
£237.00/US$368.00/€386.00

Computer Modelling of Seas and Coastal Regions III

Editors: *J.R. ACINAS, Universidad de La Coruña, Spain and C.A. BREBBIA, Wessex Institute of Technology, UK*

"...an excellent book, which includes a number of state-of-the-art papers on modelling of seas and coastal regions. The book is well worth acquiring for those with an interest in the subject and for libraries where the subject is taught at MSc level or pursued for a research degree."

ECOMOD

Addressing the subject of computer modelling of seas and coastal regions under both normal and extreme conditions, this book contains the proceedings of the third international conference on this topic.
ISBN: 1-85312-499-0   1997   464pp
£139.00/US$223.00/€234.00

Maritime Engineering and Ports II

Editors: *C.A. BREBBIA, Wessex Institute of Technology, UK and J. OLIVELLA, Universitat Politecnica de Catalunya, Spain*

Examining the rapidly changing management, operation, design and building of maritime works and ports, this book includes papers originally presented at the Second International Conference on Maritime Engineering and Ports. Emphasis is placed on new areas of research and advanced subjects while specific topics discussed include: Port Management; Private and Public Ports; Ship and Port

Operators; Multimode Transportation in Ports; Environmental Aspects; Financial and Legal Aspects; Multiuse of Ports including Tourism, Marinas and Port Issues; Information Systems for Ports and Shipping; and Construction of Ports.
Series: *Water Studies, Vol 9*
ISBN: 1-85312-829-5   2000   400pp
£149.00/US$231.00/€242.00

Maritime Engineering and Ports

Editors: *G. SCIUTTO, University of Genova, Italy and C.A. BREBBIA, Wessex Institute of Technology, UK*

"A must for port operators and students."
CARGO TODAY

The proceedings of the First International Conference on Maritime Engineering and Ports.
The papers featured are divided under the following headings: Port Management; Ports Infrastructure - Design and Construction;   Port Infrastructure - Maintenance; Port Operation; Information Technology;   Environment and Ports; Maritime Market and Ports Strategies; Port Planning.
Series: *Water Studies, Vol 5*
ISBN: 1-85312-601-2   1998   360pp
£128.00/US$196.00/€205.00

WIT*Press*
Ashurst Lodge, Ashurst, Southampton, SO40 7AA, UK.
Tel: 44 (0) 238 029 3223
Fax: 44 (0) 238 029 2853
E-Mail: witpress@witpress.com